DERICK HOWELL

ANXIETY MANAGEMENT TECHNIQUES

5 Books in 1

STOP ANXIETY NOW,

ELIMINATE NEGATIVE THINKING,

STOP PANIC ATTACKS,

OVERCOME SOCIAL ANXIETY,

MASTER STRESS MANAGEMENT

Your Free Gift

This book includes a free bonus booklet. All information on how you can quickly secure your free gift can be found at the end of this book. It may only be available for a limited time.

BOOKS

Stop Anxiety Now

End Nervousness for Good and Experience Relief With 42 Effective Anxiety Management Treatment Techniques.

Get Your Happiness Back and Find Your Inner Peace

Derick Howell

TABLE OF CONTENTS

INTRODUCTION

Psychological and mental health conditions affect so many people in society today. In this book, our main focus will be on anxiety disorders. Research shows that anxiety disorders have become prevalent among the population. They may even affect you!

In this book, we will learn about anxiety disorders, the symptoms of different anxiety disorders, and some of the ways to effectively address anxiety in your life.

Anxiety in itself is not entirely a bad thing. At times anxiety can be a lifesaver since it triggers our awareness of the potential threats to the safety or comfort of our lives. It is an evolutionary trait that is meant to protect us from danger. Normally, it works as a natural personal alarm system that motivates us to avoid threatening or dangerous situations. For instance, when you are anxious and use the energy in a positive way, you might have the extra adrenalin to meet a difficult project deadline. In normal cases like that, anxiety is supposed to be a temporary motivator; however, at times, it may exceed its normal function and take you to uncomfortable places.

When anxiety overflows and we are unable to turn off our heightened state of mind, anxiety may flood the mind with toxic thoughts and worries. This results in the body releasing excessive amounts of stress hormones. You may become scared, nervous, overwhelmed, or even physically ill due to the heightened level of stress you are in.

When this happens, you may be confused about what is happening to your body and mind. Rest assured; you are not alone! Many people suffer from anxiety, and we will help you learn about how anxiety makes you feel, and what to do to minimize the level of impact that anxiety has on your life.

This book will help clarify facts about anxiety and give you useful tools to assist you when you experience anxiety in your life. If you have an extreme anxiety condition and are worried about the impact of anxiety on your health, consider consulting a medical practitioner instead of relying on self-diagnosis and self-treatment.

CHAPTER ONE:

Everything You Need to Know About Anxiety

Stress is a natural part of life, but sometimes our bodies may not handle stress well. Sometimes stress can become anxiety. Anxiety can be a helpful, natural response to stress. It can be classified as a feeling of fear or extreme apprehension. You may be afraid of what is about to happen, or what will happen in the future. As a child, you may be fearing your first day of school. As a parent, you may be anxious about your child's first day and how they will get along without you. When you attend an interview, you may be stressed and anxious about your performance. In most cases, people become nervous about various explainable reasons. This anxiety is normal and natural, and most people can control it well enough to function successfully at home, at work, and in the community. However, some people may have extreme feelings of anxiety and have difficulty coping with it. Such feelings may interfere with your life drastically and may indicate that you have an anxiety disorder.

Anxiety Explained

Anxiety disorders are classified by The American Psychiatric Association (APA/Parekh, 2017) as one of the most common types of emotional disorders. Anxiety affects both children and adults and has no racial or gender boundaries.

As we have already learned, sometimes people feel anxious about things that have happened, are happening or are going to happen. It is normal to wonder and worry about things. It is natural to be anxious when moving to a new home, taking an exam, or interviewing for a new job. Such stress and anxiety can be unpleasant, but for most people, it can be managed. It may even motivate you to work harder. Ordinary anxiety usually comes and goes, and it does not interfere with your life very much.

On the other hand, for those with anxiety disorders, fear and worry may overcome their lives, and the intensity of the feelings can be debilitating emotionally, psychologically, and physically. If anxiety and being in a state of constant distress affects you, you may not be able to lead a normal and healthy life. Anxiety may affect your life so much that you are unable to enjoy events and activities with family, friends or colleagues. Some people are unable to attend events, go shopping, cross the street, ride an elevator, or even leave their home. Anxiety may give you a range of debilitating symptoms including panic, sweating, heart palpitations and illness.

Generally speaking, when anxiety is not treated, it gets worse over time; however, if you learn how to control and manage these feelings, you can move beyond anxiety and lead a full and normal life.

If you suffer from anxiety, it is important to know what kind of anxiety disorder is impacting your life. This knowledge will help you identify your symptoms and triggers, as well as help you understand what you need to do to manage your symptoms.

Aren't All Anxiety Disorders The Same?

There are a variety of different anxiety disorders and they are not the same, although they may seem similar. All of them render a person unable to cope with the normal and extranormal things that life throws at us. These disorders have unique characteristics. An anxiety reaction may be triggered by something specific, or it may be an ongoing underlying factor in someone's life. Depending on the type of anxiety disorder, the impact on a person's life can range from a minor ongoing issue to a complete inability to function. The severity of the disorder will vary from person to person. Depending on the severity of the symptoms, anxiety may have a profound effect on the life of the sufferer of the anxiety, and on those around them, especially loved ones. There are many anxiety disorders that have been categorized and described. Some of the most common ones are described below.

Generalized Anxiety Disorder (GAD)

People with GAD experience excessive anxiety and worry constantly about many things including their health, daily activities, and routines, social and work interactions and circumstances that may come up unexpectedly. If you have GAD, you are likely considered "a worrier" by your friends and family. You may review pending events over in your head trying to figure out all the things that could go wrong. You may be persistently nervous about everything, and you have trouble sleeping because your mind is racing with all the worries you have. You may be tense and irritable and feel fragile all the time as you try to go through everyday life.

Social Anxiety Disorder

This is a condition whereby people worry excessively about being in social situations. They may fear interacting with strangers or family because of a fear of being judged, or "saying the wrong thing" or being inappropriately dressed. There may be a fear of embarrassment. People with social anxiety tend to avoid situations such as parties, gatherings, and other events where they will have to interact with people. Such people tend to suffer from self-imposed isolation. This is also known as a social phobia, whereby you are overwhelmed by the demands of a social situation. You may constantly think about being ridiculed, among other things. Sometimes it can manifest as being afraid of being away from home or our loved ones, but most often it is associated with a fear of interacting with others.

Panic Disorder

People with panic disorder tend to suffer from episodes of intense fear and dismay which usually comes upon them suddenly. These episodes are called "panic attacks". A panic attack may occur unexpectedly and be brought on by a trigger such as an object or situation that a person may fear. This is a disorder whereby your body takes over and you experience a physical reaction as a result of the stress. You may begin hyperventilating, have heart palpitations or chest pains, become physically ill, start crying hysterically, have hot and cold flashes or experience genuine terror, among other things. Panic attacks trigger the "freeze, fight or flight" reaction in us. You may feel able to cope with a situation right up until the moment before it happens, and then be struck down by a debilitating panic attack that prevents you from continuing with the pending event. A person who has had frequent panic attacks may live in fear of planning events or trying new things. This is because they worry they may suffer from a panic attack at the last minute, or at some point during the event.

Post-Traumatic Stress Disorder (PTSD)

PTSD is an anxiety disorder that many people suffer from. Some people think PTSD only affects military personnel who have been through battle; however, it actually is a disorder that can impact anyone that has been through a major traumatic event. Not everyone who has been through traumatic events suffers from PTSD, but PTSD is always a result of experiencing significant negative events.

Although this list is by no means complete, here are some examples of events that may lead to PTSD. PTSD may affect you if you have been to war, been physically and/or sexually assaulted, suffered an accident, lost a child, been emotionally or physically abused or seen something horrific.

PTSD can cause a variety of difficulties for those who have it. There is generally a pattern of recurring invasive thoughts. These thoughts are usually a replay of all or part of the traumatic event. These thoughts may come to you when you are least expecting it, and they may make the whole world grind to a halt for you. You may also suffer from anxiety and/or depression, have difficulty sleeping, be hyper-vigilant, and be triggered easily by situations or sounds into a state of fear, panic or distress, indecision, a near-catatonic state or be unable to leave your home. You may be unable to interact at work, at home or in the community because you are unable to cope with the stressors that you face. You may be unable to go to certain places or do certain things because they remind you too much of the past trauma.

Although you "may know" or be told by others that your reaction to your current situation is disproportionate to the actual level of risk, you are unable to deescalate your reaction.

Specific Phobia

Specific phobias are rooted in an intense fear of identifiable things, situations or places. Having a phobia is more than being just scared of something. A phobia is like a fear that is so extreme that you are unable to convince yourself to move past the fear. Other people may try to convince you that "there is nothing to be afraid of", but obviously, they don't feel the same panic and terror that overcomes you when faced with the thing, place or situation. There may or may not be a genuine level of actual danger or consequence that may come about as a result of that situation. Fear of heights, flying, elevators, snakes or dogs are examples of common phobia. (In this context we are not discussing specific social phobias such as homophobia, xenophobia, or other fears related to people who are different from other people).

Illness Anxiety Disorder

This is a condition whereby a person continually lives in fear of becoming ill, or where they believe they are becoming ill or are already ill. Whenever they detect a minor change in their perceived health, they may convince themselves that it is the manifestation of a serious illness. This may lead to other behaviors, such as an obsession with thoughts of dying from illness, frequent self-examination and self-reflection about the condition of the body and how it feels and functions, self-diagnosis and treatment, and/or unusually frequent trips to the doctor or emergency room. This belief about being ill generally persists even after a doctor examines them and confirms specifically that the person is not sick. This disorder is also known as hypochondria.

Do You Have Symptoms of Anxiety?

Although there are many types of anxiety disorders, you may have noticed some similarities between them. Anxiety is unique to the personal experience of each person; however, there are some symptoms and reactions that tend to be common among sufferers. These feelings may be manageable, or they may interfere with your daily life, and impact your ability to enjoy activities.

Depending on the disorder that you have, and to what degree it affects you, you may experience a variety of emotional and physical symptoms and reactions. Emotionally you may be unable to cope with an upcoming event. You may be plagued by self-doubt, feel out of control, start crying, or be fearful or panicky. Physically you may have reactions that include or range from butterflies in the stomach to a racing heart, hot and cold surges, and even throwing up. You may feel a complete disconnection between the body and the mind.

Some common symptoms of general anxiety are:

- Difficulty falling asleep due to not being able to stop thinking about things.
- Restlessness and the sense that something is always about to happen.
- A sense of doom or apprehension about the present or the future.
- Difficulty enjoying anything because of feelings of worry and fear.

- Increased heart rate and racing palpitations that come on suddenly when thinking about something or trying to do something.
- Trouble concentrating because there are too many thoughts racing through your mind.
- Rapid breathing or hyperventilating when faced with an idea or situation.

As previously indicated, you may experience some or all of these symptoms to varying degrees of severity. There are many more extreme symptoms of anxiety including panic attacks, nightmares, and disturbing intrusive thoughts that you are unable to control. You may be completely unable to go to some places or do certain things because you are unable to control extreme symptoms. Some people may even go into a dissociative state where they are unaware of their actions or are unable to communicate and function normally.

Have You Had An Anxiety Attack?

Have you ever been faced with a situation that caused you to feel completely overwhelmed by fear, panic or distress? Did this feeling build over time or progress from mild worry to an almost panic-like state? You may have had an anxiety attack.

The outward expression of an anxiety attack can vary significantly from person to person, and the feelings, symptoms, and behaviors of the person having the attack may also vary. The symptoms of anxiety may not affect everyone the same way. The symptoms may also change over time as the disorder progresses or regresses, or the situation reaches various states of resolution.

Common symptoms are similar to general anxiety, but an anxiety attack may specifically include:

- Worry and apprehension about pending situations
- Restlessness and continued attempts to get everything done

- Obsessively ruminating about the potential outcome of everything.
- Shortness of breath and hyperventilating when thinking about the tasks ahead.
- Feeling dizzy or off-balance or overwhelmed to the point of emotional fatigue.
- Hot flashes with sweating or cold chills or both.
- Dry mouth or other physical distress such as headache or stomach illness.
- Fear of people, places or the outcome of situations.
- Distress or hypersensitivity about what is happening or might happen.

Are Anxiety Attacks And Panic Attacks The Same?

While anxiety attacks and panic attacks share some common symptoms, they are not the same. The difference is easiest to understand in terms of the time they take to develop.

An anxiety attack develops progressively and is usually brought on by an upcoming event or a situation that is evolving and has an uncertain outcome. For many people, an anxiety attack may progress from a mild concern to especially acute reactions that can't be controlled. These reactions may be so severe that the person is unable to cope with continuing participation in the event, despite their original appearance of calm or competence.

In comparison, a panic attack is a direct, acute and sudden reaction to a situation, thought or event. It does not build over time into a panic state; the panic state comes upon the individual quite suddenly. A panic attack is a physical reaction to an emotional state of extreme distress about the current or shortly pending situation. You may be dressed up and ready to go, and looking forward to something, and then suddenly, you are overcome with feelings of illness or begin hyperventilating or crying as you prepare to leave. You may not understand what you are afraid of, but you are unable to move forward due to the debilitating sudden physical manifestations of panic.

What Causes Anxiety?

There are many theories about what causes anxiety disorders. Some are more forgiving than others in the amount of blame they place on the individual with the disorder. Researchers have theorized about various causes and treatments, but no one is completely sure why some people suffer and others don't.

In the case of PTSD, most people can understand that a severely traumatizing event may cause an anxiety disorder. They understand that extreme trauma will have lasting effects upon the psyche and that these effects may manifest in symptoms and behaviors that are difficult to cope with.

For those with less obvious cause and effect type conditions, it may be difficult to explain or even understand why we have these symptoms and behaviors. Doctors are still trying to understand mental health and studies are ongoing. There are many theories, but it is generally agreed that a combination of different factors may impact a person's likelihood to develop an anxiety disorder. Some factors are genetic and include brain chemistry or inherited conditions. It is also well understood that brain injuries may cause damage to the brain in a way that makes it unable to process stress in a manageable way. Some are caused by environmental factors such as living in a dangerous place, and some are a direct result of experiences that had negative consequences on us. Researchers know that there are some areas of the brain that are responsible for controlling fear and that when those areas are impacted the person may develop anxiety disorders as a result.

In general, it is agreed that anxiety is a reaction to stressors in our lives. The role of "stress" cannot be overlooked.

Anxiety And Stress

Stress and anxiety have a direct correlation. Stress usually comes about as a result of the brain's demands about a situation. When it evaluates the situation, a decision is made to be either okay with the situation, or to be "stressed about it". If you are worried about something, and it develops into stress, that may evolve into anxiety. Stress is caused by a situation that makes you uncomfortable or worried. If the mind is unable to resolve the stress in a healthy way, it may develop into anxiety, which is a more serious expression of the emotional and physical state of extreme stress.

Anxiety and stress have many of the same emotional and physical symptoms, but for those with anxiety, they are unable to resolve the stress and stop worrying. Some people are able to deal with stressors, and some people have anxiety disorders whereby they are unable to manage stress, and it takes a toll on their emotional and physical health.

Stress and anxiety can be bad, but they can also activate our body and mind to work harder and give us the adrenalin that we may need to "power through", "get through it", or "get it done". It can also ensure that you are aware of the dangers around you and take precautions. When stress and anxiety persist in a way that interferes with your enjoyment of the activities of your life, you may have developed an anxiety disorder.

How Is Anxiety Diagnosed?

Many people know they have anxiety but are unsure if they have an actual anxiety disorder. There is no single test used to diagnose anxiety disorders. Instead, an anxiety disorder diagnosis usually requires a lengthy examination carried out by a mental health professional.

Mental health evaluations are carried out by means of conversation, question and answer, and the use of psychological questionnaires. The use of a questionnaire allows the mental health professional to rate your symptoms on a standardized scale of severity. Questions are used to evaluate depression, anger, mania, anxiety, recurring thoughts, etc. and then the patient is classified based on the responses.

Some doctors may also recommend or conduct physical exams including urine and blood tests in order to rule out any underlying health conditions that may be contributing to your symptoms.

Anxiety Combined With Other Disorders

Sometimes, we may have a very complicated mental health situation. It is quite common to have an anxiety disorder combined with other conditions such as depression.

Depression

If you have an anxiety disorder, you may also suffer from depression. Anxiety and depression both impact the ability of the mind and the body to achieve joy. The symptoms of depression may worsen when they are triggered by the symptoms of an anxiety disorder. A person may be depressed because they can't control their anxiety and feel like they can't function in society. A person may be anxious because their depression is making them afraid to interact with others who might judge them because of their condition. With both depression and anxiety, being impacted in a way that is debilitating to your ability to function may require professional help to properly address.

Chapter Summary

In this chapter, we learned that stress and anxiety is a natural response of the body when we are confronted with a challenging situation. The nervous system has a natural evolutionary response to potential danger, called "freeze, fight or flight". This is triggered when the body releases adrenaline and the stress hormone known as cortisol. Anxiety is a natural response of the body to stress; however, when the response to the stressor becomes too extreme, it may signal the presence of an anxiety disorder.

We also learned how to recognize anxiety disorders, how different anxiety disorders are defined and how they are similar and different. You may have been wondering if you have an anxiety disorder, and if so, what are the symptoms? Although each person experiences anxiety in the context of their own experience, there are many similarities in the general symptoms experienced by sufferers of anxiety disorders. Reactions may be emotional and/or physical and can range from rapid breathing or hyperventilating, increased heart rate including palpitations, hot and cold flashes often accompanied by sweating, having invasive thoughts that can't be put aside, being constantly worried or scared about everything, and difficulty sleeping due to racing thoughts. You may even experience other physical symptoms such as being physically ill, catatonia, rashes, crying or hysterical panic.

Anxiety disorders are not yet fully understood, but the science of mental health is continuing to evolve. In some instances, there are easily explained life experiences that may lead to an anxiety disorder. In other cases, there is seemingly no explanation why some people are impacted and others aren't. A true diagnosis of a specific anxiety disorder requires collaboration with a mental health professional. If you have a mental illness that has debilitating negative impacts on your life, seek the help of a professional who can supervise your diagnosis and treatment.

If you are now comfortable with your general understanding of anxiety disorders and are not sure about obtaining professional intervention at this time, you may find the information and tools that follow to be valuable assets to you as you work to manage the anxiety in your life.

In the chapters that follow you will learn a variety of different techniques you can use to deal with anxiety

CHAPTER TWO:

How To Enjoy The Present By Using Mindfulness To Minimize Anxiety

It has been shown that practicing mindfulness can help reduce the symptoms of anxiety. In this chapter, you will learn how mindfulness is defined, how anxiety is influenced by the human consciousness, how the study and practice of mindfulness have evolved, and how you can use it to manage anxiety in your life.

What Is Mindfulness?

The practice of modern mindfulness is rooted in ancient Buddhist traditions. Mindfulness requires an individual to be present in the moment and to cast aside the thoughts that distract the mind from achieving the objective that is sought at that time.

Mindfulness is a state of non-judgemental awareness of ourselves and others. Let's review this very important concept again.

Mindfulness is based on acceptance and awareness of yourself. You must foster awareness of your inner experiences, thoughts, beliefs, and processes. This awareness and consideration must be accomplished without judgment. Depending on what you have experienced in your life, you will have different things to consider.

The Role Of Human Consciousness

You may be wondering, how does mindfulness work? In order to truly understand mindfulness, we need to consider the theories related to the state of human consciousness. A keen understanding of the state of consciousness is required to understand how mindfulness contributes to better overall mental health, and specifically in the management of anxiety disorders.

The "domains of human consciousness" have been discussed, theorized upon, and judged since humans began wondering about what makes themselves think and act the way they do. The current thoughts on the domains of consciousness (Henriques, 2015) include three main areas:

Experimental domain: This is sometimes referred to as the theatre of consciousness. This part is activated and deactivated by our state of being asleep or awake. This domain is based on personal experience. It is the domain that evaluates the facts of what is actually happening or being considered at that time.

Private self: This is the part of your consciousness that provides the ongoing narrative about what is happening to you. It may be evaluating the situation through the lenses of your personal experience or worldview.

Persona: This is the side of you that you show others. Your persona is what you consciously display to others as a means to express yourself with actions and words.

The consciousness may have additional filters that allow varying degrees of consideration by our consciousness about the situation at hand. For example, each domain of consciousness is influenced by the brain's ability to ignore some things and focus on others. We may do it intentionally or unintentionally. We may give emphasis to one fact over another, or one potential outcome over another. We may think obsessively about one potential outcome when other outcomes are just as likely. Similarly, we may deliberately ignore or suppress certain things in an effort to "get over them". These filters shield the mind from the full picture. Some filters are intended to protect the private self from the public persona. For example, you may not be comfortable being alone, so in a public place, you may focus on your cell phone instead of interacting with others around you or just peacefully observing and experiencing where you are at that moment in time. Similarly, you may tell people that you're fine when really you are very anxious about something that is about to happen. These are ways that human consciousness tries to protect us from the things that give us anxiety.

One of the things about the human domains of consciousness is that they tend to try to protect us. When the subconscious is aware of trauma, it may protect us by putting up filters in the form of blockages in our memories so that we are not regularly confronted by our negative experiences. When you forcibly (whether consciously or unconsciously) block traumatic memories or are ingenuine about how your life makes you feel, your system may become unstable and negatively impacted by anxiety and stress. Due to the instability, you may be unable to cope with the things in your environment that trigger those memories or feelings. These triggers may be events, places or people that remind you of trauma.

Controlling Your Personal Narrative With Mindfulness

You may be in a state of perpetual self-evaluation and self-judgment. People with anxiety disorders often are. Now that you understand the role of the human consciousness in dictating how we think about the world around us and our place in it, imagine considering all that without the self-judgment! That is what mindfulness allows you to do.

When we expose ourselves to a full spectrum of thoughts about our reality, such that the thoughts are not filtered by denial, self-criticism, and self-judgment, we have a better, truer understanding of self and others. This understanding can help us to react to things in a way that is not influenced by our negative beliefs about ourselves or the situations we may be in or are anticipating. This is why mindfulness is so helpful in handling anxiety.

The Power Of Mindfulness

Mindfulness techniques have been used to treat a variety of anxiety disorders including generalized anxiety and PTSD, as well as related conditions such as depression and obsessive-compulsive disorder (OCD).

As early as 1979, programs such as "*Mindfulness-Based Stress Reduction*" at the University of Massachusetts Medical School were established to pursue the study and practice of mindfulness. The creator of this program, Jon Kabat-Zinn, built upon his studies of Zen Buddhism and yoga, to develop a concept about mindfulness that could be taught to others. He wrote the book *"Full Catastrophe Living*" which advocated awareness on a moment to moment basis and the consideration of things we would usually ignore or discard (Wiki, 2020; Henriques, 2015). This concept has been adopted by many medical centers and mental health practitioners to assist patients to cope with anxiety and other conditions.

The reason why Buddhist teachings are often used as a base for understanding mindfulness is because of the profound belief in the inevitable suffering of life. If suffering is inescapable, then there is no need to escape it. It needs only to become part of the full landscape of our life. Trying to banish negative thoughts creates an imbalance in us that leads to negative consequences. Being aware of the totality of life, and the balance of good and bad allows us to more easily cope with the things that unsettle us, as we are aware of them without judgment of ourselves.

In 2012, mindfulness gained further public acclaim when Tim Ryan published "*A Mindful Nation*" and was subsequently given a large grant to teach mindfulness in schools. Other noted specialists, including Richard Davidson, an accomplished neuroscientist, and the interpersonal neurobiology community used mindfulness to better understand psychodynamic perspectives, emotions and how to optimize the function of the brain. (Henriques, 2015)

Mindfulness is often expanded to include meditation, which is the ancient form of attaining total awareness and peace through the practice of sitting still, clearing your mind, and coming into a state of complete oneness with the universe. We will go further into meditation in Chapter 9.

Chapter Summary

In this chapter, you learned about mindfulness and how human consciousness works to filter our thoughts, reactions, and behaviors in the world around us.

Mindfulness is based on being aware of and considering yourself and your experiences without judgment. It can be further expanded to gain an understanding and acceptance of the situations that you are in or about to face. Being aware of and focused on what you need to do in this moment prevents you from ruminating upon what might happen later. When you practice mindfulness, you can counteract anxiety because you are considering or doing only what needs to be done in the present moment.

If you experience anxiety in any form, you may achieve great success using mindfulness. You may be afraid of the future and what may happen in your life. Consider how mindfulness can be used to focus you on what you need to do at this moment in time. Mindfulness involves paying attention to the specifics of your daily life and all the things that you usually rush through or take for granted. Focusing on being mindful of your present makes your mind unavailable to worry about what is making you anxious.

Mindfulness can be practiced consciously throughout your daily activities. It can also be practiced through meditation, which forces you to stop everything and take time to be present and aware of the totality of existence, instead of our small part in it.

In the next chapter, we will learn about what happens and what to do when anxiety attacks…

CHAPTER THREE:

What To Do When Anxiety Attacks

Anxiety and panic are real reactions that real people have to the situations around them. They may not want to feel this way but have no control over how their body reacts to the stressors in their lives. We know that the physical symptoms of anxiety may include unpleasant physical sensations and impacts upon our emotional and physical wellbeing. These sensations of doom, overwhelming inability to cope, dread, nervousness, physical illness, and emotional dismay are all real symptoms that people with anxiety strive to cope with.

Typical Anxiety Indicators

There are three predictable types of reactions that people going through anxiety may experience. Let's review each of them.

Physically Heightened State That Is Similar To Terror And Panic

This is a state of the body that is characterized by heart palpitations, shortness of breath, muscular tension, crying or hysteria and even physical illness. This happens when the body releases the stress hormones adrenaline and cortisol. As we discussed before, this is often referred to as a panic attack and is usually an immediate reaction to a specific trigger or stressor. An ongoing state of heightened anxiety that persists can have serious health consequences and has been known to lead to heart attacks and elevated blood pressure.

A "Wired" Feeling Of Tension That Is Associated With Being "Stressed Out"

Many people with generalized anxiety disorder experience the feeling of tension, stress, and dread in reaction to or anticipation of current or future activities. This can be a cycle of self-perpetuating worry that inevitably leads to increasing levels of stress as the body anticipates a resolution. When the body is constantly on edge, persistent restlessness, agitation and worry can have negative impacts on your overall health.

The Mental Anguish Of Rumination

When your brain won't stop thinking distressing thoughts, and you are routinely plagued by reruns of previous events, or anticipated scenarios, it can impact our ability to think positively and to take action. Rumination can also be associated with depression and dissociative behavior because the individual recedes into a reflective, contemplative, or worrying state that may last for long periods of time. It may cause persistent nausea and tension, or a sense of suffocating under the weight of the things you are thinking about. The ruminations may persist when we are trying to do other things, resulting in problems with concentration, and an inability to interact successfully with others.

Understand Why Anxiety Happens To You

Understanding why anxiety happens to you is often referred to as recognizing your triggers. There is usually a direct correlation between a specific stressor and the reaction of anxiety. For example, you may have been attacked by a dog when you were young. Ever since then, you have a terrible fear of dogs, and the idea of going to a park may terrify you to the point where you are unable to enjoy taking your children out in nature. An invitation to a new friend's house who has a dog may cause you to get progressively more and more anxious until right before the event, you have a panic attack and are not able to attend. Because you don't want to be judged for your fear, phobia or anxiety, you might tell them you are sick with the flu. Then you may have further anxiety because you disappointed yourself by not being able to go, and you have lied to a new friend.

A lot of anxiety revolves around the question of "what if". Often, if you are able to effectively predict the specifics of a situation, you have no reason to fear it. That is why a lot of people with anxiety disorders prefer reliable routines where things are predictable, and there is little variation. This allows for less possibility of the unknown impacting your life.

Knowing what your stressors are can help you to organize your life such that you have fewer stressors and more predictability with situations you know will trigger your anxiety. For example, you might rather miss the event than risk being judged by your new friend. However, if you tell your new friend that you are terrified of dogs and you are not sure if you can come to their house, they may just surprise you by saying, "no problem, my neighbor sometimes dog sits for us, I'll ask them if the dogs can hang out over there for the night, really, it will be less chaos in the house anyway."

Understanding why anxiety happens is the first step to managing your symptoms and finding ways to manage your stressors so they don't have such a negative impact on your life.

Fear is one of the most common reasons why symptoms of anxiety, including panic attacks, may be perpetuating a cycle of negative impacts on your emotional and physical health. If you can tell yourself that your anxiety is a normal response to a perceived threat and that you are likely "overreacting", that can be a useful tool, allowing you to talk yourself into other calming behaviors and thoughts.

Remember It Will Pass

No matter how severe your reaction to stress is, even when it is a serious panic attack, it is helpful to remember that it will pass. It may be hard to understand that when you are in the middle of a high anxiety state. No matter how "jacked up" or "obsessed" or "panicky" you feel, there is a point where another physical or emotional reaction will take over. Tell yourself, "this will pass, this will pass", and practice some techniques of managing your symptoms. The sooner you do this, the sooner the intensity of your anxiety will decrease.

Techniques For Managing Panic, Feeling Wired and Excessive Rumination

Take Care Of Your Body

It may seem like common sense, but we often forget to take care of ourselves, which can impact our ability to handle stress. This can include not eating properly, not sleeping properly and not getting any exercise. When the body is deficient in nutrients and energy, it is not capable of handling stressors in a healthy way. Some people believe that a diet that is low in caffeine, sugar and alcohol results in the body and mind being more resilient to stress and a decrease in the symptoms of anxiety. We will talk more in a later chapter about how diet and self-care routines can enhance your ability to cope with anxiety and make your reactions to stress more reasonable.

Use Deep Breathing

People often say, "just breathe", and they are right. Sometimes when anxiety is heightened, we start breathing in short jagged bursts, and may even hyperventilate. This reduces the available oxygen to the blood and brain and compounds the effects of anxiety as the state of physical distress elevates.

When you stop and take long deep breaths, slowly and deliberately, it calms the body and mind and makes us more able to attend to the situation at hand with calm and clarity. Some people call this diaphragmatic breathing or belly breathing. It is characterized by taking air slowly into your lungs and letting your belly expand with air instead of your chest, and then letting the air out slowly as you allow your belly to deflate. You can also do a version where you expand your belly first, and then your chest, and then breathe out slowly in the reverse order.

Some people swear by sessions of deep breathing, done lying down in a quiet undisturbed environment. This is, of course, the optimal practice of deep breathing for therapy. However, don't underestimate the powerful calming effect of a few deep breaths anytime you are waiting for something or feel your level of anxiety rising.

Mindful Awareness

As you learned previously, there are many benefits to a state of mindful awareness, also called mindfulness. When you are overcome with feelings of heightened anxiety or are caught in a cycle of rumination, use mindfulness to reorient you to the specifics of the present.

What can be observed at that moment? What are you doing that needs your full attention? If you want to do a full exercise, you would still your body and close your eyes. Consider how your body feels, concentrate on how you feel when you breathe, and try to take inventory of your physical sensations. Then, with your eyes still closed, shift your attention away from yourself and become aware of the sounds and smells around you, and what is happening around you. This practice is a tool that can help you to move beyond your feelings of distress because you have to deliberately silence those thoughts in order to become aware of what is around you.

Distract Yourself

Another way to be present in the moment, and effectively put anxious thoughts at bay is the time-honored tradition of distracting yourself. When you are having feelings of intense anxiety or are caught in a cycle of overthinking and rumination, it can be hard to focus on anything but your anxiety, and this can just intensify the symptoms.

It can be extremely useful to choose an activity and concentrate on doing that instead. This is especially useful if the activity requires concentration or movement. It can be hard to focus on anything other than how you're feeling during an anxiety attack and this can intensify symptoms.

If you can get your mind to focus on something else, there is less room for the anxiety in your active reality, and you may experience a significant decrease in the severity of your symptoms. There are many activities that may help. For example, listening to an audiobook, playing a musical instrument, loading wood, doing laundry, gardening or running an errand. It can sometimes be a benefit to select a chore so that you can feel good about getting something productive done. If you use a personal reward distraction, like reading or listening to a book, or singing along to some favorite music, congratulate yourself on making quality personal time for yourself.

Walk Around A Bit

You might feel as if staying in one safe contained space is best for you when you are feeling anxious. Although this can be comforting because it is predictable, it can allow you to sink further into a cycle of anxiety or other negative feelings. Like with choosing a distraction, walking around a bit can be an effective way to change your state of mind. It will help to burn off some of the adrenaline and get your blood moving, which will assist to clear your mind. Staying in one spot for too long may cause our body to stiffen and even cramp up, causing us additional physical distress. We may not realize it until we get up, so get up often and "stretch your legs" as they say. This might be the last thing you want to do when you're feeling panicky but it will help you get out of the state of mind you were in.

Release Some Tension

When the body is stressed and anxious, it often reacts by becoming tense, and we may develop pain or stiffness related to immobility and/or tension. Releasing tension is effectively done by deliberately physically changing the state of your body. If your body and mind are currently feeling bad because you are holding onto stress or anxiety, make efforts to release this tension. This can be done by breathing deeply and then exhaling all the air in a "whoosh", imaging your tension leaving your body on the breath you expel.

One of the best and most effective ways to release tension is through stretching and exercise. This forces the body into a new position and gets blood and oxygen moving through the body and brain. This movement can change your perspective and make you feel less muscular stiffness. As you stretch, your body will reward you with happy hormones like endorphins, instead of negative hormones like adrenaline and cortisol.

Summary

In this chapter you learned about typical anxiety indicators such as a physically heightened state similar to terror, being "wired" or "stressed out", and the anguish of persistent rumination. Being plagued by the constant worry of "what if" can be exhausting both emotionally and physically. Understanding why you have these reactions to anxiety is critical and being able to identify your triggers is key to improving your mental health.

You also learned some effective techniques for managing these symptoms of stress. Some of the most effective ones are taking care of your body, using deep breathing and distracting yourself to name a few.

In the next chapter, you will learn more about how to handle tension, stress, and dread…

CHAPTER FOUR:

What to Do When There's Tension, Stress, and Dread

As we have already learned, anxiety disorders can manifest in a variety of negative ways, ranging from extreme panic and anxiety attacks to a sense of perpetual tension, stress, and dread.

In order to handle your emotional and physical reactions to the stressors in your life, you must recognize your triggers and symptoms when you are faced with them. Sensations of ongoing tension and dread are managed differently than acute reactions such as panic attacks. Some of the techniques for addressing symptoms are similar because these techniques are so effective for a variety of conditions. For example, deep breathing and mindfulness are effective ways to calm and reorient yourself.

Perpetual tension and dread may be a result of the continual narrative in our minds that recycles worry and causes us to think constantly about terrible things that might happen as a result of our decisions or actions.

Don't Listen To Your Own Negative Feedback

Sometimes you may be filled with dread and feelings of tension because you are convinced of your own inadequacy or inability to cope with potential events. Because the negative voice in our head tends to be loud, persistent and domineering, it can be easy to focus on what it is saying. It is important to realize that you can change the narrative in your mind by consciously telling yourself to put aside the negative feedback and make room for the positive feedback about yourself or your situation. Tell yourself something like, "yes, yes, I know it could all go wrong, but what would it look like if it was going well", or "we've been over this before and there are other more positive ways to look at this". Envision that positive outcome and focus on letting that make you feel good.

This is similar to the idea of not believing the lies your mind tells you. The mind may lie to us to trick us into staying mentally in one place and obsessing about something. It may be telling you that you need to use all your energy worrying about a certain outcome, or that you will never get all the things done that you need to. You can choose to not believe what your mind is trying to convince you of. Don't be afraid to say to yourself and your negative thoughts, "I don't believe you. You sound really convincing, but I don't buy it. I have other options."

When Worry Calls To You, Don't Listen

When our mind and body are in a state of perpetual worry, it can be an automatic reaction to evaluate every situation or plan with a mindset of anxiety or doom. Perpetual worry and a sense of impending doom may manifest as hypervigilance in some people. This is when someone is fixated on making sure everything is safe and okay and going precisely as intended.

A state of continual focus on our fearful state can be hard to escape. This is especially true if we are busy, with many things on the go, and thus, we may feel that we have lots of things to "worry about". There may be a voice in our head that prompts us to look for something to worry about, especially if we have a free moment. This "voice of worry" is hard to turn off, and it is easy to let it dominate the theatre of our consciousness. Once you recognize that voice, however, it is easier to make choices about whether you will listen, or how much time or energy you will devote to its concerns.

When worry comes calling, tell it that you're busy actually doing something useful. Then focus on or do something positive. It may be as simple as focusing on all the things that went right today or doing something to occupy your mind with other thoughts. When you feel your body tensing up with stress, take a moment to relax your body and mind with a deep breathing exercise or a good stretch.

Make A List And Then Either Act On It Or Ignore It

This may sound like an odd strategy, but it is a way to give body and form to concerns which may be clouding your perspective and making you anxious. You may not even realize why you feel so tense, stressed out or filled with dread. Take the time to sit down and make a list of all the things that are nagging at your mind and giving you distress. Seeing your worries in a tangible form may have several benefits, including giving clarity to the reasons why you are in distress.

Seeing a list of your issues allows solutions to present themselves, which then puts your mind and body at ease. You may not realize how worried you were about getting the kids to camp until you wrote it down, which made you remember that your neighbor had already offered to take your kids with hers. This allows the identification, legitimization, and resolution of one of the things that was giving you anxiety. Add a column to the list that itemizes the ways you have planned for the item to go well, and check things off your list as you identify resolution.

Sometimes you may not have an obvious solution to all the things on the list. Sometimes the things on the list may not even make sense. They may not be anything you have any control over. That's okay! Making a list of the things that you are anxious about allows you to give them deliberate time and space in your theater of consciousness.

You can choose to come back to the list or to put it aside and ignore it. This allows you to empty your mind of the worries since you can always refer to the list if you really want to or need to. Once you have the list, you must then make a conscious choice to put the list and its contents aside and move your attention to other things. These should be things that have a positive impact on you.

Focus On Fun For A While

This concept is based on the old expression that "laughter is the best medicine". When our mind is obsessed with anxiety, feelings of tension, stress, and dread, we rarely make time for or accept the potential for fun in our lives. After all, it is hard to have fun when you are overcome with worry, stress or dread! We may ignore opportunities for fun because we don't feel we deserve it. We may even feel guilty for enjoying something because we have not overcome the barriers to resolving the other issues we face.

Doing an activity that causes us to smile or laugh or play removes us from the state of worry and dread and fills us with happy hormones such as endorphins. When we are consumed with anxiety, it may be challenging to create that opportunity for fun in our lives. Take the time to play a game, go to the park with a ball or a camera, watch a funny show or listen to a funny book, play with a child or do something impulsive that you used to enjoy back when life seemed easier. If you can get yourself to laugh and lose yourself in some fun, your feelings of dread will be minimized or eliminated. We will talk more about embracing joy in Chapter 7.

Chapter Summary

At times, we are unduly affected by tension, stress, and dread. We may experience regular intervals of persistent anxiety and have difficulty moving beyond those feelings to function effectively.

In this chapter, you learned that we can make choices about what to focus on and take active steps to control our thoughts. Some of these useful techniques include not listening to your own negative feedback, not listening when worry calls to you, making a list and then either acting on it or ignoring it and focusing on fun for a while. Using these techniques gives you an opportunity to recognize what is causing you to focus on your stress and anxiety, and then put them aside in favor of more opportunities for positive outcomes.

In the next chapter, you will learn about overcoming excessive worry and thinking…

CHAPTER FIVE:

Overcoming Excessive Worry and Overthinking

In this chapter, we are going to focus more on the behavior of rumination and overthinking that keeps us in a constant state of worry.

Rumination, also called "brooding" or "overthinking" is a state of perpetual consideration of the challenges we face, or the things we have been through, or the potential outcome of future situations. It is considered a cyclical self-perpetuating behavior that can be difficult to interrupt. Like any object in motion, it is easy to keep in motion, but when it stops, it is harder to get going again. That is why interrupting the pattern of overthinking is critical to overcoming this symptom of anxiety.

Realize You're Doing It

The first step to overcoming excessive worry and overthinking is to realize and admit to yourself that you are doing it. This may not be easy, because no one wants to admit they have a debilitating condition that causes them to think obsessively about things to the point that they have no room for happiness, joy or positive thoughts. Once you realize that you are exhibiting this negative and destructive behavior, you can take action to overcome it.

Switch It Off

Once you realize you are caught in a cycle of perpetual worry, it can be hard to just "switch it off". Some people are able to just tell themselves not to worry, and their mind moves on to other things. For those with the tendency to worry obsessively about things, they may need to use deliberate exercises to assist them.

Some therapists use a method of extracting, compartmentalizing and then shelving or releasing the things that are causing our anxiety. This requires a conscious awareness of what is causing our distress. This is where that list might come in handy again! This technique requires you to close your eyes and focus on a box that is open and empty. Then you itemize an item that you are anxious about and mentally put it in the box, put a lid on it, then place it on a shelf in your mind. Tell yourself that those boxes are there for you to reference if you need them, but that you don't need them right now. The result can be a mind that is clear and uncluttered.

If you want to practice this technique in a more literal tangible way, you can expand on the use of your list. Get slips of paper and write one worry down on each piece of paper, and then put them all in a box or bag. There are various things you can do with the box or bag, including put it on a shelf, burn it or put it in the recycling to be repurposed into something new. When you acknowledge the things that you are worrying excessively about and take action to put them away, you are able to "switch it off" because you have given it meaning and a place that is external to your own mind.

Interrupt Your Thoughts

When you find yourself caught in a cycle of excessive worry and overthinking, you must make a persistent effort to interrupt those thoughts as soon as you become conscious of them. If you notice you have been thinking intently about one of your concerns, tell yourself firmly, "stop that, you're overthinking again, move along", and then consciously choose a different thing to think about, preferably something tangible to your present situation. This brings you back to the practice of mindfulness and being present for the activity we are supposed to be paying attention to. It may take hundreds of interruptions per day, but if you are consistent, you can break the pattern of your mind sinking into overthinking, just by consciously interrupting and redirecting your thoughts.

Designate Official Worrying Time

Much of the time, the things we worry about are tangible and have to be resolved at some point. If we just let our mind obsess about all of it at once, and it does this all the time, we can be overwhelmed and suffer the negative impacts of anxiety. By designating a time for worries to be recognized and processed, the mind can rest easier knowing that the issues will be addressed and that it doesn't have to constantly bug you for resolution.

Choose a time that you will dedicate to processing through your current concerns. Decide in advance how long you will spend on this activity so that you are not drawn into a long unproductive state of overthinking and worry. Carefully and thoroughly go through one or all of your worries, making a list if you want to. Identify the things that can be acted upon in the short term, make a list of those and resolve to accomplish them at a particular time. Set a time when you will revisit these worries and determine the status of the items of concern. Faithfully review the items at the designated time. This way, when persistent worry starts to creep in, you can tell it, "Hey, I already worried about you, and you're scheduled again for later, now go away".

You can take this philosophy one step further by following the practice of "only worry once". Once you have gone through the worries and given them voice and form, put them aside and move onto other things.

The extension of this is to plan instead of worry. When you identify your worries and then make a plan to resolve them and act on that plan, there is no need for the mind to obsess about them, because the outcome is determined and there is nothing left to worry about.

Go Out Into The Community

Sometimes a change of scene can make us "forget about our worries". This can be as simple as going for a walk in your community or traveling to a different town or country. Seeing how other people live and interacting with others may give us a useful perspective on the scope of our problems or help us forget our own worries for a while. Just being exposed to new input may be enough to get us out of the mental rut that rumination puts us in. If you can find something to take your mind off your worries, you may find that you are able to enjoy the things that you have been too anxious to notice.

Switch Gears

When your mind is clouded with worry and you are overthinking every situation and potential scenario, it can be useful to confuse the senses by switching gears from a state of mental fixation to a state of physical activity. This can help to shock your system into getting into a different frame of mind, one that is not obsessed with the worries you have. The transition from mental activity to physical activity may also trick the system into focussing on the needs of the body instead of the mind, providing a welcome distraction. Depending on the level of activity you engage in, you may get the added benefits of better health.

Shocking the senses interrupts the flow of negative thoughts, which can help to shut them off, or redirect them. For example, splashing cold water on your face may interrupt symptoms of hot flashes brought on by anxiety. You may take a moment to say to yourself, "wow, that's refreshing", and feel a moment of comfort and respite.

Summary

In this chapter we learned how to move beyond overthinking and excessive worry. The most important step is to realize that you are doing it. If you can identify the behavior when it happens, this awareness gives you the opportunity to stop the behavior. Some people may be able to just switch it off by saying, "now is not the time or place for overthinking this". Others may have success with visualizing the thoughts going into boxes that are arranged on an imaginary shelf, only to be accessed when we want them. Some may go even further and write these thoughts down and put them in an actual box on a shelf or take the symbolic action of burning them. Sometimes, if we designate time to address our worries and plan for their resolution, the mind will consider that enough effort spent, and restrict its worrying to that designated worry time. It can also be useful to get a change of scene by going out into the community and being exposed to other things and people to give us either perspective on our situation, or as a distraction from it. Similarly, a switch from a mentally involved state to a physically active state of the body may be enough to shock the body into releasing excessive worry and stop overthinking.

In the next chapter, you will learn how you can turn your nervousness and anxiety into excitement…

CHAPTER SIX:

Turning Nervousness and Anxiety into Excitement

We all experience emotions differently. There are so many kinds of emotions and we all go through a range of emotions in our lives. These emotions are typically generated as a response to stimuli in our environment and the expectations that we have of ourselves.

Many emotions like happiness, amusement, contentment, and love are positive and make our lives fulfilling and enjoyable. Excitement is another positive emotion. A positive emotional state can come from our own approach to life, or as a reaction to the good things that we experience. Negative emotions such as fear, nervousness, anxiety, and anger all have detrimental effects on our psychological and physical health. Negative emotional responses can come upon us as a result of fear and doubt in ourselves or as a result of things that happen to us. Nervousness and anxiety are negative emotions that hold us back from fully engaging with the opportunities in our lives.

Sometimes, we need to take time to honor emotions that put us in a negative, depressed or somewhat anxious state of mind. For example, the grief of bereavement may lead to crying and sadness, and that's okay. Give those emotions the time and energy they need. That is a positive choice. At the point that these emotions and energy drain begin to have an overwhelmingly negative impact on your life, it is time to redirect yourself into more positive expressions of your grief and lost love.

If you are experiencing nervousness and anxiety, those negative emotions may be dragging you down and making it hard to function effectively. What if you could take your nervousness and anxiety and focus all that emotional and physical energy into something positive like excitement? This is possible because the manifestations of nervousness and excitement are similar in many ways. For example, butterflies in the stomach, or feeling on edge and jittery. These signals from our body can be a positive form of energy that propels us towards completing our goal. However, when these physical expressions of nervousness build to a point of extreme anxiety, it can be debilitating.

Before that nervousness builds, try to redirect that energy into a positive outcome, like excitement.

Identify The Root Cause Of Your Anxiety

It is undeniable that people are different and so is our reaction to things. It is important for you to know that the expression of nervousness in different people can be from a variety of causes. The degree to which that nervousness turns into debilitating anxiety can depend on the intensity of exposure to the cause of the anxiety.

People have many fears about themselves and their interactions with others in the home, the workplace, and the community. Fear of failure or embarrassment, or a fear of not belonging are common. Fear is considered one of the major causes of anxiety. There are many times that you will fail to reach your full potential simply because you fear the unknown and are not able to follow through on your desired plan. So many people are inconsiderate and say, "well, you should just get over it". That may be easy for others to say, but they probably don't understand how real the feelings are for you, and how much they impact your ability to function effectively. As insensitive as their statement may have been, there is some value in finding ways to move beyond your fears and accomplish your goals, whatever they are. In order to do that, and before you can devise a lasting solution, it is important to fully understand the causes of the fear you face and eventually develop tools that help you to recognize the onset of symptoms, and redirect them into other more positive emotions.

Nervousness may also be as a result of a medical condition that you inherited. Genetic conditions and inherited traits are commonly passed down through DNA, from one generation to another. Perhaps your mother was considered a jittery woman with a lot of nervous energy. Perhaps you are also this way. Likely, you both have chemical imbalances that cause surges of adrenalin in you and make you restless and nervous as a response to stimuli in your environment. Just because she was that way doesn't mean that you have to accept this as "your lot in life". It just means that she didn't have the necessary tools to understand and treat her condition. It doesn't have to be the same for you. You don't have to accept that it is something you can't influence, manage or control. If you understand what initiates the nervous behavior, you can devise ways to manage it.

In some cases, such conditions and others may require medication and the collaboration of a psychological care provider. That's okay, and you will learn about working with a therapist in a later chapter. There are other cases where these outward symptoms of nervousness are the result of legitimate medical conditions that have nothing to do with anxiety or emotional distress. Other causes of nervous, jittery behavior may be the result of neurological medical conditions, brain injury or other physical disabilities. These conditions all require medical intervention and treatment. Other causes may include exposure to toxic substances or the use of illicit drugs like methamphetamines.

Other times, the outward expression of nervous tension and anxious behaviors may actually be the result of a positive emotion such as excitement. In these situations, the anticipation of the outcome causes jittery, on edge, hyper-focused behavior with emotional bursts and exclamations. This happens when people are focussed on watching a competitive sports game like football or hockey. Maybe your team is almost winning. Maybe this game is a "do-or-die" situation in that they might be eliminated from a championship series. Similarly, the movie or TV series might be so suspenseful that you can barely contain yourself to find out how it ends? Maybe you are waiting for someone at the airport that you haven't seen in a long time, and you are acting jittery and nervous. These are all positive expressions of excitement.

Developing a strong sense of self-awareness can help us recognize how our behaviors express our feelings. Since we understand both nervousness and excitement, and how they share many of the same physical and emotional characteristics, we can use that information to our advantage. Nervous energy may be unavoidable, but what if we could use our understanding to help direct the energy from negative nervousness to positive excitement? It is possible!

To accomplish this, try to be self-aware and understand the underlying causes of the anxieties you are trying to deal with. Since each person is different, complete your own self-assessment to determine what behaviors you express in different situations, and how close the line is between nervousness leading to anxiety, and the expression of nervous excitement.

Find Out What Triggers Initiate Your Anxiety Reaction

After developing an understanding of the ways in which your mind and body express anxiety, you are better positioned to examine what triggers this behavior. Being able to identify the causes of the nervous and anxious behaviors you may have allows you to identify what things in your environment are a catalyst for the onset of these physical responses. Understanding what causes the anxiety to dominate your mind and body is not always easy. It requires an honest effort to self-assess and observe the world around you to really understand how you feel when things happen. The specific things that trigger anxiety and anxious behavior vary from people to people, but there is a lot of common ground. It may be helpful to start with trying to understand your triggers from a broad perspective and then from a specific perspective.

For instance, students experience varying degrees of stress related to final exams. Some people handle stress with grace and calm while others suffer from anxiety and depression. They may be equally smart and have studied for the same amount of time. Why does one person become nervous and sick with anxiety? No one is really sure, but those that experience acute anxiety in some situations often have an underlying fear of failure. Also, the students may have a different expectation of the consequence of the outcome of the exams. Imagine that in your case, the results will determine whether or not you qualify for a scholarship for college. If you have other means of paying for college, then the loss of the scholarship may not cause too much anxiety for you. On the other hand, if you will not be able to go to college without winning the scholarship, the thought of not getting a good enough grade may cause debilitating anxiety. Such a dire consequence of failure may result in an inability for you to settle your mind until the results are finally released. In this case, it could be said that the exam itself is the cause of the nervousness and anxiety, but in fact, it is the fear of failure that is the root cause. Qualifying for a scholarship for college is not the cause of the nervousness, it is merely an instrument for the fear of failure resulting in a negative impact on personal or family income.

This person may have a similar emotional and physical reaction every time they are faced with a task that may have a high impact on their quality of life or basic survival needs. After all, don't forget, anxiety is an evolved trait, a characteristic of our survival instinct that feels it is necessary to identify and handle threats to our wellbeing.

Let's further consider the fearful, anxious student mentioned above. If the student develops a sense of mindfulness and evaluates their situation without judgment, they may use their observations to identify that trigger for themselves. Once they realize that the exam triggered the fearful anxious reaction and that they are scared because failure may mean not going to college, they can focus on a plan to convert that energy into positive acceptance, scheduled worry time, distractions or even planning for success.

Other triggers for these behaviors may include visible competition with others. When our failure is public and not just private, the consequences can seem so much bigger, and this naturally drives the anxiety level higher. Anything that causes uncertainty for the future can trigger nervousness and anxiety. Things that challenge our self-confidence and make us confront perceived challenges or shortcomings can also trigger a negative emotional state.

Let's use an example from the workplace. An upcoming project deadline may be causing you an undue amount of stress and anxiety. You have started to act nervous and jittery and are having trouble concentrating on your work. Furthermore, you are not able to function effectively at home due to your preoccupation with the project. When you do a careful self-examination, you may discover that the anxiety you are feeling has been triggered by a fear of failure, because your project teammate and you are both being evaluated for a promotion. You may not have told your domestic partner, and you don't want to get their hopes up. You don't want them to see you as a failure and are worried they will be disappointed in you.

Whenever you have an activity or task where the consequences of the outcome are significant to you, it is natural to be nervous. When that nervousness turns into debilitating anxiety, it is critically important to identify the source of your anxiety and take positive steps to manage it. This benefits both you and your loved ones, who may be troubled by your emotional or physical state and want to help you.

Studying and identifying your triggers and understanding the root causes of your anxiety are the only way you can move beyond them and transform the negative physical responses into positive energy.

Transforming Anxiety And Nervousness Into Excitement

Understanding the root causes of your anxiety, recognizing your triggers and using coping techniques previously discussed, you are well-positioned to consider the challenge of transforming your negative, nervous, anxious energy into the positive energy of excitement. This is not to be undertaken with the belief that it is easy, and it doesn't just happen because you want it to. You have to maintain constant awareness of your state of mind and body and be able to redirect that energy when you feel it coming over you. It may sound exhausting but once you have trained your body to redirect itself, it will require little effort. As with many things, "practice makes perfect". You may consider the occurrence of such anxious behaviors as a downfall. However, with the right tools and attitude, it is also possible for you to be able to turn the anxieties and nervousness into something positive and useful.

There are various ways to approach transforming negative nervousness into excitement. One method was developed by Cung Khuu, a personal development writer (Khuu, 2018). He discusses the fact that we often try to go from anxiety to calm. This is very hard to do since the emotional and physical responses to anxiety and calm are so different. On the other hand, since anxiety and excitement are so similar in how the body reacts, it is easier to convince the mind that the feelings are tied to something positive.

He suggested that you can reduce anxieties and nervousness through self-development, determination and the following of four simple steps. It starts with the simple statement of "get excited". Some people are able to make that switch easily. They feel the symptoms of nervousness coming on, such as sudden flashes of hot or cold, nausea or jittery movements. Then they say to themselves, "I'm not nervous, I'm excited!" and they then think about all the potential positive outcomes of the situation instead of the negative ones.

Cung Khuu suggests that when you are in a situation that makes you nervous or anxious, and you are not able to convert your negative energy into positive excitement, you should follow four simple steps. Let's identify the steps, explain them, and then consider the ways that we can use them to move from nervousness and anxiety to excitement.

Embrace The Emotions

Take the time to examine your physical and emotional response. Recognize how you feel. Are you hyperventilating, are you sweating, are you jittery and can't stop moving, or are you unable to move because you feel so ill? Give the emotions a moment of thanks for making you so aware of the potential dangers to you, and then recognize how these symptoms are similar to excitement. In talking about embracing your emotions, Cung Khuu, encourages you not to fight the emotions you are experiencing. This does not mean you should encourage the escalation of the emotional or physical condition. This is to help you identify it and deal with it within a shorter period of time. You may tell yourself, "wow, this is how I'm feeling and that is legitimate, but I will only let my mind and body indulge in this behavior for a designated period of time". After all, the expression "time heals everything" is indicative of the diminishing impact of anxiety on our body the further we move away in time from the triggering event. Giving it recognition makes it less mysterious, and that gives it less power over you.

In addition to embracing the emotions, it is also important that you conduct positive self-talk and try to convert your feelings into positive manifestations of excitement. Making deliberately positive statements about yourself or your situation has immediate benefits to your emotional and physical state. Tell yourself nice things and believe them! Invest your energy in thoughts of personal development and the embracing of positive ideas.

Most people can understand that someone who is in mourning is naturally consumed with grief and may cry for long periods of time. That is an example of accepting the emotions and allowing yourself to go through them. Most people also understand that at some point you have to move beyond that emotion to another state of mind. Although this is different from embracing the anxious responses of the body to stress, it is a good example of how people have been encouraged to embrace emotion, give it value, space and time in an effort to move beyond the emotion into a different one. Recognizing the intensity of your emotions without judgment is less burdensome on the psyche than criticizing yourself for the perceived weakness of succumbing to negative emotions. Facing your emotional state head-on is usually a better way to deal with it, and by doing so, you have a higher potential of being able to redirect that energy.

Stop Beating Yourself Up

You are really hard on yourself. Sometimes the things we are nervous about are out of our control and we must simply wait for an outcome. The outcome will be the same whether you worry about it or not. Stop focusing on all the ways you believe you have caused your own demise or all the ways things could go wrong. Stop it! Remember to tell yourself that despite any perceived obstacles, there are many advantages to putting your worries aside. You have made efforts towards your goal, and you deserve to congratulate yourself on that.

Cung Khuu also encourages us not to be so deeply consumed by the negative thoughts that we have. Nervousness and other signs of anxiety are often an outward expression of overthinking. When these symptoms are acute and debilitating, they may be at a point where they are dangerous to your health. You may develop additional negative symptoms such as migraines or even have a heart attack or experience dangerous spikes in your blood pressure that could lead to a stroke. These are serious medical conditions that may be avoided if you properly manage your anxiety.

Don't beat yourself up for not achieving everything you want to right now. Stop beating yourself up over the fact that you are not dealing with your stress and anxiety very well. Give yourself a break!

Sometimes things happen that we are unable to control, but we are able to control our reaction to them if we give ourselves the chance to move beyond our emotional state.

For example, imagine a college student who has an academic scholarship and is fully sponsored by an organization. The money the student receives is just enough to pay the bills, and there is none left over to save for an emergency. At some point, the scholarship money is delayed due to an administrative error at the institution's accounting department. For this reason, the student is unable to pay their rent because they have not received the money in time. When they tell the landlord what happened, they are threatened with eviction if they don't pay on time. In order to meet their financial obligations, they decide to borrow money from their parents because they are worried about eviction for non-payment. This situation would be very upsetting to many people. Some people would escalate their negative feelings to include berating themselves. They might berate themselves for failure to manage their money, the nervousness of asking for a financial loan, and the anxiety of potentially losing their housing. Once you recognize that you have these feelings ask yourself if you are being unduly hard on yourself. Stop beating yourself up! For example, you can confidently tell yourself that everything is okay because you did not fail to manage your money. The scholarship money failed to arrive on time. That was not because of anything you did. Furthermore, your parents had the money to lend and understood that it was just a temporary cash-flow problem caused by no fault of your own. To continue in this vein, there is no reason to be anxious about getting evicted because you were able to secure the loan to pay your rent. You should feel good about how you recognized the problem in time, rallied your resources, and solved the issue before it had any truly negative consequences for you.

Try To Convince Yourself You Are Excited

Make a conscious effort to reframe your emotions. Your body currently believes that these emotions are a reaction to negative stimuli; dangers that we must be protected from. What if your body believed that these physical responses were a sign of excitement due to the potential of something good happening? Tell yourself why this is exciting. Could the outcome have positive benefits for you? What are all the good things that could come out of it? Instead of the emotions signaling impending doom, tell your body those emotions signal the approach of a new exciting opportunity.

Sometimes our mind and body develop an attachment to the relationship between stimuli and reaction and it is familiar, though may not be comfortable. The body immediately responds in the same way to the same triggers. When we feel anxious and nervous, we are often thinking about all the negative potential of a situation and all the ways in which we could fail or let ourselves down. For this reason, the body and mind are associating this kind of situation and the emotions you feel with a negative outcome.

Because of this tendency of the body and mind to go to the most familiar place, it can be hard to redirect those feelings and have breakthroughs in challenging situations. Instead of going to the same negative place in our mind, when you are feeling anxious and nervous, think consciously of all the ways the situation could be successful and work out for you. Then your body will start to associate those same feelings with the positivity of success.

You need to convince yourself that at that moment of distress, the feelings are the signal of the beginning of an exciting thing yet to come. It can be hard not to focus on the negative because it is so powerful and occupies so much of our consciousness. It may take some time, but you can train yourself to recognize the negative feelings of anxiety and nervousness and convert them into a state of excitement. You will stop dreading those feelings and start using them as a way to bring more excitement into your life.

Visualize Success

People often talk about visualization, and there is a reason why it is so popular as a tool for accomplishing many great and challenging things. Visualization is an effective tool for moving our brain from negative to positive places. When we imagine all the ways in which we could succeed at our endeavor, and what that would look like, our emotional state switches from negative nervousness and anxiety to a state of positive excitement and anticipation.

To get past negative emotions, we must take the time to consciously do something different with our minds and imagination. Instead of imaging all the things that could go wrong, imaging all the things that could go right. This will help convert your emotional energy from negative to positive because of the power of association discussed above.

You may have to work very hard to transform your perception of yourself and concentrate on the possible success that might come from the situation you are in. Focus on visualizing yourself being on the other side of the anxiety and feeling better. Imagine how far forward you can move if you focus on moving towards the successful resolution of your situation. This is something that you can do to effectively get yourself to the point where you recognize the triggers of your anxiety and can redirect your thoughts before they have a negative impact on you.

Chapter Summary

In this chapter, we learned that it is possible to convert anxiety and nervousness into a state of excitement.

In order to do that, we must first review and understand what the triggers are for our anxiety, and how they manifest in physical responses by our body. Anxiety and nervousness may be expressed by the body in the form of shaking, jittery movements or speech, short breaths, hot flashes and nausea. You may also experience an increased heart rate, restlessness, and insomnia. Coincidentally, those are also some of the symptoms of excitement.

Cung Khuu, a personal development writer, espouses the transformation of nervousness and anxiety into excitement. He teaches people a very useful set of tasks that can lead you to that positive place. These four steps require you to:

- embrace your emotions.
- stop beating yourself up.
- tell yourself to get excited.
- visualize success.

Learning to convert your negative emotions and physical reactions to stress into something more positive like excitement has many long-term health benefits, both physically and emotionally. Untethered stress and anxiety can lead to many of the modern killer diseases like heart attack and stroke.

Do not despair if at first you find it difficult to convert your anxiety and nervousness into excitement. It may take some time to train your body to recognize and redirect negative emotions and physical responses into a more positive place, but you will get there.

In the next chapter, you will learn about the importance of making a list of joyful activities and then engaging in them...

CHAPTER SEVEN:

Making Your List of Joyful Activities

In this chapter, you are going to learn about how making the conscious decision to seek out joy in our lives can have many benefits. When we accept joy into our lives, it takes up space in our emotional and physical landscape. Depending on how much space and time we allocate to joy, there is less room for anxiety, nervousness, and the debilitating effects that overthinking can have on our wellbeing. When we make time and room in our lives to find and experience joy, we are making ourselves available for the positive feelings it brings with it.

As you clearly know, we are all very different people, who go through different things in life. It is important to remember that although the specifics of what we are going through may vary, there are likely general similarities with the experiences of others. We all have some degree of worry over finances, success, health, etc. We all have different ways of dealing with the issues we face. Some people are able to accept these challenges with calm and grace. Others may ruminate excessively, have panic attacks or experience surges in emotional stability. Some people may take longer to find a way out of their difficult situations. Others may have instant and definite solutions. Either way, we must all commit to moving toward the resolution of our concerns in a way that is healthy for our body and mind.

As a result of the amount of time and energy we spend on the emotions and symptoms of anxiety and obsessive overthinking, we may have little time to think about anything else. There comes a point when it may be necessary to make the decision to make room in your consciousness for the experience of joy.

Making Room For Joy

When you are able to experience a joyful or enjoyable event, it causes surges of endorphins which make you feel good. Furthermore, your body may relax, your mind might clear, you might laugh or smile and your nervousness will subside. These overall effects result in a more positive outlook on life. During the time that you were "having fun", you were not thinking about your anxiety. Isn't that a relief?

We all have different things that bring us true joy. You may have very specific things that trigger feelings of happiness and joy. We have focussed on negative triggers for much of this book, but let's take a moment to talk about positive triggers. There are some things that we may have done in the past that we know bring us joy, enjoyment or excitement. It is time to call upon those memories, and if possible, recreate them. For example, you may have a favorite song that you associate with a particularly fun evening you had. Whenever you hear that song, you are instantly transported to that memory, and your body experiences those feelings of joy again. These are positive triggers. You may love to swim, and every time you drive past a recreation center with a pool, your body remembers how good it feels to dive in that first time when you get there.

Develop An Inventory

We previously discussed making a list of the things that cause you anxiety. For similar reasons, it is useful to make a list of the things that cause you joy, give you enjoyment or that get you excited when you think about them or engage in doing them.

When you have a list to refer to, it can make it easier to make positive decisions when you are in a challenging situation. Consider it your "finding joy cheat sheet".

Don't be shy. Take the time to self-evaluate. It may not be easy because you have had so little joy in your life recently that you can't remember clearly what things you used to enjoy. Maybe you feel like even if you could make a list, it wouldn't matter because you don't have either the time, money or energy to do those things. That's okay. Make the list anyway. You can sort it into categories later and use it to make plans. The list has all sorts of uses. For example, you can use it as a trigger to just remember good things, which will have an immediate positive impact on your outlook. If the list is short at first, just add to it as you think of things. You can even put things on the list that you think you might enjoy and try them to see if you liked it. Don't feel as if the things on the list need to cost money to do. There are a lot of enjoyable things that you can do that are free.

Maybe what gives you joy or enjoyment is not the same as it is for other people. In fact, that is what makes these lists so interesting. You might be surprised at the things you put on there. Maybe it is a special food or a special song or hiking with your special someone. Maybe it is planting seeds in your garden. Maybe it is watching birds. It doesn't matter what is on the list, as long as you are honest with yourself about what gives you enjoyment. This is because this list is your own personal toolbox. The items on this list will become the go-to things that you can draw upon when you need to reorient your mental and physical state.

After you have made your list, make a plan to incorporate those activities into your life. Whatever you do, make time to actively engage in activities that make you feel good. In addition to giving you the opportunity to experience positive emotions, there is less room for the influence of anxiety on your life. Also, because you are in a more positive mental and physical state, you are more resilient to the triggers that you might encounter.

There are some activities that are commonly enjoyed either alone or with others, and these may be a starting place for your list if you are having trouble getting started.

Activities That Might Be Enjoyable

Once you have conducted the appropriate self-reflection, you will have a list to work with. This list should only be of things that bring you joy, enjoyment or excitement. These are things that have the ability to knock you out of your negative state and put a smile on your face or make you happy in some way. For the items that you know to give you joy, make a point to schedule them into your life. Don't leave it to chance that you will spontaneously make time to engage in your preferred activities. You have to actually do the things on your list to get the full benefit. It is okay to just think about them and use it to remember when you were feeling joy, but it is even more powerful if you go through the experience again and recreate those feelings so they are fresh in your mind and you can have the benefit of the actual physical reaction that can be so transformative.

Let's review some of the things that are commonly done to bring people joy, enjoyment, peace, contentment and other positive emotions. Some of these activities might not be of interest to you at first but do consider trying new things. You might be surprised what your body reacts to. Many of these activities are regularly used by people seeking to bring more joy into their lives.

Watching A Funny Movie Or Show

It is often said that laughter is the best medicine. That is really true! While some people say that watching any show is a distraction, shows that are funny have a way of transforming our mood. They have a way of making us forget our troubles, and they let us just sink into another reality. Before you know it, you are laughing at a joke and you get a rush of endorphins. Success! You have switched your mind from a state of anxiety to a state of joy. You may notice that your physical tension drains away and you are less jittery and irritable. You might not have thought about your problems for a whole half hour! If you resolve to do this once a day at least, you will be able to look forward to this time when you will be treating yourself to the emotional and physical benefits of laughter. If you need a longer dose of light-hearted laughter, try a comedy stand-up special or a comedy movie. Even if you find them "stupid" or "infantile", don't underestimate the value of those couple of laughs you might indulge in. Even if you don't get a lot of laughs, you will have spent time not thinking about your problems. If your problems keep seeping to the forefront despite watching these shows, don't despair, try a different show or comedian.

Sometimes we can get a great benefit from watching any kind of movie or show that takes our mind off our problems. It is important not to choose shows that will upset you, trigger negative memories, or remind you too much of your own situation. The idea is to add positive input to your life. Maybe you find it easier to lose yourself in a good action film, or a nice romance. As long as you are feeling good when you watch it, you are on the right track. This is why it is important to try different things, and variations of different things until you are fully successful in identifying the perfect go-to activity when you need to be lifted up.

Spend Time Doing Or Appreciating Artistic Activities

Over history, some of the world's best artistic works, and especially paintings, were done by artists in a profound emotional state. They may have been in love, happy and well-fed, or they could have been persecuted, angry and poor. Some were even bored and just making something on a commission that didn't inspire them at all. The artist may have had an easy upbringing in a country that is at peace, or the artist could have grown up the offspring of a revolutionary, fighting for human rights in their country. All of these factors influence the emotion that is expressed in the art we look at. As with the extreme emotions that may lead to the creation of a genius work of art, the viewing of incredible art can evoke strong and profound emotions and physical reactions in us. We may look at a painting and get a sense of longing or contentment from it. For someone else, it might be boring. Another might give us joy because it shows a subject that is dear to our heart, like a child with a puppy or a smiling woman collecting shells on a sunny beach.

You don't have to have a lot of money to be an appreciator of art. Some of the best art is on display in free galleries and museums. Also, libraries and used bookstores have a huge selection of books on art that you can look at and experience at your leisure. Walk into an open art gallery or artisan gift shop wherever you live. Take out books from the library that display art from various eras and artists.

When you are exposed to artwork, you will find that you have an emotional reaction to some of them. When you find images that make you feel happy or joyful, take note of them, and return to them often in order to recreate that good feeling you have when looking at it. If you are able to get a copy of the art piece or image, it may be advantageous to display it in a section of your home where you can see it often. This way, you will have many opportunities to recreate the feeling of joy that you got when looking at it the first time.

A lot of emotion goes into creating art and making your own art can be an excellent way to generate a regular influx of joy into our lives.

Creating art is an impactful outlet for your negative energy, and it can be a way to bring more positivity into your world. If you are angry, you may be able to express this anger, and purge it from your system by making an intense art piece that demonstrates your emotional state. Artists are often able to communicate the emotions they are going through in their paintings, sculptures and other artistic works.

Paintings, drawings, sculptures, photos, tapestries, and other art forms can express anger, confusion, anxiety, despair, horror and a wide range of negative emotions. They can also express love, admiration, calm, adoration, joy, amusement, and other positive emotions. Just as artists throughout the centuries have used art as an outlet for their emotional and physical energy, you can benefit from using the creation of art as an outlet for you to release negativity and invite in joy.

You do not need to even be a good artist to use this tool, nor do you ever need to show anyone what you have created. You don't even have to keep what you have created. You just have to commit to putting your feelings into the art instead of internalizing them. It is the act of internalizing our negative emotions, often through overthinking, rumination and self-doubt that causes our body and mind to express signs of distress.

Think about the thing that is upsetting you and create something that expresses this for you. It can even be abstract and look like nothing at all. As long as you use this as a chance to channel the distress you are feeling into the art. This is you giving it time and a voice. When you are finished, you can walk away and think about other things, or nothing at all. This opportunity to expel the emotions from your body can be very freeing, as it gives you an opportunity to let go of those emotions and "leave them on the canvas".

Art can be a powerful outlet for negative emotions, but many people prefer to focus on positive thoughts when they create art. They do this in order to invite joy and contentment into their lives. They may enjoy the act of creating something, no matter what it is. They may try to recreate something they find beautiful or calming, and in recreating the calming image, they are able to bring calm into their own body and mind. The act of creating something can have positive benefits to your perspective and your self-esteem. There is joy and pride in saying, "I made that". Every time you look at the item you created, you have an opportunity to recreate positive emotions associated with joy and personal pride. Maybe you tried and you don't think you are good enough to keep going. Don't sell yourself short. It is the act of creation that is important, not the quality of the result. You don't even have to keep it if you don't want, but you will always have the pride of spending that time completely engrossed in trying to create something beautiful and joyful.

When you go looking, you will find some amazing art, including paintings, drawings, photographs, tapestries, sculptures and many crazy fun crafts. Open your mind to artforms you may not have seen or tried before. You may be surprised what brings you joy. Exploring the art of others can inspire you to try creating art of your own. You might see or try something new and find that you like it very much and that it brings joy or other positive emotions into your life. Regardless of what art form you choose to make, use it as a tool to purge negative emotions and express or create positive emotions.

Listen To And Make Music

We've all said, "oh, I love that song!" at some point when a song we like comes on. We are filled instantly with feelings of joy, a smile comes over our face, and we might start tapping our toes or even start dancing a little. That is what spontaneous joy feels like, and we should endeavor to repeat those feelings whenever we can. It is hard to focus on our anxiety when we are singing along to an upbeat song.

Listening to music is a great way to give yourself something to do besides worry. In order to be truly effective though, you have to listen actively, and not let your mind wander. It is best when you can sing along, as this fully engages your body in the activity. Not only can you hear the music, but the act of singing creates endorphin surges that have beneficial effects on our breathing and we are more likely to move around. If you are somewhere you can't sing along, listen intently to the words and the music. Try to think only of the lyrics and the beats, and don't let your mind wander.

Further to the act of listening to music is the act of making music. It can be very joyful to play an instrument, even if you are not very good at it. If you have the opportunity, practice making music. It is a great distraction since it fills your mind and body with the need to focus on a specific activity. You may also be singing, which fully engages the mind and body to the exclusion of negative thoughts. Maybe you used to play an instrument in school but haven't played in years. Try to find that instrument at a thrift shop and start playing again. You would be surprised how fast it comes back to you. Maybe you have always wanted to learn a specific instrument. Get one and start learning. The internet and the library have lots of resources if you don't want to spend money on lessons. Maybe you were given or you inherited an instrument from a friend or family. This is the perfect opportunity to try something new. If you have no access to instruments, drumming is a great option, because you can use anything as a drum, and use either your hands, cutlery or chopsticks to tap on the surface. Just tapping along on the table to the beat of a song that you like can be tremendously enjoyable and is highly recommended.

There is one very important thing to remember about using music to change your mood. You have to make sure to listen to and play upbeat, cheerful, or hopeful songs. When you are anxious about finances or the potential of losing your job, a sad song about someone who just went broke may sink you deeper into despair.

At the heart of this plan to use music to find joy is that you must find music that resonates joyfully within you, and repeatedly expose yourself to it, so that you have more joy in your life.

Do Some Charity Work

Sometimes the best way to distract ourselves from our problems, or transform our emotional state is to help others. This is especially true if you are consumed by nervous energy and need an outlet for it. Similarly, when you are focussed on helping others, your mind and body is too busy to worry about your own problems. Sometimes seeing the problems of others gives you perspective about your own situation, and you feel better about where you are in life. Sometimes you can meet other really great, genuine and caring people who are also doing charity work. These are the positive types of people that you want to be around.

When we help others, we can derive a great sense of pride from a job well done, or from seeing the joy on someone else's face when they get something good that they weren't expecting. Stress and anxiety can often be replaced by joy and happiness when we involve ourselves in charity activities. It does not matter if you only have a little time to give, find a charity in your community that you feel passionate about, and offer them your time. When most people think about charity work, they automatically think of food banks and soup kitchens, but that is only a tiny fraction of the organizations that could use your help. If you are good with kids and youths, you may want to be involved in a youth mentoring program or community center. If you are good with animals and they give you joy, you may want to volunteer at a local animal shelter to walk dogs or play with cats. Help raise money for or participate in environmental clean-ups. Type out letters for the elderly or help them with their shopping. This may involve giving your time and energy to others, but since you were just wasting it on being anxious, use it to help others.

Giving hope to other people and putting smiles on the faces of others is very rewarding and creates a variety of positive emotions for us, and this translates into less anxiety. There is a lot of satisfaction to be had when you make a positive impact in the life of another person.

Attend More Social Gatherings

Many people just love their own company and prefer to be alone. Sometimes people don't love their own company but are nervous about interacting with others. Sometimes we just get so busy that we don't make time for people outside of our immediate circle of family and co-workers. Either way, being alone too much or not making time for socializing can have a very detrimental effect on our emotional health. It is easy to stay wrapped up in your anxiety when you are alone and have no other opinions or perspectives to interrupt your negative thought patterns. If you suffer from anxiety, there can be many benefits to getting out of your solitary state where you are likely ruminating upon all the things that make you anxious.

If, for whatever reason, you don't have friends to socialize with, there are still many opportunities in the community for social interaction. Socializing can be as simple as starting a conversation with the counter attendant at your grocery store. It can be as simple as having coffee with a colleague at lunch. It can be as extravagant as accepting an invitation to a dinner party or a mixer for work or attending a wedding. You might also be able to join a local club or class at a community center. These are all ways to engage socially with others and give ourselves the opportunity to experience enjoyment.

When we have positive interactions with others it takes our mind off the source of our anxiety. We may find that listening to others speak exposes us to things that are interesting or amusing. Also, when we see that others are able to enjoy our company and that we are interacting well with others, it gives us an increased sense of self-worth and opens us up to feeling more joyful about ourselves and our situation.

When we "step out and socialize", attend public meetings or events, we are assailed by a whole new set of stimuli, and some of them may result in feelings of enjoyment. We may meet someone interesting and learn something new. We may hear someone tell a really funny story and it makes us laugh. We may have an opportunity to watch some really skilled musicians play and maybe even dance. This will cause the influx of positive emotions and get our body into a different physical and emotional state.

Going to a social event, or even the thought of going to social events, may be something that you find stressful and anxiety causing in itself, so you will have to work through that or make decisions that you are comfortable with. You may be terrified to go out and interact with others due to your anxiety, but ironically, that may be the best way out of your poor emotional state. Embrace opportunities for social gatherings, and if you find them difficult, work on becoming progressively more tolerant of the extra stimuli and getting used to trying to interact with others. Tell yourself that you don't have to stay, you just have to go and try. If you have a positive interaction, you might just find yourself sticking around.

Family And Friends Time

Family can be an important part of our support structure. We may depend on family for various things, and some people have more family support than others. When we have a supportive family, we are able to count on them to be a part of our lives. This interaction with people who love us can be a source of great joy and enjoyment. You may really enjoy listening to your grandmother tell stories about the old days, and it may give you a different perspective about how hard your life is. Your uncle might have great advice for you about how he handled a stressful situation once. You might see a cousin who expresses a mutual interest in a music group or artist. Someone might remind of a really funny thing that happened, or they might give you a hug or tell you that they are proud of you. Sometimes they may do nothing other than be company that you can count on. These are all family situations that can bring us joy if we embrace them.

Some families and family homes may not be supportive and welcoming and healthy for you. When this is the case, seek out other family type groups. There are many different types of families, and many "family members" may not be biologically related. Some people consider their friends as their family and trust them more than anyone. The important thing is that you spend time with the people who you trust, who support you, and who you enjoy spending time with. These should be people that bring out the happiness in you, not the ones who bring you down with constant negativity.

If you have friends, this can be the best social outlet and an effective way to "cheer you up". Socializing with someone you know and trust is the best way to create opportunities for meaningful positive interaction. Being with someone who is non-judgemental of us, and who knows how to "cheer us up" can be a great resource. Be sure to use these opportunities to do fun things together and do not use it as an opportunity to focus on your anxieties out loud. The point of social engagement is to get us out of our negative headspace and fill that space with happy and joyful things. This can include all sorts of things like playing a game with your friend, watching a funny show together, taking a walk, going to a gallery or to a music venue, or eating some amazing food that you cooked together.

Interacting With Nature

One of the most profound ways to change your negative mindset and counteract the symptoms of anxiety and nervousness is to spend time outside in nature. Taking the time to go outside and breathe fresh air gives us an opportunity to clear our head and move our bodies, and to see beautiful things. When we go to the park or interact with the natural world, we may enjoy the feeling of the wind in our hair, find contentment in a good stretch, find laughter in watching a dog chase after a toy, or find wonder in the beauty of a flower. Forests of any kind are rejuvenating and can bring us to a place of wonder as we contemplate the interconnectedness of the species of flora and fauna that exist there together.

The Japanese have a practice called Shinrin-yoku which literally means "forest bath" You and I know it as a "walk in the woods". Japanese researchers measured changes in the bodies of people who walked for about 20 minutes in a beautiful forest, with the woodsy smells and the sounds of a running stream. The "forest bathers" had lower stress hormone levels after their walk than they did after a comparable walk in an urban area, and that these effects lasted up to a month. (Li, 2018; Livni, 2016)

There is no doubt of the calming effects of walking in a park, forest or garden. Camping and hiking are wonderful opportunities to focus our minds on something bigger than ourselves. When we interact with nature, we can see ourselves as a smaller part of an interconnected world. The positive aromatherapy benefits of being in an environment that smells fresh and of trees and flowers are tremendous. While we are in the natural environment, we are likely walking around, and this physical movement causes surges of positive endorphins and can give us an outlet for our nervous energy.

Challenges That May Be Faced When Seeking Joy

There are many things that we can do in an effort to bring more joy into our lives. We have explored some very effective and common activities that are known to be effective in lifting people's spirits and transforming anxiety into joy.

It is important to acknowledge the fact that not all of these activities will be enjoyable to all people. Explore different activities and keep building your list of things to do. Try what you think will bring you the most, or even some, joy.

You need to be careful and sensitive with yourself when you take on activities in an attempt to deliberately challenge your body and mind to find enjoyment. For example, if we have a terrible fear of heights, accepting an invitation for lunch on a rooftop patio might be more than you can handle, and you should not add to your stress by attempting to confront that fear when you are simply trying to find some joy in lunch out with a friend. In this scenario a true friend will understand when you say, "if it's okay with you, I would be more comfortable in a restaurant that is on ground level".

When you reach that level where you are able to confidently identify the things that hinder you from achieving joy, you may have to carefully come up with ways to eliminate them from your life. Forming habits at your workplace or home that progressively eliminate your exposure to negative stimuli and increase your exposure to positive stimuli will result in a greater degree of joy and happiness.

Chapter Summary

We all deserve to be happy and to experience joy. In order to maximize your potential for joy, you need to always be on the lookout for both the things that you know trigger anxiety, and also for the things that trigger joy. Increasing our exposure to the things that trigger joy for us has a transformative effect on our emotional state and on the emotional and physical expression of anxiety.

Often, we are consumed with negative thoughts and our anxiety may be at a peak. When this happens, you must make a conscious effort to expose yourself to the things that give you joy. Once you make a decision to make room in your life for joy, you may need to develop a plan of how to do that. We may have forgotten what gives us joy because we have been anxious for so long. We may have few resources at our disposal for doing things that cost money. That's why making a list is so important. The list may be small at first and it may take a while to get enough things on it that you feel you have a lot of options. Put things on the list that you think might be enjoyable. Put anything on the list that you can think of, and then just start trying things that are appropriate at the time. The truth is you really only need to start with one thing. Be on the lookout for the things that increase your anxiety and sap your happiness and joy, and then do away with as many of them as you can.

Some of the joyful activities that we've discussed include watching funny shows, spending time on artistic endeavors, listening to music, attending social gatherings, and others. Embrace these opportunities to experience joy and repeat them as much as you can. This will keep the anxiety at bay, because your emotions and your body are engaged in something else that is keeping you focused on positive things.

In the next chapter, you will learn more about the many natural remedies for anxiety…

CHAPTER EIGHT:

Natural Remedies to Beat Anxiety

Sometimes the best remedies for the anxious mind and body is a proper regime of healthy choices in various areas of our lives. These choices are largely in the area of self-care, and they may include a commitment to a healthy lifestyle that includes exercise and the proper diet.

Self-Care

Generally speaking, when you are in a state of heightened anxiety, your self-care regimes may be pushed aside in favor of rumination and panic, self-doubt and the attempt to accomplish everything that we set out to do. When we are too busy or too preoccupied with our anxiety, we may stop taking care of ourselves properly. We may let our bodies get run down, stop exercising, cut back on sleep or sleep poorly, and we may not eat properly. This compounds the negative effects of anxiety because our body is less resilient to the impacts of stress.

For example, if you have a deadline, or many things on the go at once, you may be pressed for time and be very anxious about achieving your goal. Since so much depends on the result of your efforts, you may have stayed up late many nights in a row in order to work or study, and maybe you've been eating fast snacks instead of cooking yourself nutritious meals. You also have probably been sitting in the same position without stretching for long periods of time. You may be berating yourself constantly and doubting your ability to accomplish your goal.

These are all examples of ways that we neglect to provide ourselves with self-care. The truth is, if you were sleeping more regularly, eating better and stretching at regular intervals, your symptoms of anxiety would probably be lessened.

There are many ways to increase our level of self-care, and we will explore some of them below.

Exercise

It is important for all of us to prioritize being healthy as a partial antidote to anxiety. We all yearn to live a healthy life, and this is especially true when old age begins to set in. With that in mind, create a plan that will ensure you remain healthy. One of the keys to good health is exercise. You may have heard this many times before, but you need to believe it and embrace it. There are many ways to exercise and you need to find the one that is best for you. Whatever you do, try to make it fun by choosing the right activities and approaching them with a good attitude, confident in the knowledge that this healthy choice will have many positive impacts upon the management of your anxiety symptoms.

You may be able to join a gym, or you may want to exercise alone at home or use the park or a community facility. The important thing is that you get your body moving and stretching and that you get your heart rate up, and that you breathe regularly and deeply. There are so many ways to do that.

If you have access to or can acquire home gym or exercise equipment of any kind, that is the best and easiest way to integrate exercise into your life. When it is at home and easily accessible, it is easy to schedule it into your daily life. Try exercising right before you get into the shower, or when you get home from work or school. This is a great way to get out your tension and channel any negative energy into a good workout. When you exercise, your body releases endorphins and that makes us feel good. Even doing a few minutes a day, or ten minutes every couple of days is better than nothing and will get you in the habit of exercising. At first, it may be hard to go longer than a few minutes, but if you keep at it regularly, you will find it easier as you become more fit. It is often helpful to listen to music or an audiobook when exercising. This is to keep you distracted from thinking about your problems while you exercise. Practicing mindfulness can also be helpful. Focus on your muscles, on your breathing and on your posture as you exercise, whatever it is. How do you feel? Fully experience the joy of your body working in a healthy, natural way.

There are many ways to exercise at home without "formal gym equipment". If you need ideas and instruction about exercises and stretches that might work for you, go to the library or the internet to research your many options.

If you want to, and are able to make it work, join a gym or register for exercise classes at a gym or community center and attend them faithfully. This may have the added benefit of social interactions that could lead to positive and interesting friendships, or at least some positive light socializing.

If you prefer to exercise outdoors, walking, hiking or running can be a great way to exercise. Maybe you have a back yard you can use to do an exercise routine or a basketball hoop you can use to shoot hoops. Taking a football/soccer ball to kick around at a park or a tennis ball to bounce around at public court can be a great way to release pent up nervous energy and anxiety.

Doing regular exercise has the added benefit of controlling your weight and helping to regulate your blood sugar, thus promoting better health. Remember, a healthy body is more resilient to stress.

There is an endless list of activities that you may consider when exploring self-care through exercise. Try to do something you enjoy, but whatever you do, do something. If you love to swim, find a way to swim regularly. If you enjoy dancing, do it regularly. If you enjoy hiking through an urban forest, do that regularly. Channel your anxiety and nervousness into intensifying your workout and be mindful of the way your body feels as you get healthier.

Exercise is a powerful antidote to anxiety and depression and has both immediate and long- term benefits.

The 21-minute Cure

Dr. Drew Ramsey, assistant clinical professor of psychiatry at the New York-Presbyterian Hospital at Columbia University and co-author of "*The Happiness Diet*" says that in order for exercise to have a beneficial effect on anxiety, you should engage in it for about twenty-one minutes. (Barnett, 2019). He attests to the fact that you will feel calmer after the workout. He asks his patients to spend 20 to 30 minutes doing any activity that gets their heart rate up. It can be anything they like, whether it's a treadmill, elliptical or rowing, or even brisk walks.

Resolve To Eat A Healthy Diet

Another secret to successful self-care and the use of self-care to reduce anxiety is adhering to a healthy diet. The ability of our body to regulate hormones and to function effectively and make us feel healthy is largely influenced by the things that we eat and drink.

We can all understand the connection between bad food decisions and stomach distress, but few people fail to associate the impact of poor-quality food on other aspects of our physical and psychological health. Furthermore, few people give credit to nutritious food as being one of the building blocks of general good health, both physically and psychologically.

When our body receives a good balance of proteins, vegetables, fruits, and grains, it is able to function at its prime. This in return makes it more able to cope with stress, which minimizes the symptoms of anxiety.

Commit to eating more fruits and vegetables. Fresh is always best since fresh fruits and vegetables have the highest amount of nutrients and fiber.

Foods that are highly processed and/or are high in sugar, salt and additives should be avoided. It is well known that high sugar intake is harmful to our bodies and can lead to conditions such as obesity and diabetes. It is also known that high salt intake can contribute to conditions such as high blood pressure.

Furthermore, the intake of caffeine-based and sugary drinks should be minimized, especially from late afternoon to bedtime.

Sometimes it can be hard to make good food decisions when we are away from the controlled environment of our own home. We may be assailed with options that seem more attractive than others, or we may not have access to healthy choices because of limited options. Sometimes we are too busy to cook and find ourselves bringing home takeout, ordering in, or just grabbing something on the run to eat in the car. These are the times when we can do the most damage to our health, as these foods tend to be high in saturated fats, sugar, salt, additives, preservatives and other artificial or highly processed ingredients.

These occasions where we have to get quick or convenient food can be minimized by good planning. For example, if you know you are going to be busy running around, pack a nutritious snack or lunch. Sometimes, however, eating out or eating on the run can't be avoided. When this happens, get in the habit of making the healthiest choice you can. At first, it may be hard to get over the automatic instinct to, for example, get fries. This is the moment when you must choose the salad and not smother it completely in dressing. Choose grilled instead of fried. Choose soda, water or juice instead of cola or coffee. If you are in a restaurant, choose your meal carefully, and make the healthiest choice you can. A lean grilled or poached protein, with salad or cooked vegetables, are available almost everywhere.

Quick, Eat Something

Dr. Ramsey and many others confirm that people's levels of anxiety and irritability increase when they are hungry. When you get overwhelmed with anxiety, it may be a sign that your blood sugar is low. Have a quick, healthy snack, like a handful of nuts and raisins, along with a glass of water or a nice hot beverage.

Don't Skip Breakfast

You are often encouraged to eat a healthy breakfast. Many people insist they aren't hungry in the morning or skip breakfast because they are so busy in the morning. A healthy daily breakfast is one of the most important tools you can give your body to work with. Skipping breakfast is a guaranteed way to find yourself suddenly hungry at an inopportune time. For example, getting to work hungry is an assured recipe for a stressful day in the office, or an inability to deal with stressors. You may feel weak or emotionally fragile, have trouble concentrating, be irritable or feel sick to your stomach.

Stop starving yourself, advises Ramsey. "Many people with anxiety disorders skip breakfast. I recommend that people eat things like eggs, which are a satiating and filling protein, and are nature's top source of choline. Low levels of choline are associated with increased anxiety." (Barnett, 2019)

Get Adequate Sleep

When the body is tired, it is unable to cope with stress and the symptoms of anxiety may be harder to manage. Make sure to make time for enough sleep every night. It may seem like a good idea to stay up to finish something, but then if you are unable to accomplish other tasks the next day because you are so tired, working late may have little overall benefit. Furthermore, it is dangerous to drive or operate machinery when we are tired.

If you are unable to get a good night's sleep, some people swear by taking naps. Some people do experience great stress release and other positive benefits from napping. Try it and see how it works for you. After a long, stressful or bad day at work, or when you feel you are in a high anxiety state, you may find it rejuvenating and calming to lay down and take a nap.

The desired result of the nap is that not only do you address some of the exhaustion you may feel from lack of sleep, but you may feel the relief of a calm body and brain. You may find a lot of peace in finding a quiet place to lay down your head for a few minutes or a few hours and then waking up to go on with your tasks.

Good Habits And Personal Traits

You could also develop some traits that help ensure your stress and anxiety is minimized. An example is making sure you are on time with everything, or that things are organized so that they can be accessed easily. You may develop the habit of planning carefully so that you are able to fit in all your activities. You may develop the habit of walking up the stairs instead of taking the elevator in order to fit in some exercise, or you might lay out your clothes the night before to avoid last-minute panic over choosing an outfit. You may get in the habit of making a batch of healthy snacks and lunches to put in the fridge so that you can grab them on the way out the door.

The Power Of The Right Tea

There are many people that swear by the calming and healthful powers of a good cup of the right tea. Hot herbal beverages have been used for centuries to calm the mind and the body.

Chamomile

Many people find a cup of camomile tea to be very relaxing, and some find it promotes good sleep. If you are feeling anxious, overwhelmed or jittery, a cup of chamomile tea might help to calm you.

Chamomile is also available as a nutritional supplement that contains apigenin as an active ingredient, along with dried chamomile flowers. A University of Pennsylvania Medical Center study found that patients with a generalized anxiety disorder (GAD) had a significant decrease in anxiety symptoms after taking chamomile supplements for eight weeks compared to patients that were given a placebo. (Perelman, n.d.)

Green Tea

Green tea contains antioxidants and an amino acid called L-theanine. L-theanine has been shown to help curb rising heart rates and blood pressure, and a few studies have found that it reduces anxiety. In a study, subjects with anxiety were given 200 milligrams of L-theanine before the test and those that took it reported that they were calmer and more focused during the test than those who did not take the L-theanine.

Although you can get L-theanine directly green tea, you would have to drink between five and 20 cups to get the same amount of L-theanine offered in a quality supplement. At that point, the impact of the caffeine may have a detrimental effect on your ability to be calm.

Herbal Supplements

Some herbal supplements are sedatives as well as having other health benefits, but this is not true of all of them. For example, L-theanine, as discussed above, may reduce the symptoms of anxiety, but it will not make you sleepy. Other herbal remedies have sedative effects that help calm us down and in many cases help us sleep. Good sleep has many positive health benefits including the minimization of anxiety symptoms. These sedative herbs should be used carefully. For example, do not take them when you need to be alert, drive or operate machinery. Barnett, 2015 discusses an assortment of herbal supplements which are summarized below

Hops

Most people associate hops with beer; however, the tranquilizing benefits of hops (*Humulus lupulus*) will not come just from drinking a beer. The actual sedative compound in hops is a volatile oil, so it is processed into extracts and tinctures. Hops is often used as a sedative and to promote sleep. "It's very bitter, so you don't see it in tea much unless combined with chamomile or mint," says Mark Blumenthal. (Barnett, 2015) It is sometimes also used in aromatherapy.

Note: Don't take sedative herbs if you are taking a prescription tranquilizer or sedative. Discuss with your doctor any supplements you are taking.

Valerian

Valerian (*Valeriana officinalis*) is a sedative that is used to treat insomnia. Due to its legitimate sedative compounds; it has been approved in Germany for treating sleep disorders.

Valerian is known to have a pungent, somewhat unpleasant smell, so it is often taken as a capsule or tincture, rather than as a tea. Valerian is often combined with other sedative herbs such as hops, chamomile, and lemon balm.

Lemon Balm

Lemon balm (*Melissa officinalis*) has been used since the Middle Ages to promote sleep and reduce the symptoms of anxiety. One study showed that lemon balm extracts of 600 mg were effective in producing a calming effect.

Lemon balm is very easy to grow, but it is usually sold as a tea, capsule or tincture. It may be combined with other herbs such as hops, chamomile, and valerian. Lemon balm should be used only in moderation because some studies have shown that high doses can increase the symptoms of anxiety. Always follow the directions on the product label and start with the smallest dose.

Passion flower

Passion flower is a natural herbal sedative that has been approved in Germany to treat nervous restlessness. It is also used to treat insomnia and reduce symptoms of anxiety. Some people have found it very effective. As with other sedatives, use it with caution.

Like other sedatives, it can cause drowsiness, so don't take it or other sedative herbs when you are also taking a prescription sedative or need to be alert.

Passion flower is recommended for short term use only. Don't take it for longer than one month at a time and never mix sedative herbs without medical advice.

Aromatherapy

There are many ways to use aromatherapy to treat symptoms of anxiety. Some of the scents are administered by deeply inhaling the scent from a small bottle that contains an oil or tincture. Sometimes, using a hand lotion with a calming scent can be a way to insert a regular soothing aromatherapy ritual into our day. Some people use potpourri or incense. Also, there are many diffuser products on the market today that release a mist into the air that is scented with whatever oil you put in it.

Lavender

Lavender (*Lavandula hybrida*) has been used as a calming scent for many centuries. The intoxicating aroma of lavender can bring us to a point of stillness and calm. Many people report feeling less anxious in environments scented with lavender oil. Many people carry lavender spray or oil to use periodically throughout the day when they feel the need to "chill".

Pine, Cedar And Aromatic Woods

A walk in the forest can be calming in part to the incredible smell of the trees and plants. It is possible to recreate these feelings by using an aromatherapy product or room scent that closely resembles the smell of a forest filled with evergreen coniferous trees.

Chapter Summary

In this chapter, you have learned about the various natural remedies that can be used to treat anxiety. There are many natural ways through which you can minimize and even eliminate the symptoms of anxiety. All of the natural remedies are rooted in the concept of self-care. When we neglect to take care of the basic needs of the body, it is not able to function effectively enough to withstand major stressors. Some of the major categories of self-care include exercise, proper nutrition and adequate sleep.

Some lifestyle changes and the development of good habits may assist to relieve stress by eliminating the sources of anxiety from your lives. Making time for exercise will have many positive benefits, including being an outlet for nervous energy, increasing the balance of hormones in our body, and keeping our body limber and fit. Being prepared for the day to come by preparing healthy meals and snacks that you can easily access and consume is an important part of ensuring good nutrition. Furthermore, making smart choices when you have to eat out is very important. Consuming healthy teas and enhancing the body's own ability to combat stress by taking nutritional supplements that promote relaxation and good sleep may be an option for you. Another option that many people find effective and pleasant is aromatherapy.

In the next chapter, you will learn about how to find peace and relieve anxiety through meditation...

CHAPTER NINE:

How to Meditate and Find Peace

Meditation is used throughout the world as a means to calm the mind and body and achieve a feeling of inner peace. Mediation has been used by Buddhists for this purpose for hundreds and maybe thousands of years. The modern practice of mediation has its roots in Asia and India, where the practice of meditation is widely spread and has evolved over the centuries to have unique cultural or religious characteristics. Despite any differences in words, actions, techniques or specifics of practice, all meditation has the same basic purpose. That purpose is to center the body, clear the mind and allow one to simply exist as an extension of the universe around you.

In today's modern world of the library and the internet, there are many ways to learn meditation techniques. There are some basic practices and beliefs that are common to most forms of meditation. Meditation requires you to train your mind and your body, and it may take time to master.

University of Wisconsin neuroscience lab director Richard J. Davidson, Ph.D. told "*The New York Times*" that in "Buddhist tradition, the word 'meditation' is equivalent to a word like 'sports' in the U.S. It's a family of activities, not a single thing," He goes on to explain that different meditation practices require different mental skills. (Gaiam, n.d)

Some people are able to meditate for hours. When you first start practicing meditation, it may be extremely difficult to sit for hours and think of nothing and have a clear, empty mind. Remember, don't beat yourself up! Don't be too hard on yourself! Focus on quality and not quantity. Make an effort to have really good but short sessions when you start and gradually increase the amount of time as you become better at controlling your mind and body.

If you enjoy nature, you may find it really helps you to center and focus yourself during a meditation session when you do it outside. The power of nature can fascinate and calm and be a path to relief from the stress you are under. Having the sounds of nature around you as you meditate can set a positive tone to your session. If you are not able to be outside surrounded by nature, you can use a nature soundtrack as the background music during your session. Some people believe that medication can only be done in silence, but that isn't true. It can be done in a loud crowded room, or with music on, or in any number of places with any number of background "soundtracks". This is because the focus of meditation is precisely about focus. Focus on both the specifics and the totality of the universe at the same time. When you are able to clear your mind no matter what distractions are around you, there is great peace and comfort to be experienced.

The Many Benefits of Meditation

Although relaxation may not always be the goal of meditation, it is often one of the beneficial results. After conducting research on people who practiced transcendental meditation in the 1970s, Herbert Benson, MD, a researcher at Harvard University Medical School, coined the phrase “relaxation response". He considered it “an opposite, involuntary response that causes a reduction in the activity of the sympathetic nervous system.” (Gaiam, n.d)

The study of meditation has proved the following short-term benefits on the nervous system:

- Less anxiety

- Lower blood pressure
- Lower blood cortisol levels
- Improved blood circulation
- Lower heart rate
- Slower respiratory rate
- Greater feelings of well-being

In the Buddhist tradition of meditation, the ultimate benefit is the liberation of the mind's attachment to things it cannot control. This may include external stimuli, situations and circumstances, including strong emotions. By being able to free oneself of the fixation on desires or experiences, an “enlightened” practitioner is able to maintain a calm mind and develop a deep sense of inner harmony.

Concentration Meditation

The practice of concentration meditation requires the practitioner to focus on a single object or thought. This could involve focusing on your breathing, repeating a single word or mantra, staring at a candle flame, looking at a picture or item, listening to a repetitive gong, or counting beads on a mala. In this form of meditation, whenever your mind wanders, you simply refocus your awareness on the designated object. Rather than allowing random thoughts to permeate your full consciousness, you let them pass by and through your mind.

Remember, it is okay to only start with a few minutes at a time. It will get easier with practice.

Mindfulness Meditation

Mindfulness meditation is a bit different from concentration meditation. It encourages the practitioner to observe any and all thoughts as they drift through the mind. This observation is not meant to lead to consideration, evaluation or judgment of the thoughts, you are only meant to be aware of each thought as it comes up and passes through.

Through mindfulness meditation, you may notice patterns in your thoughts when you are anxious or calm. Finding stillness in this observation without judgment can give your thoughts and emotions a place to wander out of your anxious mind and out into the universe, where they will no longer impact you. With practice, you may find it helps you find a sense of inner peace.

Teresa M. Edenfield, a clinical psychologist in the Veterans Administration Medical Center in Durham, N.C., often uses mindfulness meditation to treat anxiety patients. "The act of practicing mindful awareness allows one to experience the true essence of each moment as it really occurs, rather than what is expected or feared," she says. (Barnett, 2019)

How do you begin the practice of mindful meditation? You start by simply "paying attention to the present moment, intentionally, with curiosity, and with an effort to attend non-judgmentally", Edenfield says.

Other Meditation Techniques

As mentioned previously, there are various other meditation techniques that are used around the world, and there is no one form that is right or wrong. Find the practice that works best for you. Some people use either concentration or mindfulness meditation. Some practitioners of meditation use a combination of meditation techniques. Most disciplines call for stillness but there are also forms of moving meditation such as tai chi, qigong, and walking meditation.

Simple Meditation For Beginners

There are many traditions of meditation. As a beginner, it can help to have a simple guide to some of the basic principles and practices of meditation. This meditation exercise has six steps and is an excellent introduction to meditation techniques.

Step 1: Sit Comfortably

Get seated in a comfortable position. You may have to try a few things before you are able to find a position that you can sit in for an extended period of time. If you sit on the floor, it is "traditional" to sit cross-legged, right leg over the left, right hand over the left hand, palms up, your right index finger gently touching your left thumb. Alternatively, place both hands on your lap comfortably. In all cases, keep your head up and your back straight. This sitting position is called the Peace Position or the meditation posture.

If you feel uncomfortable in this position, you may sit on a chair or sofa. Adjust your position until you feel completely comfortable. Ensure that you are in a position that will not restrict your blood circulation.

For those who are not able to sit up comfortably, it is also possible to meditate while lying down. Really you can meditate in any position, even standing up.

Gently close your eyes. Don't squeeze them shut tightly. Just drop your lids into a comfortable resting pose. Put a gentle smile on your face.

Step 2: Take Deep, Full Breaths

Next, take a deep breath. Hold it for 2 or 3 seconds and then exhale fully. Repeat inhaling and exhaling up to 10 times, and just breathe deeply in and out. Breathe in deeply until you feel the air pass through your lungs and reach the middle of your abdomen. Imagine that each cell in your body is fully taking in the feeling of happiness and joyfulness. Observe the way your body feels as it takes in air and lets it out. Some people swear by slowly breathing out through your nostrils, but others breathe out through their mouth with no truly detrimental impact on their positive experience. When you breathe out, consciously expel all your worries, stress, tension and negative feelings. Don't forget about what we learned earlier about deep breathing and apply it when you are meditating.

Step 3: Bring The Body And Mind To A Place Of Stillness

Take this time to just let go of all of your worries and anxieties. This is not the time or place to give them the stage in the theater of your consciousness. This is the time to stop thinking about the responsibilities of work, personal commitments to family or friends, or whatever else is making you anxious. Let your mind be relaxed and free from worry.

Keep breathing deep, full, regular breaths that feel natural and comfortable. Next, you should deliberately relax every muscle in your body. Start at the top of your head and make your way down to your toes.

When you are fully relaxed, try to maintain this state as long as you can. When your body is fully relaxed, it can more easily accept the sensations of lightness, joy and other positive energy that exist in our bodies or are available for us to experience.

Empty your mind and imagine you are sitting alone in a large open field. This space is peaceful where you have no attachments or problems. Then, imagine that your body is empty and hollow. Allow your body to feel lighter and lighter, as if it were becoming weightless, gradually melting away and becoming one with nature. What is left is your consciousness and a sense of oneness with the totality of the universe and the positive energy within it.

Step 4: Accept And Expand Upon This Feeling Of Peace And Calm

Next, focus on the center of your body about two finger widths above your navel. Simply concentrate on this area of your body with gentle sustained awareness, like a feather floating down from the sky to rest on a calm surface of a lake.

Imagine how soft and light the feather is when it touches the surface of the water. Imagine how soft and light you would feel if you were that feather. Hold onto the feeling of relaxation and keep your mind focused on the center of your body. Once you have centered your body, slowly and gently begin to imagine a neutral object that your mind can focus on so it does not wander. The moon, the sun, the flame of a candle, or the waves on a sandy beach are all good choices, but any object that makes you feel calm, peaceful and content will work.

Relax and simply picture the object resting in the middle of your peacefully resting body. It doesn't matter if you can picture it clearly. Think of your chosen object continuously, and don't let your mind wander.

Another way to focus the mind is to recite a short, soothing phrase. This is called a mantra. Recite the chosen word phrase softly in your mind and let the words resonate in the center of the object you envision in the center of your body. Keep your mind on the object and the phrase until your mind is still.

Step 5: Resist Outside Thoughts

Once your mind is completely still, you may just want to be still without your mind thinking about anything or even reciting your mantra. Once you have achieved stillness, it is okay to do that. If you lose your sense of meditative calm, simply back up a step and re-establish the use of the calming image and mantra until the feeling of peace and calm overcomes your body again.

Do not do anything beyond this. Let your mind be neutral to the thoughts that try to invade your carefully constructed sense of calm. Observe any new thoughts with a calm mind and remember to relax and let them pass through without judgment. Just keep observing and do not think of anything specific.

If you do this correctly, meditation will become easy and comfortable. Soon you will be able to get into this state effortlessly.

Your mind will enter into a state of clarity, calm and contentment, and true inner knowledge may be revealed to you by your psyche.

Step 6: Send Your Positive Energy Out Into The World

Sharing positive energy with others spreads joy and compassion throughout the world, but we are not always in an emotional or physical state to be able to offer that to others. After meditation though, our minds and bodies are in a state of positivity that lends itself well to sharing.

The benefits of sharing kindness and other forms of positive energy include radiating a happy feeling from ourselves towards others and having it reflected back to us. We can share positive energy like love and kindness with the world by doing the following:

- Before ending your meditation session, when your mind is peaceful and still, you may find yourself filled with feelings of happiness. Focus your mind at the center of your body where you feel true love and good wishes. Then imagine condensing those good feelings into a bright sphere. Imagine this sphere or ball of love is effortlessly expanding in all directions away from your body, and then imagine it touching everyone in its path as it expands away from you.

Chapter Summary

You now have a firm handle on how to get started with the ancient practice of meditation. Use it to bring calmness and peace to your mind and body. Meditation has been proven over centuries to be an effective tool for managing anxiety and stress. Achieving stillness and a clear mind frees us from the negative outward expressions of our anxiety. Furthermore, meditation may have significant positive health benefits including lowering your blood pressure and improving blood circulation.

When you are preparing to meditate, there are some things that it might be helpful to prepare in advance. For example:

1. Select a comfortable and quiet place to sit in.
2. Select the item that you will use as your focusing object.
3. Choose a word phrase, or "mantra" to recite repeatedly to yourself, for example, "Clear and Bright" or "Beautiful World".

Summary of Meditation Steps

4. Assume the meditative posture of sitting comfortably with your hands at rest.
5. Relax your body and then your mind.
6. Become aware of and concentrate on a central area of the body, then imagine your focus object resting gently there.
7. Bring your body and mind to a point of calm, stillness and peace. Think of nothing, and if your mind becomes distracted, recite your mantra or picture your focus object.
8. Before getting up, make a conscious effort to spread your positive energy out from yourself to the entire world.
9. Get up carefully and slowly. Take some deep breaths and resume your day.

Now that you know how to meditate, you will be able to experience all the benefits it can bring to your life. Use it to calm yourself down and to clear your mind. You will find the calm you attain during meditation will seep over into the rest of your life.

In the next chapter, you will learn more about how to approach going to a therapist or other mental health professional...

CHAPTER TEN:

Tips for Going to A Therapist

In this book, we have focused on things that you can actively do to address your own personal battle with anxiety. As you learned, anxiety can include nervousness, self-doubt, worry, overthinking, and express itself in negative ways including nausea, sweating and panic attacks. By understanding your triggers and the underlying cause of your anxiety, it may be possible to interfere with its patterns, reduce your symptoms and find joy, peace and calm.

When the overwhelming and recurring symptoms of anxiety have a significantly negative impact on your life, it's time to get outside help. In Chapter 1 you learned about anxiety disorders such as PTSD, social anxiety disorder and generalized anxiety disorder, among others. Sometimes, despite our desire to manage our symptoms and underlying conditions on our own, we fail to achieve the results that we want. When this happens, or when you are in a state of overwhelming despair and are not able to cope with the negative impacts of anxiety on your mental and physical health, it is time to seek additional professional guidance to assist with the management of your condition.

Don't feel bad or beat yourself up for the fact that you need help. It's a sign of emotional maturity to recognize, seek and go through therapy. Mental health professionals may use a range of tools to assist you. There are many forms of therapy, but most commonly you will be offered some kind of talk therapy or medication, or both.

How Does Your Anxiety Express Itself?

It is important for every anxiety sufferer to understand the process involved in diagnosing a mental health condition. The underlying causes of your condition may be unique to you, and you may or may not understand what triggers your anxiety.

People show their anxiety in various ways. Some people become extremely talkative but they don't really make sense. They may be fixated on particular things. Other people become withdrawn and isolate themselves. Even individuals who usually seem outgoing can become fearful and withdrawn. All too often, a person's anxiety is caused by intrusive and obsessive thoughts. Therefore, that person may often feel confused or find it challenging to concentrate. Other people can feel restless and have a lot of nervous energy, while others may feel sick and depressed regularly. These are all major physical signs of anxiety. Other physical symptoms of anxiety may include tensed muscles as well as high blood pressure. Trembling and sweating can be common. Anxiety can cause digestive issues, difficulty in breathing, a racing heartbeat, insomnia or dizziness.

When your symptoms are something that you worry about, or if you are unable to manage your anxiety using the tools in this book, or if you are overwhelmed to the point of desperation, you should seek medical attention. Work with a professional to develop a treatment plan for your anxiety. Once you decide to get therapy, you will have to find and work with a mental health professional and get the most out of it that you can.

Tips About Working With A Therapist

Seeking therapy may seem mysterious. What will you discuss with the therapist? Are you capable of being honest? Is it possible to know if you are making progress? Prior to walking into the room, you need to be clear about your intention to seek help and be open to accepting it. Take some time to analyze your feelings and beliefs about therapists. If you have the belief that, "a head-shrinker is just going to talk about a bunch of emotional stuff, and that won't help me", then you are unlikely to open your mind up enough to accept the help that they offer. If you have difficulty interacting with others, group therapy may not be effective for you. You may need or want intensive individual counseling. You may be contemplating or need medication that helps to effectively manage your symptoms. You may need both medication to manage your symptoms and talk therapy to help you understand the underlying cause of your anxiety and what triggers your negative responses.

Choose Carefully

Once you have decided to seek professional help, you now face the challenge of finding a practitioner that you can work with. In some cases, as with prescribing psychiatrists, you may be referred to the only in your area or the only one that is currently taking patients. Work with whoever you are referred to and try to get the most out of the experience. Ask questions about their areas of practice and expertise, and how they typically handle cases like yours. Don't be afraid to get a second opinion, but also don't be afraid to take their advice and the medication that they prescribe to you. Do your research, however, and make sure that you are comfortable with what you learn about the medication they have prescribed, and that you feel safe working with them. See if there is any kind of feedback about their practice. Remember, a psychiatrist is usually focussed on prescribing medication, and may not practice any forms of therapeutic talk therapy at all.

When you are looking to work with a psychologist, you are likely to have more choices of practitioners. You may be able to get a referral, or you may have to research and select a practitioner yourself. It is important that you have a psychologist that you feel safe with and that you trust. You will be telling them your most personal secrets and you need to feel like they are on your side. Select a therapist carefully. Don't be afraid to speak to them on the phone and ask what their experience with counseling anxiety sufferers is. Ask them what kind of methods they use, or what type of practice they have. For example, are they followers of the Freudian methods or do they practice modern techniques such as cognitive behavioral therapy, tapping therapy, or art therapy? Do they typically work with people who have been through similar types of trauma as you have? Are they located somewhere that you can conveniently access? Do they have office hours that work with your schedule? Do they have fees that you can afford? If after your initial inquiries, you feel somewhat comfortable with what they can offer you, consider attending three sessions of therapy and see how you feel about it. It may take many sessions to make a lot of progress, but you may also find that you improve by leaps and bounds in a very short time. Everyone has a unique and personal experience with therapy, and it is meant to be tailored to your specific situation. Of course, because the therapist has likely worked with many others who also suffer from anxiety, they will be able to give you many useful insights about your condition and offer you viable ways to cope and manage on both a short-term and a long-term basis.

Schedule Your Sessions At The Perfect Time For You

Don't pick a time for your therapy that gives you extra stress. Schedule your appointments when you are capable of giving them your full attention. Specifically, you need to completely avoid scheduling your sessions when it is time to work or when you know that you will be pressed for time. If you are not very communicative in the mornings, and you have a lot of obligations during the day, a midday session may cause more harm than good. This is because these sessions can be very emotionally intense, and you may want to just go home and contemplate your session after you are done. If you are distracted by all the things you must still accomplish after the session, you may be excessively focussed on that, and not absorb all the insights of the session. On the other hand, the therapist may be able to give you useful short-term tools to help you get through the anxiety of that specific day. In these cases, you may not be focused on the overall underlying causes of your stress, but on coping strategies.

Whenever possible, consider giving yourself time and personal space in order to process and reflect upon your therapy.

Let It All Out In Therapy

Most people begin psychological therapy (talk therapy) by censoring themselves. It is difficult to be vulnerable, and we may not want to be judged. We may feel ashamed or embarrassed or angry about what we've been through. We may be afraid to relive our experiences in full. Be assured that therapy is meant to be a safe place. It is a safe place to talk about things you may have never told anyone. It is a safe place to cry. It is a safe place to ask questions about yourself and why you are the way you are.

Experts in the field encourage clients to say what they want and to not fear judgment. The role of the psychologist is to listen without judgment, help you come to terms with how you feel, and give you tools to improve your life. In doing so, you will be making progress every time you go to therapy.

Getting the most out of therapy does not mean you have to be on your best behavior or only talk about specific things. Getting the most out of therapy requires that you are authentic. You must believe that there will be a positive outcome if you talk about the things that have happened to you or that have been significant influences in your life. You must believe that the therapist will have ways to help you, or that just the act of releasing all of the emotion will help in itself. That way, your therapist can more effectively work on solutions that will help you to recover.

You Need to Be Orderly

The first thing you should do when booking a session is to check with the receptionist or administrator about how payment is handled.

Make arrangements so that you don't have to pay on the way out when you are potentially in a rush, or in a vulnerable emotional state.

The next thing you need to consider is making a list of the urgent issues that you are facing. Remember making the list of all the things that cause you anxiety, or cause you to have anxious behaviors such as nervousness, invasive thoughts, and panic? If you didn't do it before, make that list now. If you have made the list, bring it with you when you go to talk to the therapist. You will be doing both of you a big favor, and it will increase the efficiency of your treatment process, as you will not be wasting time trying to figure out what your issues are. Having a good idea of what your symptoms are, and how your anxiety manifests itself gives the therapist "something to go on ". This may lead to the therapist asking you questions about the details of an event, or how it made you feel. They may ask you to divulge uncomfortable information about your experiences. This is all in an attempt to understand what the underlying causes and triggers of your anxiety are. Sometimes we may get angry or upset with our therapist for pushing us to an emotionally vulnerable place. You may feel that it isn't helping you because you don't see or feel any immediate relief from your symptoms. Don't be afraid to tell your therapist. They are used to these reactions and can explain the process to you and maybe even point out some of the improvements they have noticed in you that you may not have noticed yourself. Maybe you have a question regarding what you discussed in the last session. This is especially valuable to both you and the therapist because it means that you have been participating in your therapy outside of the sessions. Don't be afraid to ask them to explain something again or give you perspectives on what you might have been thinking or wondering about. Raise any concerns or questions at the onset of the next session. That way, you will have time to viably process the issues. In many cases, this will strengthen the alliance between you, as it indicates that you are actively engaged in your therapy. Some therapy takes time to work through, but it is valuable work, and you will reap many benefits in the end.

Stick to The Issues

It is critical to set boundaries for yourself and stick to the important issues during therapy. It may be difficult to "get right down to it", but this is what you are paying for. Resist the urge to make too much small talk or to merely go over the events in your life since the last appointment. Get right to business after saying your initial hellos and getting comfortable. Talk about what gave you anxiety since the last appointment. What triggered it and how did you feel? Did you cope better with it than last time? What have you been thinking about since your last appointment? If you are not sure what to say, let the therapist ask you questions and answer them honestly. If the questions upset you because they make you think of things that remind you of past trauma, that is okay. You are there to "unpack all your issues" and have the therapist "help sort them out".

Treat Therapy as A Collaboration

I'm sure it is now clear to you that therapy is an interactive process. It requires you to honestly share your memories and feelings with someone you may not have known at all before therapy started. You must rely on your therapist to help you, and the therapist must rely on you to come to your appointment and participate in a meaningful way so that they can help you. This collaboration is a give and take relationship that can give you great strength. This collaboration, when successful, will give you the confidence and tools that you need to address the sources of your anxiety and make changes in your life that allow you to manage the symptoms of your condition. Express yourself and your needs. Ask questions and read extra books or articles that may further your understanding of your condition.

Chapter Summary

Sometimes when we have anxiety we are able to control our symptoms on our own, using helpful techniques such as distraction, positive self-talk and meditation, among other things. Unfortunately, however, sometimes we are not able to fully cope with the stressors in our life, and we need professional help to understand our issues and develop effective coping mechanisms. When you notice that you are suffering from debilitating anxiety, you should see a therapist.

A psychiatrist and a psychologist are different, although some people are both. A psychiatrist will prescribe you medication, whereas a psychologist will talk to you about your problems and potential solutions. Some mental health issues, such as those caused by chemical imbalances in the brain require medication to be effectively treated. A proper diagnosis is important. Talk to the professional that you can get access to, and work with them to develop an understanding of your condition.

Make sure that if you are seeking medical help that you take a path that will not cause you extra anxiety. Make sure your appointments are scheduled at times when you are not super busy with other things before and after. Be honest with your medical care provider and tell them everything you can about what you know about your symptoms, triggers and underlying causes. As you talk about your life and your symptoms, your doctor will be able to form a diagnosis and help you develop tools to assist you in your daily life. Commit to honest, collaborative issues and stick to the issues. If you aren't sure what to say, let your therapist ask questions and answer honestly and fully. Get the most out of your sessions by practicing mindfulness and focusing entirely on the appointment. If you are distracted, tell your therapist why. It may be related to your condition and be a sign of a current anxiety reaction that they can help you with.

Making the decision to seek professional help is not always easy, but if you think you may need the advice of medical professionals, you probably do! At the very least, explore what therapy might be able to offer you. Go in with an open mind and a willingness to work with the therapist in an open and collaborative way. Many people benefit enormously from the help of a therapist. Maybe you will be one of them.

FINAL WORDS

In this book, you have learned about anxiety and how to stop it. Anxiety is a natural response to stress. When the mind and body are confronted with a stressor, the nervous system may be triggered to release adrenaline and cortisol, which can make us jittery and unable to handle stimuli. This is usually caused by the body's fear response that initiates the "freeze, fight or flight" behavior in us. The different impacts of stress may be expressed differently by various people. Anxiety may cause a rapid heartbeat, flashes of hot or cold, nervous behaviors, panic and gastrointestinal distress. Some people are able to manage stress and anxiety very well, but for others, it can have a debilitating effect on their lives.

Over the course of this book, we have reviewed everything you need to know about anxiety. You learned about what anxiety looks and feels like, and what the common symptoms are. In addition, we went over some of the major anxiety disorders that some people suffer from.

You have also learned a variety of tools and techniques to handle the symptoms of anxiety. When you are able to recognize the triggers for your anxiety, you can engage in positive self-talk, thought interruption and switching gears. Making a list of what you know about your anxiety helps you to understand what is happening to your mind and body. Also helpful in list form is all the things that bring you joy. Make a commitment to those things regularly. Making concerted efforts to incorporate joy into your life is very important to overcoming anxiety. The active pursuit of joy will increase the amount of happy hormones such as endorphins in your body and give you a positive experience that you can draw on later to rekindle feelings of contentment or joy.

For centuries, people have practiced various forms of meditation to help them calm their mind and body. Sit comfortably and clear your mind using focusing objects or a mantra. Meditation is an effective way to practice stillness and to bring peace and balance into your life.

Other natural remedies to anxiety include exercise, a nutritious diet, adequate sleep, and herbal supplements. Whether it be the practice of mindfulness and meditation, or the use of exercise and proper diet, there are many ways to influence how our body reacts to stress.

If you are experiencing debilitating anxiety and you find no relief from the techniques in this book, you may benefit from the assistance of professional mental health practitioners such as a psychiatrist or psychologist, or both. There is no shame in actively seeking out the help you may need.

Regardless of what method you use to reduce your nervousness and anxiety, the most important thing is that you are taking active steps towards managing your mental health, and that is a positive and healthy thing. Find ways to understand yourself better, recognize your triggers, and use this understanding, along with techniques for managing anxiety, to get your happiness back and find your inner peace.

RESOURCES

American Psychiatric Association & Parekh, Ranna, M.D, M.P.H. (2017) What Are Anxiety Disorders? https://www.psychiatry.org/patients-families/anxiety-disorders/what-are-anxiety-disorders. (accessed 2020).

Barnett, Robert A. (2019). 19 Natural Remedies for Anxiety. https://www.health.com/health/gallery/0,,20669377,00.html. (accessed 2020).

Brady, Krissy (2019) 13 Signs You're Sabotaging Your Own Progress in Therapy. https://www.huffingtonpost.ca/entry/signs-sabotaging-therapy-progress_l_5d40ac12e4b0db8affafb0a2. (accessed 2020).

Calmer You (2018) What To Do During An Anxiety Attack. https://www.calmer-you.com/anxiety-attack/. (accessed 2020).

Cooke, Justine (2016) Using Mindfulness to Overcome Anxiety. Visions Journal. https://www.heretohelp.bc.ca/visions/mindfulness-vol12/using-mindfulness-to-overcome-anxiety. (accessed 2010)

Daskal, Lolly (n.d.) 10 Simple Ways You Can Stop Yourself From Overthinking. https://www.inc.com/lolly-daskal/10-simple-ways-you-can-stop-yourself-from-overthinking.html. (accessed 2020).

Ferreira, Mandy (2017) 14 Mindfulness Tricks to Reduce Anxiety. https://www.healthline.com/health/mindfulness-tricks-to-reduce-anxiety#1. (accessed 2020).

Gaiam (n.d.) Meditation 101: Techniques, Benefits, and a Beginner's How-To. https://www.gaiam.com/blogs/discover/meditation-101-techniques-benefits-and-a-beginner-s-how-to. (accessed 2020).

Gottern, Ana (2018) 11 Ways to Stop a Panic Attack. https://www.healthline.com/health/how-to-stop-a-panic-attack#happy-place. (accessed 2020).

Headspace. (n.d.) Meditation for Anxiety. https://www.headspace.com/meditation/anxiety. (accessed 2020).

Henriques, Gregg, Ph.D. (2015) What is Mindfulness and How Does It Work? https://www.psychologytoday.com/ca/blog/theory-knowledge/201502/what-is-mindfulness-and-how-does-it-work. (accessed 2020).

Hofmann, Stefan G, Ph.D. (n.d) Facts about the effects of mindfulness. https://www.anxiety.org/can-mindfulness-help-reduce-anxiety. (accessed 2020).

Holland, Kimberly (2018) Everything You Need to Know About Anxiety. Healthline. https://www.healthline.com/health/anxiety. (accessed 2020).

Hovitz, Helaina (2018) Some Simple Ways to Turn Anxiety Into Excitement. https://greatist.com/live/how-to-turn-anxiety-into-excitement#3. (accessed 2020).

Jaworski, Margaret (n.d.) Living with Anxiety: How to Cope. https://www.psycom.net/living-with-anxiety/#anxiety-mind-andm. (accessed 2020).

Khuu, Cung (2018) How to Instantly Turn Anxiety into Excitement. https://medium.com/publishous/how-to-instantly-turn-anxiety-into-excitement-2c6c9495bc1. (accessed 2020).

Kind, Shelly (n.d.) Facts about the effects of mindfulness. https://www.anxiety.org/can-mindfulness-help-reduce-anxiety. (accessed 2020).

Li, Qing, Dr. (2018) Forest Bathing is Great for Your Health. Here's How to Do It. https://time.com/5259602/japanese-forest-bathing/. (accessed 2020).

Livni, Ephrat (2016) The Japanese practice of 'forest bathing' is scientifically proven to improve your health. https://qz.com/804022/health-benefits-japanese-forest-bathing/. (accessed 2020).

Matthews, Dan, CPRP (2020) 15 Ways to Stop Overthinking and Worrying About Everything. https://www.lifehack.org/articles/communication/how-to-stop-overthinking-everything.html. (accessed 2020).

Mayo Clinic, Anxiety Disorders. https://www.mayoclinic.org/diseases-conditions/anxiety/symptoms-causes/syc-20350961. (accessed 2020).

Mays, Mitchell, Dr. (Mindful Staff (2019) How to Meditate. https://www.mindful.org/how-to-meditate/. (accessed 2020).

Moffitt, Debra (n.d.) Nine Simple Practices to Embrace Joy. https://www.beliefnet.com/wellness/personal-growth/nine-simple-practices-to-embrace-joy.aspx. (accessed 2020).

Perelman School of Medicine (n.d.) Generalized Anxiety Disorder. https://www.med.upenn.edu/ctsa/general_anxiety_symptoms.html. (accessed 2020).

Risher, Brittany (2018) This Is When to See a Mental Health Professional About Your Anxiety. https://www.self.com/story/when-to-see-professional-anxiety. (accessed 2020).

Roselle, Tom, Dr. (2017) 19 Natural Remedies for Anxiety. https://www.drtomroselle.com/19-natural-remedies-anxiety/. (accessed 2020).

Spiritual Progress Guide Admin (2015) Meditation for Inner Peace. http://spiritualprogressguide.com/blog-post/meditation-for-inner-peace. (accessed 2020).

Tartakovsky, Margarita, M.S. (2018) Therapists Spill: 10 Tips for Making the Most of Therapy. https://psychcentral.com/lib/therapists-spill-10-tips-for-making-the-most-of-therapy/. (accessed 2020).

U.S. Department of Health and Human Services (n.d) What are the five major types of anxiety disorders? https://www.hhs.gov/answers/mental-health-and-substance-abuse/what-are-the-five-major-types-of-anxiety-disorders/index.html. (accessed 2020).

Wehrenberg (2005) 10 Best-Ever Anxiety-Management Techniques. https://www.psychotherapynetworker.org/magazine/article/774/10-best-ever-anxiety-management-techniques. (accessed 2020).

Werner, Carly (2019) I'm Afraid of the Future. How Can I Enjoy the Present? https://www.healthline.com/health/fear-of-the-future#1. (accessed 2020).

Wikipedia (2020) Jon Kabat-Zinn. https://en.wikipedia.org/wiki/Jon_Kabat-Zinn. (accessed 2020).

Eliminate Negative Thinking

How to Overcome Negativity, Control Your Thoughts, And Stop Overthinking. Shift Your Focus into Positive Thinking, Self-Acceptance, And Radical Self Love

Derick Howell

TABLE OF CONTENTS

INTRODUCTION

Negative thinking is a very common problem that most people have encountered at some point in their lives. Although positive thinking is widely advocated by many health and wellness experts, getting yourself out of the rut of negative thoughts can be very challenging. Even if you are a person who analyzes their thoughts frequently, it can be difficult to tell the difference between negative thinking, and the everyday worries and anxieties that everyone deals with.

While it is normal to worry about issues such as divorce and financial problems, when these thoughts become too intrusive and unrelenting, they may wreak havoc not only on your personal life but also on your career and professional relationships.

It is for this reason that you need to understand what negative thinking is, how it manifests in your life and how you can overcome it. In doing so, you will be able to safeguard your mental health, become more resilient to change and be more capable of dealing with any challenges that come up in your personal and professional life.

So what is negative thinking and how do you determine which thoughts represent normal levels of concern and which are overly negative?

In general, negative thinking refers to a thought process in which one only sees the worst aspects of things, events, people and experiences. A negative thinker will always expect the worst possible outcome from every situation. Most people who engage in constant negative thinking also tend to reduce their expectations. They do this by considering only the worst possible scenarios in order to shield themselves from disappointment. Moreover, it is not uncommon for individuals who engage in negative thinking to suffer from low self-esteem and low self-confidence, since they are likely to focus on the things they consider inadequate about themselves.

Negative thinking may arise due to several factors. One of the most common causes of this type of thinking is depression. Most people experience a balanced mix of positive and negative thoughts throughout their day. Someone who has depression experiences a distorted view of the world, often through a filter of constant negative thinking. They may perceive themselves as a failure in life and unworthy of love or success. They may also view the world as inherently cruel and hostile. In addition to negative thinking, depression also affects the way individuals feel about themselves. People who are afflicted with this illness tend to feel very sad, despondent, fatigued and lethargic. This can compound the negative thinking and lead to even more serious health problems and sometimes, sadly, suicide. In most instances, people never realize that their negative thinking stems from depression. They may brush it off as simply being a normal part of who they are.

Another mental health condition that is closely associated with negative thinking is obsessive-compulsive disorder (OCD). Individuals who suffer from OCD typically experience unwanted, recurring thoughts and sensations which compel them to do certain things repeatedly, or in a very specific way. For instance, an OCD sufferer might feel the need to double-check their looks excessively, be fixated on organization, or repeat certain words or tasks repeatedly. Moreover, they might spend time "over cleaning" their clothes or washing their hands excessively due to an irrational fear of germs. This mental health condition is categorized as an anxiety disorder since the affected individuals perform these actions to lessen their anxiety. Due to this constant worry, people who have OCD tend to experience negative thinking more than those who don't. They may perceive themselves as being at risk of some impending danger if they do not satisfy these impulsive thoughts and needs. Even though most OCD sufferers tend to have an awareness that their obsessive thinking is not rooted in reality, they still find it difficult to control the behavior.

Fortunately, this mental health condition, like many others, can be managed with the right help and support.

However, this does not mean that normal, healthy individuals are immune to the perils of negative thinking. In fact, there are plenty of reasons why even the most optimistic people find themselves in "negative thinking loops" at one point or another. Negative thoughts in most people arise out of fear of the future and anxiety about the prevailing circumstances in their lives. For instance, due to aging or time limitations, a person may worry about not achieving everything they had hoped to do in their lives. This might lead to feelings of anxiety, which if not confronted and dealt with, can affect one's mental and physical health. Some individuals may also feel anxious about past events, and how they have shaped their lives. This often leads to self-criticism, which may exacerbate negative thinking.

Regardless of where your negative thinking stems from, there is absolutely no reason why you should continue to wallow in these thoughts if they are affecting your life in negative ways. There are numerous techniques that can help you intercept your negative thoughts and manage them effectively when they arise.

I have been an anxiety coach for more than a decade. During this time, I have taught many individuals how to properly use these techniques to counter negative thoughts. I have also conducted numerous training workshops and seminars designed to help people overcome negative thinking loops which are holding them back from living their lives to the fullest.

There are many benefits to learning how to control negative thinking. Firstly, by countering your negative thoughts with positive thinking, you will be able to overcome mental illnesses such as depression and anxiety. You will also develop a more balanced perception of the world and yourself. In addition to this, you will be better equipped with the skills to cope with stressful life events and situations in a healthy way.

It is also no secret that anxiety and incessant worrying contributes to health problems such as hypertension and heart disease. By learning how to counter your negative thought loops, you can significantly reduce the risks of developing these health issues, which can be fatal if not managed effectively. So, by extension, getting yourself out of the rut of negative thoughts will help you increase your lifespan!

Unfortunately, overcoming negative thinking patterns is not as easy as most people think. As a person who has suffered from persistent negative thinking and anxiety, I can assure you that there are many challenges and obstacles that you will encounter along the way. This, however, should not cause you to lose hope! As long as you make a conscious resolve to end your negative thinking and are persistent about this goal, you will begin to enjoy remarkable results very soon. The tricks and techniques outlined in this book have helped not only myself but also thousands of other individuals throughout the world. I have no doubt, therefore, that they will work for you too, in your journey to overcome negative thinking.

So, if you are tired of negative thoughts getting in the way of your personal life, professional career or relationships, now is the time to nip this problem in the bud! I hope that you will find this book instructional and enjoyable, and that the wisdom contained herein will aid you in overcoming negative thinking, overthinking and anxiety, for good.

CHAPTER ONE:

Ineffective Ways to Stop Negative Thinking

If you struggle with negative thinking and anxiety, you are probably aware of how challenging it can be to change your mindset. Being stuck in negative thinking loops can feel like an internal struggle. On one hand, the psychological discomfort can be a strong motivator to pull yourself out of the rut, while on the other, you may not know exactly how to do so. This can leave you feeling very hopeless and frustrated.

Many people who engage in constant negative thinking resort to ineffective coping behaviors out of desperation (O'Brien, 2019a), which only makes the problem even more complex and much harder to solve.

In this chapter, we will discuss some of the ineffective ways of approaching negative thinking, and why you need to steer clear of them if you hope to get rid of your negative thoughts.

Ignoring the Negative Thoughts

Persistent negative thinking and overthinking can be very uncomfortable and disconcerting regardless of who you are. If you are constantly assailed by intrusive negative thoughts, you can feel very powerless and out of control. This is why most people resort to trying to ignore the negative thoughts in the hope that if they do not pay attention to them, they will magically go away. However, this doesn't always work out as expected. Negative thinking is usually a deep-seated internal problem that has taken a foothold in one's psyche. It is not something that can be easily wished away or ignored. While you might temporarily feel a sense of relief from not having to think about your negative thoughts, this relief is usually very short-lived and sooner or later, the negative thoughts may come bubbling to the surface once again.

Using Distractions and Diversions

Some people immerse themselves in their careers or hobbies in the hope that by distracting themselves from their negative thinking, it will somehow magically stop. People use expressions like "I'll just throw myself into my work," and "I'll just stay busy." However, this can be counterproductive, as it only shelves the problem rather than addressing it head-on and finding long-term solutions.

Indulging in Drugs and Alcohol

Constant negative thinking often leads to stress and anxiety, which can be very difficult to cope with. That is why many people resort to using products such as tobacco, marijuana, and alcohol in an effort to silence the negative thoughts in their head. However, while smoking and drinking alcohol can provide a temporary sense of relief, these are not very effective ways of dealing with negative thinking in the long-run. As a matter of fact, they can even lead to even more serious health problems such as dependency and addiction. It is worth noting that these methods of coping with negative thinking only offer temporary relief. While you might feel a sense of calm for a few hours, this soon dissipates once the effects of the drugs or alcohol wear off. Then you find yourself back in the cycle of negative thinking. In essence, drugs and alcohol only exacerbate the problem of negative thinking, and should, therefore, be avoided as a coping mechanism.

Bargaining with the Negative Thinking

It is not uncommon for some individuals to resort to bargaining with their negative thinking in an attempt to make it stop. They may be convinced that by trying to rationalize their thinking, they can pull themselves out of their negative thinking cycle. The problem with this kind of mentality is that it assumes that negative thinking is rooted in some kind of rationality. While this may be true in some cases, it does not apply in all instances. For example, the negative thoughts associated with depression may be the direct result of chemical imbalances in the brain.

Sleeping it Off

Getting adequate and quality sleep every night is beneficial in a number of ways. It helps in rejuvenating the body and the mind. It can also boost our thinking and memory.

However, despite its numerous benefits, overindulging in sleep as a means to counter negative thinking is not very effective. It only postpones the problem rather than solving it. This is not to say that you shouldn't use sleep as a temporary relief when you feel burnt out physically or mentally. In fact, sleeping can feel very refreshing, and be beneficial to your physical and mental well-being. However, you are advised not to use it as a crutch to avoid negative thinking patterns, as it may prevent you from dealing with the root of the problem. Remember, the goal is to find long-term solutions for your negative thinking problem. This is not something that sleeping will provide you with.

Resorting to these ineffective ways of dealing with negative thoughts has been shown to work only in the short term. Therefore, if you are trying to get rid of negative thinking permanently, it is absolutely crucial that you learn the proper techniques to approach the problem.

Summary

Now that you understand the ineffective ways of dealing with negative thinking, you are more likely to avoid them in the future. So, to recap this chapter, here are some of the big takeaways:

- Negative thinking is a problem that should never be ignored since this only postpones the solution and makes it more difficult to resolve.
- Using distractions to avoid your negative thoughts is counterproductive, and only delays and hinders you from coming up with long-term solutions.
- Drug and alcohol abuse only offers temporary relief from the discomfort of negative thoughts rather than providing permanent solutions.
- Do not try to argue with or rationalize your uncomfortable thoughts since negative thinking is an inherently irrational process.
- Sleeping does not effectively get rid of negative thinking. Rather, it shelves the problem, which means you will still have to deal with it later, when you wake up.

In the next chapter, we will cover ways in which you can clear your mind of negative thinking. The techniques and practices that will be discussed in the next chapter will be useful and handy to you. Pay close attention to them and see how they are applicable in your situation.

CHAPTER TWO:

Clear Your Mind of Negative Thinking

Negative thinking is a habit that can develop over time without the conscious awareness of an individual. If you allow negative thoughts to take hold in your mind, it will become very difficult to overcome them. However, this does not mean that you should immediately force negative thoughts out of your head the moment you become aware of them. As a matter of fact, the more you try to resist the thoughts, the stronger they become (Bloom, 2015). So what should you do in such a scenario?

Well, there are several practices and techniques you can employ to help you clear your mind of negative thoughts whenever they present themselves. Here are some of the ways in which you can counteract your negative thinking as soon as you become aware of it.

Change Your Body Language

Body posture is known to exert a significant influence on the way our minds work. For example, if you are slouching in an uncomfortable manner, you are likely to experience more negative thoughts than if you are at ease. In addition to this, poor body language can affect your self-image and confidence. This makes you more vulnerable to negative thinking and you may be prone to self-criticize.

Therefore, it is vital to develop an awareness of your body language in order to get rid of persistent negative thinking more quickly.

Talk Them Through With Someone

There are times when negative thinking arises out of pent up emotions and feelings. Granted, most people find it uncomfortable to share their innermost feelings out of a fear of being judged by others. Other times it just seems like talking about your emotions with others amounts to burdening them with your problems. However, there are many benefits of sharing your uncomfortable emotions with people you trust. These include:

- You stand to gain a better perspective of your problems.
- You will be more likely to find a solution.
- You will be happy to know you are not alone.

Failing to share your uncomfortable feelings can seriously exacerbate the problem of negative thinking, and make you feel even more hopeless. Don't be alone with your negativity! Talking it out with someone you trust, on the other hand, can provide you with a sense of relief, and help dissipate your worries.

Spend a Minute Calming Your Mind

Negative thinking can become very overwhelming sometimes, causing you to feel anxious. Keeping your mind relaxed and at ease can be very challenging when you have a million thoughts racing around; therefore, it is very important to take some time to calm your mind. This will enable you to perceive things in a clear and unbiased way.

This requires taking a step back and letting the thoughts pass through your mind without offering any resistance or judgment. You can think of it as a kind of meditation. Once your thoughts have settled and your mind has calmed down sufficiently, you can then assess your thoughts from an objective point of view.

Change Your Perspective

Very often, we are plagued by negative thinking because of our poor perspective on the situations we encounter in life. Sometimes we find ourselves blaming the challenges we experience on a deficiency in ourselves. This can cause us to have a very poor self-image. However, all that is needed in some cases is simply a change of perspective. Instead of considering yourself as a failure when going through challenges, you can decide to think that you are no different from others who face day-to-day problems.

By changing your point of view whenever you feel assailed by negative thinking, you can develop self-confidence and clarity. Being able to look at your situation with an open mind will help you to identify the root cause of your negative thinking and assist you to troubleshoot it effectively.

Take Responsibility for Your Negative Thoughts

Many times when we are plagued with negative thoughts, it can be tempting to blame other people for the unpleasant situation which we may be facing. We might adopt a victim mentality or point a finger at other people as we try to avoid being accountable for the situation. This, however, is not a very effective way of dealing with uncomfortable or negative thoughts. While it might provide us with some temporary relief, it prevents us from considering the actual problem, thereby hindering us from finding long-lasting solutions. It is important to remember that even though you are not in control of everything that happens in your life, ultimately you are responsible for the choices you make and the outcomes which emerge as a result of those decisions. You should, therefore, learn to hold yourself accountable for any negative thoughts you may be experiencing. Take the initiative to seek out permanent solutions for them so that they do not interfere with your internal state of wellbeing.

Get Creative

While negative thoughts can be very unsettling psychologically due to the anxiety that they bring, they can also act as a catalyst for creativity. Whenever you feel overwhelmed by uncomfortable thoughts, you can use that opportunity to express yourself in creative ways.

You can channel your anxiety and frustration into creativity by writing, drawing, painting or even making music about it. Doing so allows you to find healthy outlets for your negative thoughts, thereby enabling you to purge them from your system. Furthermore, creating works of art also enables you to explore your emotions on a deeper level, thereby helping you to develop a better understanding of why you think the way you do.

Another fundamental benefit of being creative is that it helps you feel good about yourself. Channeling your mental discomfort into creativity can significantly lift your mood and pull you out from the slump of anxiety or depression that often accompanies negative thinking.

Employ Positive Affirmations

Positive affirmations are statements that are meant to help you overcome negative thoughts and they challenge you to believe in yourself. When you repeat these statements to yourself regularly, they become imprinted on your consciousness, and you begin to realize the truthfulness in them. Reciting positive affirmations can not only help you to get rid of uncomfortable negative thoughts, but it can also motivate you to start acting positively in order to achieve the outcomes you desire. Furthermore, positive affirmations can help you alleviate the effects of stress and anxiety that comes from overthinking about negative things. Just like workout exercises, positive affirmations trigger the release of feel-good hormones in the body and increase the generation of new clusters of "positive thought" neurons in the brain.

If you are struggling with negative thinking cycles, here are some of the best positive affirmations that you can repeat to yourself in order to begin thinking more positively:

- I am in control of my life today, and I choose to think positively today.
- I refuse to allow negative thoughts to rob me of my peace of mind.
- I am enough and I possess all the qualities to direct my life as I please.
- I am powerful enough to conquer any challenges which I may face today.
- I acknowledge my uniqueness and the talents which I possess.
- I am strong enough to face this day with an open heart and clarity of mind.

Take a Walk

Staying in one place for too long can make you feel grumpy and anxious, which often triggers negative thinking. Sometimes all that is needed to reset the mind is a simple walk in another location. When you feel like negative thoughts are distracting you, one of the best ways of clearing the mind is to take a stroll in a scenic place. There are plenty of great places where you can go for a walk whenever you feel assailed by negative thinking. Parks and forests are good places to start. Of course, it's nice if you have access to parks and other beautiful places, but any location will do, as long as you get out and get moving. If you live in a place where there are none of these, you can still go on a walk in or near your neighborhood. It is advisable to avoid crowded streets and busy commercial places since the noise and bustle of activity can be uncomfortable when you are feeling negative.

Keep a Gratitude Journal

Very often, we get so caught up in our lives and the challenges that we are facing that we end up losing focus on all the ways in which life has been kind to us. Just because you are experiencing a challenging situation at present doesn't mean there's nothing good going for you in your life. So, when you get stuck in a cycle of negative thinking, it is a good idea to take a step back and take an inventory of how life has been good to you.

Rather than focus on the negative thoughts running through your mind, create a gratitude journal and list all the things you are grateful for in your life. These may include good health, a career that you enjoy, meaningful friendships and relationships in your life, and so much more. Record the good things that have happened and the things that have given you joy recently. Remember that nothing is too small or too big when it comes to gratitude. Even something as trivial as having an easy day at work can be something to be thankful for. Maybe you saw a beautiful bird, or someone held a door for you. Take the time to list everything in your life that you are happy about or thankful for, regardless of how small or insignificant it may seem. Keep in mind that sometimes the best things in our lives are right in front of our eyes waiting for us to notice them.

Approaching your negative thinking with gratitude can help you develop a greater appreciation of your life. Gratitude for what we have helps us view situations more positively no matter how challenging they may seem.

Change Your Environment

It is very easy for us to become so accustomed to a particular location that we become weary and bored of it. This can lead to feelings of restlessness and may trigger negative thoughts that we cannot escape. If you are feeling overwhelmed by negative thinking, a change of scenery can help you clear your mind of negative thoughts. This does not mean you have to permanently move to a different location. A simple act such as spending a few hours somewhere different, especially if it is a beautiful spot such as a park, can work wonders in terms of providing you with relief. You might also have a favorite coffee spot or a nicely decorated part of a mall or a community center that you like. Use these places to spend time away from home or work and bring variety to your life. You will be able to relax your mind and be able to think more clearly.

Engage in Workout Exercises

As we discussed in the introduction of this book, anxiety is one of the most common causes of negative thinking. In some cases, this anxiety arises out of pent up tension in the body and mind. One way of releasing all this frustration and tension in the body is to engage in workout exercises. There are numerous benefits to exercising whenever you feel overwhelmed by anxiety or negativity. One of the advantages of keeping yourself active by working out is that it triggers the release of feel-good endorphins such as dopamine and serotonin, which can greatly lift your mood. Working out also enhances blood circulation in the body, and can help alleviate symptoms of stress and depression.

Studies have shown that regular exercise can significantly improve one's cognitive processes. You don't need to engage in intensive fitness training at a gym. Even simply taking a few minutes to jog, walk or get on your exercise machine can significantly improve blood flow in the brain and help clear your thoughts. So, next time you feel assailed by negative thoughts, take a moment to stretch, do exercises or even go for a short walk or jog? If you are in an apartment or office building, climb a few flights of stairs. Your body and mind will surely thank you for it.

Practice Deep Breathing

Deep breathing is a very effective way of clearing your mind of negative thoughts. This is because when you breathe deeply, it signals your brain to relax. This message is then relayed to your body, telling it to relax. Performing deep breathing exercises allows your body and mind to calm down whenever you find yourself overthinking. By practicing deep breathing, you allow your body to release any tension that you may be experiencing. This can help you ease any anxiety or stress you may be feeling. When you feel overwhelmed by negative thoughts, take a few minutes to perform a routine of deep breathing. Draw in controlled deep breaths through your nostrils and expel all the air (slowly) from your diaphragm. Doing so will help you feel calm and relaxed almost instantly.

Employ Humor

It is often said that laughter is the best medicine, and this certainly rings true when it comes to dealing with negative thinking. Laughter, just like fitness exercises, is known to release feel-good hormones, which can help lift your mood whenever you are feeling overwhelmed with negative thoughts. Of course, it can be very difficult to bring yourself to laugh when your mind is constantly being bombarded with uncomfortable thoughts every minute of your day. However, using humor to counter your negative thinking is very effective, and produces positive results almost instantly.

Therefore, whenever you feel like life is happening faster than you can keep up with, or you are feeling overwhelmed by negativity, you can derive a lot of comfort by taking a step back and laughing at the quirkiness of it all. Watch a show that is funny, and even if you don't feel like it, make a point to laugh at it. The action of laughter will release those feel-good hormones.

Remember not to take life so seriously all the time, since this negatively impacts how much you are able to enjoy it.

Summary

Negative thoughts can seem very overwhelming and cause you to feel like you are losing control over yourself and your life; however, it is possible to overcome them. With the right strategies and practices, you can clear your mind of negative thinking and regain your self-confidence (Bloom, 2015).

In this chapter, we learned about the many ways we can clear our mind of negative thoughts. In summary, here are the things you need to do whenever you feel overwhelmed by negative thoughts.

- Pay close attention to your body language and readjust any aspects that may be triggering your negative thoughts.
- Share your uncomfortable thoughts and emotions with someone you trust.
- Take a few moments to relax and calm your mind such that you begin to view your negative thoughts from an objective state of mind.
- Try to gain a different perspective of your negative thinking by looking at it from a new point of view.
- Use your anxiety and frustration as forces for good by channeling them towards creation. Painting, writing and composing music can act as outlets for your negative thoughts.
- Take frequent walks in serene environments to relax your mind whenever you feel bombarded by too much negative thinking.
- Recognize, focus on and be grateful for all the good things you have going for you in your life, no matter how insignificant they may seem.
- Spend some time in your favorite outdoor and indoor locations where you feel comfortable and relaxed. This can help calm your mind whenever you spiral into negative thinking and overthinking.
- Exercise in order to give your body an outlet for anxiety and stress. This will relax your body and mind when you feel

assailed by negative thoughts. This can be as simple as jogging for a few minutes, climbing some stairs or performing some stretching exercises.

- Practice deep breathing exercises to release tension in your body and mind whenever you feel overwhelmed by negative thoughts. This helps you to attain some clarity of mind.
- Use laughter to counter your negative thinking; you should not take life so seriously all the time.

In this chapter, you learned about the different methods you can use to clear your mind of negative thoughts. I have no doubt in my mind that you now have all the tools to help you counter negative thinking whenever it arises in your day to day life.

In the next chapter, you will learn some of the ways you can deal with the problem of negative thinking and permanently eliminate it from your life. If you have noticed that you have a tendency of obsessing over your negative thoughts more than you should, and you want to stop this behavior for good, then this next chapter is going to be very helpful for you.

CHAPTER THREE:

Eliminate the Bad Habit of Negative Thinking for Good

If you constantly struggle to overcome negative thinking, you might worry that there is something inherently wrong with you. However, this couldn't be further from the truth. Negative thinking is a normal part of being human. Over the course of our evolution, we naturally developed this trait as a survival strategy. Being aware of the negative potential in a situation or environment can help us become more aware of the issues that threaten our survival. This means anyone can be trapped in a cycle of pessimistic thinking at some point in their lives.

Although negative thinking is innate in us as human beings and can often be a motivator for us to act, when the thoughts become too intense and too frequent, they can interfere with our lives. It is therefore important not to allow your negative thinking to develop into a habit. Nevertheless, if you feel like you have already sunk into a hole of pessimism and negative thinking, this does not mean that you are doomed! As a matter of fact, there are several ways that you can rein in your negative thinking and eliminate it for good.

This chapter will present useful tools to help you eliminate the bad habit of negative thinking from your life for good.

Recognize and Step Back from Negative Thought Patterns

If you are constantly bombarded by negative thoughts that are intrusive, you know just how stressful they can be. That is why you need to take immediate steps to neutralize negative thinking patterns.

The first thing you can do in this regard is to recognize the loops of negative thinking that you often get stuck in and to take a step back to view them from a detached state of mind (O'Brien, 2019b). Easier said than done, right? Actually, gaining awareness of your negative thinking patterns is very simple to do as long as you have the right tools. The primary tool you require to achieve this is "cognitive defusion". The process of cognitive defusion is probably something you are already familiar with, you just don't realize it.

What is Cognitive Defusion and How is it Helpful?

Cognitive defusion is a mental process that is commonly associated with Acceptance and Commitment Therapy (ACT). Essentially, defusion is based on the idea that taking our thoughts too literally can lead to mental and psychological problems. Cognitive defusion techniques are designed to put our thoughts together with our experiences in order to allow for the distinction between the two to be recognized.

To better understand how cognitive defusion works, let us consider how our minds work. Generally, in our day to day lives, everything we experience or see is subject to labeling, categorization, evaluation, and comparison. This is a process that unfolds automatically, and it is facilitated by our cognitive analysis functions. This means that all these processes happen even without our conscious awareness, which is very useful when it comes to problem-solving.

However, a problem arises when these mental processes that facilitate comparison and pass judgment are directed inwards. This typically yields negative judgments upon ourselves and causes us to become hypercritical of ourselves and others. Eventually, when these processes merge with our psyche, we begin associating with them in a manner that is not reflective of reality. This results in problems such as overthinking and intrusive negative thoughts.

The aim of cognitive defusion is to allow us to recognize these processes without forming an attachment to them. It enables us to form partnerships with our thoughts (both negative and positive) without ceding control over our lives to them. This mindset requires that we do not suppress or try to deflect our thoughts, but rather observe them and acknowledge them from a distance. By developing cognitive defusion, we are able to distinguish the thoughts that are workable from those that are not. Unproductive thoughts are encouraged because they help us to pursue our visions and aspirations in life. On the other hand, thoughts that are not productive or positive are only meant to be observed and acknowledged but not acted upon since they lead us nowhere. They can be considered and then treated as background noise.

There are several skills that are involved in the process of cognitive defusion. These include:

- The ability to evaluate whether a thought is workable and productive. Does it align with your values and aspirations in life?
- Developing an acute ability to view thoughts simply as mental impressions rather than tangible things that exist in reality. This skill is very valuable because it enables us to be less caught up or entangled in our thoughts, particularly the negative ones.

Cognitive defusion is a very important skill to develop since it can be applied in various ways. Some of the scenarios where this skill can come in handy include:

- When you have patterns of thought that are repetitive or recurrent, especially if they have to do with your opinion or perception of yourself. For instance, “I’m not good enough" or “I will not amount to anything." These thoughts may seem benign and harmless at first, but once they take root in your mind, they can lead to anxiety and self-doubt which can result in negativity.

- When you are unable to determine the accuracy of our thoughts (also known as cognitive restructuring). Cognitive defusion can help reduce the psychological impact of thoughts without altering their content or frequency.
- When your negative thoughts become barriers to your progress. Sometimes when we are about to take a risk towards something that we actually want, we are plagued by thoughts such as, “What if I fail?” or “I’m not talented enough.” Through cognitive defusion, we can bypass these thoughts so that we act in ways that will catapult us towards the things we desire, even if it involves taking risks.
- When we are faced with a serious problem which we should otherwise be dealing with in a realistic way. Cognitive defusion can help us alleviate the stress of opening up to the possibilities that exist in situations that may seem very daunting.

There are various techniques that are employed in cognitive defusion. These techniques can be applied to any stream of thought, although they are most helpful when one is faced with intrusive negative thoughts.

The first thing you need to do when applying cognitive defusion is to think about a negative thought that you are constantly plagued by. This could be something like, "I am not worthy enough," or "I will never succeed at this." Once you have identified the negative thought, focus on it for a moment in order to get in fusion with it, then make that thought the target of your cognitive defusion practice. Here are some of the techniques which you will need to apply.

Recognize and Acknowledge

The first thing you need to do when applying cognitive defusion is to recognize and acknowledge the negative thoughts. This entails adding a cognition phrase such as, "I notice I am having the thought..." to the repetitive uncomfortable thought. Doing this will allow you to alter your relationship with your difficult thoughts.

Name It To Tame It - Assign a Label to Your Thoughts

Very often, we get trapped in our cycles of negative thinking because we try to fight or argue with negative thoughts, or we try to push them away. However, trying to cope with negative thoughts in these ways only amplifies them, and further reinforces their power over our lives.

So, how do we deal with the negative thoughts that plague us in a way that is effective and practical? The "name it to tame it" technique will help free you from negative thinking loops without having to fight them (O'Brien, 2019b). Here is how it works:

Once you recognize and acknowledge your negative thoughts, the next thing you need to do is label them. You can approach this technique in two different ways.

Your thoughts usually fall into the category of evaluative or descriptive. Descriptive thoughts are those that are related to our direct sensory experience, such as things we see, hear or touch. Evaluative thoughts, on the other hand, consider our experience and are mostly based on concepts such as good-bad, right-wrong.

When observing your thoughts, you should be able to label them depending on what kind of thoughts they are. For example, is the negative thought that you are having an image, a question or a statement of blame? Once you have identified and labeled your recurring negative thought, you can give it a label to address it whenever it pops into your head. You may have already noticed that most of our negative thoughts are recurrent, and usually involve the same storylines, such as, “I’m not good enough to succeed.” You might respond to yourself by saying, "There's my self-blaming thought," or “There’s my fear of inadequacy again.” whenever such a thought appears in your mind. This allows you to create distance from your thought, and perceive it as something conceptual rather than actual. The goal is to realize that it’s only just a thought, and it doesn’t necessarily reflect reality. Once you have assigned the label, simply try to “let it go”. Give it a name, and then put it in the background while you consider other ways to think of the situation you are in. In doing so, you prevent the negative thought from overwhelming your mental state and mood.

Appreciate Your Mind

The idea here is to refrain from giving your negative thoughts too much importance since this creates tension and struggle. Give it a moment of consideration and then put it aside. Whenever that recurring thought pops into your mind, you need to “appreciate” or “thank” your mind for giving you that thought, but in a kind of sarcastic tone similar to how you would respond to a nagging teenager who says something provocative to trigger a reaction out of you. For example, tell your mind, “Yes, yes, I know, very scary, it could all go wrong. Got it.” Be thankful that you have been informed of that potential outcome, and then consider other more positive perspectives of the situation.

Mindful Observation

Mindful observation involves considering your thoughts with an attitude of curiosity and openness. Spend some time observing your flow of thoughts without trying to analyze or judge them. This might be challenging to do since our minds are naturally designed to evaluate things, including our own thoughts. However, if you notice that you are trying too hard to analyze your thoughts, take note of that and then continue to observe the thoughts that follow.

There are various images that may help you become good at mindful observation. For instance, you can think of your thoughts as boats floating on a lake. In this case, the lake represents your mind, while your thoughts are represented by the boats. Try to observe your thoughts the same way you would watch the boats gliding peacefully over the lake. Similarly, images of birds soaring effortlessly through the sky is another image you could use.

Approaching mindful observation using these images will help you overcome the tendency to negatively analyze, evaluate and judge your thoughts. It will allow you to observe your thoughts with a sense of curiosity and detachment, thus helping you to achieve relaxation and peace.

Come to Your Senses

If you pay close attention to your negative thoughts, you may already be aware that most of them arise from one of two sources.

The first is an obsession over the past. Perhaps you spend a lot of time thinking about past actions which you regret, circumstances that didn't turn out as you had hoped, or bad things that happened to you. This can result in a perpetual feeling of guilt and sadness, and make you predisposed to negative thinking.

The second factor that contributes to negative thinking is constant anxiety about the future. As humans, we are naturally prone to experience fear about the uncertainty of life. Maybe you find yourself worrying about the future of your family, relationships or career. This can put you in a state of constant worry and negativity.

When you investigate your negative thinking loops carefully, you will realize that your mind is focused on the future or past.

The problem with these negative thought patterns is that they steal our focus away from the real world. When you get too invested in them, you lose track of your life. You may also end up losing connection with the people in your life and the world in which you live.

In order to begin living in the present, you need to divert your attention from your negative thoughts and direct your attention to the world around you. You can do this by practicing the "coming to your senses" technique. The technique involves redirecting your attention away from your thoughts and focusing on your senses. Be aware of your surroundings, and focus on what is happening. What can you hear, what can you see? How does it relate to your situation at that moment? You will experience a greater awareness of yourself and the world around you. You will also gain a sense of calm and relaxation which will help ground you when plagued with difficult thoughts.

Helpful Questions

Negative thinking patterns tend to be very relentless. No matter how hard you try to overcome them, they can persist. If you find yourself plagued by negative thoughts, there are several tools that you can use to unshackle yourself and change your situation. These tools are in the form of questions that are used in Acceptance and Commitment Therapy (ACT). The questions are designed to help you challenge your negative thoughts in order to shift your focus.

The best approach to this method involved asking yourself questions and answering them in your head (O'Brien, 2019b). Here are some of the questions you need to consider in order to overcome negative thinking patterns.

- Is this thought helpful or useful to me in any way?
- Is this thought grounded in reality?
- Is this thought important or is my mind just engaging in mental chatter?
- Does this thought help me to take action towards achieving my objectives?

Once you ask and respond to these helpful questions, you can follow up with some positive questions that will help you redirect your focus towards constructive thoughts. Ideally, you should handle these questions one at a time and only move to the next one after you've sufficiently answered the one before it.

- What do I consider to be true?
- What outcome will I get out of this situation, and how can I make it happen?
- What should I do to make the best out of this situation?
- Will I be better off without this thought?
- What are some of the things I can focus on now?
- Can I view this from a different point of view?
- What can I be grateful for at this moment?

Asking and answering these questions can change your perspective and redirect your attention from your negative thoughts to the potential of positivity in your everyday reality.

Summary

In this chapter, we have looked at some of the tools and techniques that can help you overcome your negative thinking patterns and take back power and control over the way we think. Whenever you feel overwhelmed with uncomfortable thought patterns, remember to:

- Use cognitive defusion to distinguish between the thoughts in your head and the reality of your situation. This will allow you to develop a positive relationship with your thoughts. It will also enable you to view your thoughts from a point of calm detachment, rather than allowing the thoughts to govern your emotions and actions.
- Learn and practice the "name it to tame it" technique. This will help you to break free from negative thought patterns without having to struggle with them.
- Be in the present by focusing your attention away from your negative thoughts and direct them to your sense perceptions

of your immediate situation. This will provide you with relief by calming your mind and freeing you of worries about the past or the future.

- Use "helpful questions" to dig deep into your thoughts and determine their veracity. You may also use follow up questions to challenge your negative thoughts and replace them with positive ones.

This chapter has focused on giving you tools and techniques to deal with negative thoughts in an effective manner. The strategies we have discussed have been proven to work. If you struggle perpetually with negative thinking, start practicing these strategies. This will help you to eliminate the negative thought patterns you are faced with and assist you to regain control of your thinking.

In the next chapter, you are going to learn how to take control of your thinking and prevent yourself from spiraling into negativity. This next chapter is undoubtedly one of the most crucial in this book, as it will show you how to nip negative thinking in the bud before it grows into a bigger problem. Pay close attention to our pointers. They will be invaluable to your strategy for eliminating negative thinking permanently.

CHAPTER FOUR:

How to Control Your Thoughts and Stop Spiralling into Negativity

Depression and anxiety are often characterized by negative thoughts that can be difficult to deal with. People often don't realize just how serious their negative thinking is affecting them until it's too late. However, even if your negative thinking has become habitual, there are mental strategies that you can employ to help you take control of your thought process. Let us examine some of these strategies and see how we can use them to deal with negative thoughts.

Making a Mental Shift

In order to take control of your thought process and prevent negative thoughts from taking hold in your mind, you need to make a conscious effort to shift your thinking. This can be very challenging to do; however, with regular practice, it will soon become second nature to you, and you will be able to shift your thinking without making a lot of effort.

So, what does making a mental shift involve? Basically, shifting your mental focus entails challenging your established perception about a difficult situation. It requires you to consider whatever worries you may be facing and directing your attention towards something different. The aim of mental shifting is to break the cycle of unwanted or uncomfortable recurring thoughts (Elmer, 2019).

A key component of this strategy involves reversing the negative thoughts that you may have picked up from other people. For instance, if you have been brought up to believe that you have to excel in academia in order to have a good future, you might feel like a failure if you do not achieve this. Holding onto these beliefs might make you very susceptible to negative thinking. This is why you need to unlearn such beliefs if you hope to get rid of the negative thought patterns you are prone to.

By deliberately shifting your focus away from negative thoughts, you can significantly alleviate anxiety and stress and free yourself from uncomfortable thought loops.

Do Your Thoughts Include Should?

When learning how to make a mental shift you must identify the common thought loops that you get caught up in, and learn how to recognize negative thinking instantly. For instance, if your thought process includes the word “should”, you need to evaluate why you think in that way. For instance, you might be having a thought loop that tells you, "I should do a certain thing," or "I should not feel a particular way." Although these thoughts might be well-intentioned, they can elicit feelings of guilt and pull you into a spiral of negative thinking.

A great way of countering thoughts like these is to change the words you use to take account of your imperfection and limitations as a human being. Instead of thinking "I should not feel this way," you can instead say, " I don't feel well right now due to the challenges I’m experiencing, but I'm sure it will pass." By shifting your approach in this way, the pressure might be significantly lifted.

To make a successful mental shift when plagued by negative thoughts, you also need to identify any patterns of negative thinking that you might be caught up in. In most cases, thoughts that express commands, such as I "should", emerge out of mental distortions referred to as automatic negative thinking.

Negative thoughts that arise due to automatic negative thinking are usually reflective of strong aversions we may have towards certain things. These thoughts tend to develop into habits and become persistent, which makes them very difficult to deal with. They are usually very common if one is struggling with anxiety or depression.

Automatic negative thinking isn't always easy to recognize since it usually develops over a long period. Most people usually don't even realize that this is the cause of their negative thoughts unless someone else points it out to them. However, you can identify these patterns of thinking by maintaining records of your thoughts.

You can go about this in the following way:

- Identify the situation that you are in.
- Recognize and note any emotions that you might be experiencing.
- Pay attention to the images or thoughts that come to mind.

Here are the steps you need to follow to figure out if your negative thoughts stem from automatic negative thinking.

1. Assess the Situation

The first thing you need to do is to evaluate the situation you find yourself in. Some of the leading questions that may aid you in this evaluation include:

- Which people are involved in this situation?
- Where did this incident take place?
- What did I do to find myself in this position?
- When did this incident happen?

2. Evaluate Your Mood and Feelings

You will need to record any emotions you may be experiencing as a result of the situation. For example, are you angry, nervous or sad? It is also a good idea to note down the degree to which you feel affected. You can use percentages or other scales to denote this. For example, today I feel 75% sad, or my sadness is a 7 out of 10. Don't worry too much about getting the percentages exactly correct. You can choose any figure depending on the extent to which you feel those particular emotions. The key here is to trust your instincts and to take time to evaluate your moods and feelings.

3. Record the Automatic Thoughts that are Going Through Your Mind

The final and most important step in this process is to note down the automatic thoughts that are running through your head. These may include thoughts such as:

- I am stupid.
- I am overreacting.
- I can't deal with this.

If you realize that you are manifesting such automatic negative thoughts, you should deconstruct the situation to make it more manageable. This will allow you to make a shift of perspective and prevent your negative thinking from affecting your mood.

You need to investigate the reasoning behind your negative thinking to figure out why the situation you are in makes you think that way. For instance, if your negative thinking story says "I will never be a good parent", you may ask yourself whether this thought stems from the way in which you were brought up by your parents. It is important to follow this thought process to its logical conclusion since this will provide you with great insights into why you are prone to such negative thoughts about yourself.

It can also be worthwhile to imagine the worst-case scenario and take note of the feelings it arouses in you. When you evaluate your situation with honesty and an open mind, you might find out that your beliefs about yourself are totally unfounded, and that you have no reason to be anxious.

Once you have identified your automatic negative thoughts, you need to scrutinize them to see whether they hold true. You may come to the realization that there is no evidence whatsoever to support your train of thought. Even if there is some evidence that is based on past experiences, it might not be exactly applicable in your current situation.

Therefore, when investigating your automatic negative thinking loops, you need to give emphasis to credible evidence rather than emotions. Weigh all the evidence before making a judgment on whether your thought is grounded in rationality or is just another symptom of anxiety. If you determine that your thought is irrational, you can then replace it with a new one that factors in all the sound evidence, and one that allows your rational mind to take charge of your thinking.

When dealing with stressful automatic negative thinking, it is also important to acknowledge when you feel overwhelmed by your thoughts. People are quick to react defensively when they encounter difficult thoughts that they are unable to control. This is not only ineffective but can also be very counterproductive. Trying to fight your thoughts only makes them persist, which can hurl you down a spiral of anxiety. Regardless of where your negative thoughts come from, the first thing you need to do to overcome them is to welcome them carefully into your mind space. This is by no means an easy thing to do. After all, no one enjoys being bombarded by negative thoughts constantly. However, by carefully embracing your uncomfortable thoughts, you significantly reduce mental strain and expend less energy than you would do trying to fight them. Rather than spending all your efforts struggling with the negative thoughts, consider the possibility that they are there to teach you something. I assure you, once you learn that stressful thoughts are there for a reason, you will be better equipped to manage the feelings of anxiety and frustration that they elicit.

Summary

In this chapter, you learned that in order to control your thoughts and stop spiraling into negativity, you need to make a mental shift. There are several main takeaways from this chapter. When it comes to dealing with negative thinking habits, here are some important things to keep in mind.

- Making a mental shift is vital to getting rid of negative thoughts for good. To do so, you must be able to challenge your negative thoughts and determine their plausibility. To achieve this, you need to redirect your thoughts from the negative story in your head and replace that with a different perspective which takes into account the facts of the situation.
- Thoughts that include the word "should" are very challenging to deal with since they create intense pressure, which has to be resolved. If you are making "should" statements to yourself, you need to break down your thinking patterns in order to make navigating such thoughts easier. Generally, thoughts such as these reflect automatic negative thinking which develops over time. It is therefore important to scrutinize these thoughts to determine whether they are backed by evidence or are simply mental chatter arising from long developed habits (Elmer, 2019).

Learning how to identify and evaluate automatic negative thinking patterns is very crucial to making a mental shift away from negative thinking. If you have been struggling with these thoughts, developing these skills can prove to be invaluable. In most cases, negative thinking tends to go hand-in-hand with overthinking, which can also be a major problem. Obsessively thinking about negative thoughts can seriously affect your mood.

In the next chapter, we are going to look at some of the strategies you can employ to deal with overthinking and overcome the tendency of obsessing over your negative thoughts. By the end of the chapter, you should be able to easily recognize how your overthinking habits arise and use various techniques to troubleshoot this problem.

CHAPTER FIVE:

How to Stop Overthinking

Overthinking is a common problem affecting people across all age groups. While it is normal to obsess over some thoughts once in a while, when you spend all your time ruminating over your thoughts, it can become a serious problem.

Overthinking typically happens when you obsess over the past or become anxious about the future. Unlike regular thinking which is geared towards problem-solving, overthinking just makes you dwell on the problem without providing any solutions (Oppong, 2020). It is normal and even beneficial to think deeply during moments of self-reflection since this allows you to gain important insights that you can use to solve the problems you are facing. However, overthinking only makes you feel powerless about your situation and does not serve any meaningful purpose.

Unfortunately, in most cases, it is not easy to tell whether you are actually engaging in overthinking. Some people might confuse overthinking with self-reflection since both involve spending a significant amount of time thinking about something. However, the difference between the two is that self-reflection leads to useful insights, whereas overthinking only drains your energy and time. It doesn't matter how long you spend overthinking. You are unlikely to find a solution to whatever problem you are experiencing. It is therefore important to recognize when you are engaging in overthinking and learn how to stop it from cluttering your mind.

Here are some of the signs that you may be overthinking:

- You can't stop yourself from thinking about a negative incident that happened in the past.
- You find yourself engaging in negative thinking very often.
- You tend to focus on the worst-case scenario in any kind of situation.
- You tend to obsess over past mistakes and failures even though they may have no bearing on your current life.
- You tend to overanalyze every detail of your everyday interactions with other people.
- You often relieve any embarrassing moments you may have had in the past.
- You find it difficult to sleep because your mind won't shut off.
- You spend a lot of time looking for hidden meaning in what others say. You might even overinflate some statements and their possible meanings.
- You spend significant amounts of time worrying about things that you have absolutely no control over.

Overthinking is certainly a serious problem that can be damaging to your self-esteem and peace of mind. However, just because you are afflicted by constant negative thoughts doesn't mean you should give up. There are several steps outlined below that you can take to reclaim a sense of control over your life and overcome the problem of overthinking for good.

Develop an Awareness of the Problem

By now, you probably understand that most of the thoughts we have occur spontaneously and automatically. In the previous chapter, we looked at how our automatic negative thoughts arise out of habits we have developed unconsciously over the course of our lives. Usually, these thoughts latch onto our minds and become repetitive, thus making it impossible to make progress in our lives. The first step in overcoming overthinking, therefore, is to be aware of your thoughts. You must begin to view your thoughts from the perspective of an outside observer in order to avoid becoming attached to them.

Becoming the observer entails more than just identifying your thoughts. In essence, you need to become aware of the sensations and feelings that accompany your negative thoughts. This is because our thoughts happen automatically, and may capture all our attention at the time. They emerge and dissipate often at lightning speeds, making it very difficult for us to focus on a single thought process and follow it down to its genesis. Nevertheless, with constant practice, self-observation is a skill that is very possible to learn.

Learning how to observe and evaluate your negative thinking from a neutral or objective point of view allows you to gain a different perspective. You will be able to understand the source of your negative thoughts and how they affect your emotions and moods. You will also be able to pick up on any counterproductive defensive mechanisms which you normally resort to when plagued with difficult recurrent thoughts. Learning how to observe your obsessive thought patterns also enables you to realize that your thoughts arise all by themselves. This realization allows you to see your thoughts from a more accepting and objective point of view. This can provide you with a lot of relief and peace of mind whenever you find yourself obsessively overthinking something negative.

Understand Your Triggers

Overthinking is a problem that profoundly affects our emotional health. That is because we rarely overthink all the positive things in our lives. Overthinking is usually rooted in a negative memory or concern. Therefore, in order to deal with constant ruminating in an effective manner, it is vital to recognize and understand the emotional triggers that lead you to overthink. Emotional triggers refer to the words, actions, opinions, situations, people, etc. that arouse strong negative emotion in you. When you are triggered, you may experience a range of emotions, including fear, anger, sadness, and rage. These emotions may, in turn, cause you to overthink the scenario. There are various reasons why you may be emotionally triggered. These include:

1. Past Trauma

An individual who has experienced a very traumatic event in the past might get triggered when they see, hear, smell, touch or taste something that reminds them of their negative experience. For instance, a person who was abused as a child by their caregivers might be triggered when they see parents who have a bad relationship with their child. Similarly, an individual whose spouse died of lung cancer due to smoking tobacco might feel triggered by the smell of cigarettes or whenever they see someone smoking.

Post-traumatic triggers are usually a symptom that one's trauma has not been resolved. Fortunately, this can be solved through guided behavioral therapy, which aims to help victims understand their triggers and develop effective ways of coping with them.

2. Conflicting Beliefs and Values

As human beings, we tend to adhere to and defend our beliefs vigorously. The belief systems which we learned and adapted to over the course of our lives play a crucial role in shaping our values. This subsequently shapes the way we think and behave. When we identify too strongly with a particular belief, we may find it difficult to be tolerant of other people's beliefs, especially if they contradict our own. This is why religion creates so much conflict and discord in society. Our beliefs provide us with a sense of comfort and safety in the challenging world we live in. So, when they are challenged, we may feel as if the entire basis of our lives has come under threat. When other people question our beliefs and values, we are likely to see this as an attack on our personhood. However, it is important to realize that belief systems, even the most enduring ones, are not set in stone. They are subject to change over time as we acquire new information and experiences.

3. Preservation of our Ego

If you possess any basic understanding of modern psychology, you may be familiar with the concept of the "ego". Essentially, the ego is the distinct sense of selfhood that every human being carries with them throughout life. It is a confluence of many things, including our preconceived thoughts and notions, cultural values, upbringing, belief systems, memories, desires, and habits. The primary purpose is to perpetuate our experience of self-hood and shield us from experiencing the death of our familiar selves. So the ego creates a network of ideas, thoughts, beliefs, and habits through which we derive our sense of identity. It is therefore not surprising that whenever our sense of identity is challenged by others, we are likely to become triggered instantly. When someone hurts us, our egos immediately spring to action in a bid to defend our identity. Some of the ways we may respond include arguing, insulting, defaming or belittling the object of our anger. In extreme cases, some people may commit serious crimes such as assault or murder when they feel that their ego is under threat. This just goes to prove how powerful this aspect of our lives actually is. However, while the ego can be very destructive, it can also be a force for good when kept in balance. After all, the ego is an integral aspect of every human being.

Every human being has an ego. The fact that we do not see a high percentage of people committing serious crimes is because a balanced ego is a desirable, beneficial and somewhat common thing. Therefore, if you have a problem dealing with people or ideas that challenge your ego, you need to learn how to keep your ego healthy so that you can accept the perspectives of others without feeling threatened. Some of the practices that might help you do so include meditation, introspection and performing acts of service to others.

By understanding how the ego works and developing a healthy ego, you can overcome the triggers that make you susceptible to overthinking.

Focus on the Big Picture

Very often, we get caught up in the small worries and anxieties of our day-to-day lives, to a point where we get sidetracked from our biggest goals. As a matter of fact, most goals in life, whether in career or relationships, take some time before they can be realized. Therefore, the longer this period is prolonged, the easier it is to lose sight of the big picture. When you focus too much on the small details affecting your ambitions, you inevitably end up with less time to think about your ultimate goals. This can have a detrimental effect on your overall drive and enthusiasm. In some cases, you may end up forgetting about your goal completely, as your mind gets distracted by immediate worries and problems. In order to maintain the integrity of your aspirations and goals, it is essential to remind yourself of the big picture.

How can you do this? Well, the secret to focusing on your big goals is to bring them back to your conscious awareness. In essence, you need to constantly remind yourself of your personal vision in life. There are several strategies that can help you to regularly recall your mission and focus on the big picture. Here are some of the tips you can employ towards this end.

1. Set Aside Some Time Every Week to Engage in Planning

You need to dedicate some hours every week to think about your goals and your overarching mission in life. The aim of doing this is to remind yourself of your aspirations and pull yourself away from all the minute distractions that may sideline you from working on your ultimate goals in life.

2. Devise a Symbol that Reminds You of Your Mission

It is essential to come up with a symbol that reminds you of your goals in life. You may choose to draw the symbol yourself if you are artistically gifted, or you can simply select one from the public domain that resonates with you and aligns with your goals. For instance, if you are an aspiring musician, you can use a music symbol, images of your mentors or other people you look up to as your symbols. Whatever or whoever you select for your symbol is entirely up to you. Print that symbol and set it in a location where it is likely to capture your attention easily. You can stick the image above your bed, on the door to your room, on your desk or even make it into a pendant which you can wear frequently. Every time you see the symbol, you will be reminded of your goals.

3. Give Yourself a Break

Sometimes we get so caught up in our careers and social lives that the positive and creative energy in us becomes sapped. This can lead to performance problems, which may end up leaving us frustrated and overwhelmed with negative thoughts. It is therefore very important to take frequent breaks to replenish and rejuvenate your mind so that you can begin working optimally again. If you are experiencing negative thoughts due to burnout, it might be wise to set aside some time to unwind. This will help you reboot and declutter your mind so that your thinking and creativity flow more freely.

4. Eliminate All Distractions when Planning for Your Goals

You are advised to steer clear of any possible distractions whenever you are planning for your goals. Ideally, you should find a quiet place with few distractions in order to be able to think more clearly when working out your plans for the future. Set aside time to focus on yourself and what you want to achieve.

5. Write Down Your Goals and Read Them Often

Committing to your goals in writing creates a personal contract, and allows you to connect with your mission statement more fully. You don't need to write an entire book describing everything in detail. A two-to-three sentence summary that captures the essence of your mission statement should be more than enough. It can even be a list in point form. Once you come up with your mission and commit to it in writing, practice reading it to yourself at least twice a day, especially in the morning when you wake up and just before you go to bed. Doing so will keep your goals at the forefront of your mind at all times, even as you navigate the minute challenges of your day-to-day life.

Realize that Chronic Overthinking is Not Permanent

When you are caught up in the cycle of overthinking, it is easy to think that this is a challenge you'll never be able to overcome. This gloomy mindset can make you very depressed and hopeless. It can also lead you to make counterproductive decisions to combat your negative thinking, hence compounding the problem.

However, just because you are dealing with constant negative thoughts doesn't mean you are doomed forever! Chronic overthinking does not have to be permanent. By changing your mindset from resignation to determination, you can begin to investigate the problem and find an effective way to move forward.

Minimize Your Daily Input

One of the main reasons why we fall into the trap of overthinking is because we expose ourselves to too much information. In the age that we live in, we are constantly bombarded by vast amounts of information coming from various sources. These sources include television, the internet and social media sites like Facebook and Twitter. This unrelenting overload of information clutters our mind with useless facts which serve no purpose other than to clog our mind and distract us from the reality of our lives.

When your mind gets jammed with too much information, you may find yourself spending copious amounts of time ruminating over issues that are not remotely relevant to your life. This can seriously upset your mental balance and affect very essential aspects of your life, including daily happiness and sleep. In order to get rid of the tendency to overthink, therefore, it is absolutely vital that you minimize the amount of information you expose yourself to on a day-to-day basis. For instance, try to cut down the amount of time you spend browsing the internet and checking social media notifications and messages. In addition to this, try to abstain from using your phone just before bedtime. This will help you avoid information that may affect your sleep.

Reconnect with the Immediate World

If you spend most of your time overthinking and worrying, you may end up living in your head too much and fail to experience the vibrant and exciting world that is happening around you. Constantly obsessing over the minute details of your negative thoughts robs you of the opportunity to actually connect with your environment and the people in it. Overthinking can cause you to live in your head so much that you lose track of the real world. In essence, when you are constantly worrying about the minute worries in your life, you may end up losing track of the most important things in your life.

Develop an awareness of your overthinking habits to prevent the tendency of living in your head too much, and take active steps to reconnect with the immediate world.

Redirecting your focus from obsessive negative thoughts and channeling your energy towards the environment around you will help you reconnect with the world around you. This will help you start enjoying life again.

Here are some of the strategies that can help you to stop living in your head and start living in the real world again.

Have Realistic Expectations

Sometimes we are plagued by negative thinking and overthinking simply because we have set expectations that far exceed our own abilities. When we set overly high standards for ourselves, we may end up getting disappointed when we fail to achieve them. Overthinking can lead to feelings of guilt, anger, anxiety, depression, and self-blame. In some cases, we may even aspire to do too much in a very limited amount of time. Not giving yourself enough time to accomplish a goal is self-sabotage. To avoid these problems you need to set attainable goals and give yourself enough time to accomplish them.

If you are prone to setting unrealistic expectations, it is important to re-evaluate your goals and assess whether they match your talents and skills. You should, therefore, give yourself ample time to plan your goals and draft a realistic plan of action. By doing so, you will be able to eliminate the tendency to overthink and develop a strong awareness of yourself and the environment around you.

Change Your Perspective

There are some instances where we struggle with overthinking simply because we hold a negative attitude towards a situation. When things do not go the way we expect, we may end up forming negative judgments about ourselves. To overcome this problem, you need to learn how to adjust your attitude towards the situation. Therefore, when a negative thought about a situation pops into your head, try to analyze whether there is something you can gain from the situation. In such cases, simply changing your attitude towards the situation can make a huge difference in how you handle it. It is important to let go of negative thoughts that do not help you in any way and replace them with productive thoughts that are designed to help you succeed. The more you practice superimposing positive thoughts over negative ones, the sooner you will turn this type of thinking into a habit. As a result, you will be able to approach even the most difficult situations with a dose of healthy optimism. This might even provide you with some fresh insights on how to solve the problem. Even if the situation is beyond your control, you might pick up some helpful lessons that may help you through a similar situation in the future.

Find a Good Distraction

When you are feeling overwhelmed with negative thoughts, sometimes it helps to find a good distraction to help you to release some of the tension and stress. There are times when all that is needed during a difficult moment of overthinking is to simply find something to help your mind calm down. When you find yourself overwhelmed with negative thinking, you can turn this energy into a creative distraction. For example, if you are artistically gifted, you can draw, paint, make crafts or play music. This will help you channel your energy in a productive way and distract your mind from the negative thought loops that you may be caught up in.

Even if you are not very creative, there are many things you can do to relax your mind when overthinking. For instance, you can read a book or watch a funny TV program to lift your mood.

Sometimes a good distraction can help you soothe anxiety resulting from negative thoughts.

Acknowledge that Some Things are Beyond your Control

No matter how much control you are able to exert over your life, there are plenty of things that are beyond your control. You cannot, for example, know whether you are going to have a bad day at work tomorrow. However, you can control how you react to the situations you face. Accepting that you cannot control everything in your life allows you to focus on changing things that you do have power over. This is a form of thinking that can help you overcome negative thoughts and the characteristic anxiety that comes with them.

Accept Your Limitations

As humans, we have a tendency to want to exert total control over our lives and our environment. This desire arises out of an evolutionary need for survival. However, the circumstances in the world aren't always in our control. While we have individual control over our lives to some extent, it is just not possible to know what will happen next in the unpredictable world that we live in. One minute you may be healthy and full of life, and the next minute you are diagnosed with a chronic illness, or you may be succeeding in a high paying career and then suddenly lose your job. Our inability to predict what happens in the world and our lives might seem very gloomy. However, this is a natural part of our reality and a fact that should be embraced. By acknowledging your limitations and lack of ability to control everything, you can ease the pressure on yourself and achieve a state of inner peace and acceptance. This will allow you to cope better with negative situations and prevent them from affecting your mental health.

You should always remember that overthinking is not a habit that yields any productive results. As a matter of fact, it only sinks you deeper into the hole of anxiety and despair. By accepting your limitations and focusing on what is realistic and achievable, you can more easily overcome negativity and appreciate all the wonderful things in your life.

Replace the Negative Thoughts

Acknowledging and releasing negative thoughts can help you generate opportunities for positive thoughts. Let's suppose that you have been fired from your job and are worried about how you are going to support your family. Rather than bombard yourself with negative thoughts such as "How will I survive without a job?", try to see any positive thing that you can derive from this situation. Consider thoughts such as "How can I capitalize on my free time?" By replacing your negative thoughts with positive ones, you may end up realizing the situation is not as gloomy as it seems. This can help you overcome the tendency to overthink and make room for positive, productive thoughts.

Talk Yourself Out of It

Overthinking often arises out of irrational fear or anxiety over certain situations. The recurrent mental chatter is usually not backed by any meaningful evidence based on reality. If you find yourself obsessing over negative thoughts, it might be helpful to interrogate yourself to find out why you are having negative thoughts. Having a logical conversation with yourself whenever you are overwhelmed with your negativity can help you determine whether those thoughts deserve to be paid any attention. In all likelihood, you will find that most of your worries are not very rational. This can help you ease your mind and stop overthinking too much.

Cultivate a Psychological Distance

One of the most effective ways of coping with negative thoughts and overthinking is to develop a psychological distance between them and yourself. As we mentioned in the previous chapter, your thoughts do not usually reflect reality. Likewise, they do not necessarily arise from you. As humans, we tend to view thoughts as things that are consciously being generated rather than images and words that occur autonomously. This causes us to identify with our thoughts too much.

However, the problem with getting too attached to our negative thoughts is that it makes us lose our sense of control when we are bombarded by them. Therefore, in order to prevent spiraling into patterns of negativity and overthinking, you need to learn how to detach yourself from your thoughts. Start using language in a way that treats thoughts as ideas that are happening separately from yourself. For instance, instead of thinking "I am a total failure," you can address your negative thought by saying, "I notice I am now having that thought which says I am a failure". By developing this kind of mindset, you will be able to cultivate a psychological distance between yourself and your negative thoughts so that they do not impact your mood or affect your peace of mind.

Practice Self Compassion

Self-compassion is a very effective way of dealing with difficult situations, including overthinking. It allows you to develop a deeper understanding of yourself, become more connected with others and increase your satisfaction in life.

By treating yourself with more compassion and understanding, you will realize that your happiness is entirely dependent on yourself. As a result, you will be able to navigate even the most difficult thoughts with confidence and optimism. This will help you eliminate the problem of negative thinking for good.

While overthinking is a very difficult problem to contend with, it should not give you a reason to despair. With the right strategies, you can empower yourself to deal with negative thoughts and overthinking in a positive way.

Summary

In this chapter, we learned how to stop overthinking. Here are the main things you need to remember when trying to overcome obsessive negative thoughts that do not help you move forward in any way.

- Practice self-observation to develop an awareness of your thoughts. This will help you gain mental clarity about them.
- Realize and understand the emotional triggers that cause you to overthink.
- Constantly remind yourself of your goals and aspirations.
- Realize and appreciate that overthinking is a problem that can be combated and eliminated successfully.

- Reconnect with other people and the outside world in order to stop living in your head and start living in the real world again.
- Learn how to replace your negative thoughts with positive ones.
- Develop a psychological distance between yourself and your thoughts to avoid becoming too identified with your negative thoughts.
- Learn to be more compassionate and kind to yourself and accept your limitations.
- Develop a stoic attitude towards life in order to become more resilient when faced with challenges.

If you have been struggling with overthinking, I assure you there is nothing wrong with you. Ruminating over negative thoughts is a problem that every individual experiences in their life (Oppong, 2020). However, by applying the strategies we have discussed in this chapter, you can develop the ability to get rid of your overthinking for good and have a more positive attitude.

In the next chapter, you will learn different techniques and practices that you can apply to cushion yourself from constant worrying, which is a side effect of overthinking.

CHAPTER SIX:

Overcoming Worry

Worrying is undoubtedly a very normal part of life. There are plenty of things that can cause you to worry. For instance, you may be apprehensive about getting to work late due to traffic gridlock or perhaps you worry that you will not be able to meet the deadline for your work project. These kinds of worries are very natural and pretty much everyone experiences them. However, when your worries become too many and unrelenting, this can be a cause for alarm.

Worrying too much not only saps your emotional and mental energy but can also be detrimental to your physical health (Robinson, 2020). People who worry constantly tend to suffer from numerous problems, including anxiety, depression, headaches, muscle tension, and poor concentration. When worry becomes too common in your life, it can even be debilitating, making it difficult for you to perform your duties and responsibilities. This can deprive you of peace of mind and sink you deeper into a hole of despair.

Incessant worry is a chronic problem that can be very difficult to deal with. You may find yourself constantly obsessing about every negative thought, leaving you no time to actually enjoy your life.

Notably, people who worry too much tend to hold both positive and negative ideas about worrying, which further intensifies the problem. For instance, some people believe that constant worrying might make them lose their sanity. Holding such negative beliefs about worry can compound the problem, and make it difficult for you to find permanent solutions.

Positive beliefs about worry can also be just as damaging and problematic as negative ones. In some cases, people believe that by worrying constantly, they will be able to steer clear of problems and trouble. Some even fall into the trap of thinking that worrying too much will help them find solutions to problems they are facing. This, however, couldn't be further from the truth. Worrying too much not only drains your energy and creativity but also distracts you from finding solutions to life's difficult situations. The stress hormones which are released when you worry too much can significantly take a toll on your health. Some of the problems associated with worry include:

- Increased headaches.
- Depression due to emotional fatigue.
- Increased production of stomach acid which leads to heartburn and ulcers.
- Increased hyperactivity of the brain which leads to stress.
- Breathing problems due to muscle tension.
- Weakened immune system.
- Rise in blood sugar which can lead to Type 2 diabetes.
- Increase in blood pressure which can lead to heart problems.
- Excess stress on the digestive system which can lead to gastrointestinal diseases.
- Low sex drive due to fatigue and loss of confidence.
- Irregular menstrual cycles due to hormonal imbalances caused by stress hormones.

Worrying is something that everyone does. However, when it becomes a constant habit, it can make you susceptible to all the problems mentioned above. In order to be able to tackle this problem, it is important to first establish whether you are just worrying about the normal stresses of life or are engaging in excessive worrying. Below, we outline some of the symptoms which will help you differentiate between normal worrying and excessive worrying.

Normal Worrying

- You take some few minutes before falling asleep to think about your upcoming challenges and tasks that you are meant to accomplish.
- People rarely describe you as a nervous or anxious person.
- You often notice a loss of appetite whenever you are anticipating a stressful event.
- Sometimes you find yourself needing to have a drink in order to relax your mind and body when experiencing a stressful situation.
- You often worry about things for short amounts of time and then move on from them after you rationalize them.

Excessive Worrying

- You find it difficult to fall asleep or get a good night's rest because you are overwhelmed with worrisome thoughts for which you have no immediate solution.
- People often describe you as very anxious and consider worrying to be a key part of your personality.
- You often experience significant weight changes due to binge eating or not eating at all when you are dealing with difficult situations.
- You tend to overanalyze every situation that you encounter regardless of how trivial or serious it is.
- You find yourself unable to enjoy your life because you are constantly ruminating over everything that happens.
- You find it difficult to go through your day without using drugs and alcohol as an escape from your worries.
- You always seem to be looking for something to be worried about. In other words, worrying is like an addiction that you cannot seem to get rid of.

While ending the cycle of constant worrying can admittedly be a very challenging thing to do, it is nonetheless very possible. There are some very effective techniques and strategies that you may employ to break out of your worrying loops.

Create a Daily Worry Period

As counterintuitive as it might seem, scheduling worry time is actually one of the most effective ways of dealing with worrying thoughts. Rather than avoiding your obsessive negative thoughts, this strategy requires you to allocate some time to ruminate over them. This strategy can be very beneficial in a number of ways. Firstly, by allocating some time to ruminate over your negative thoughts, you will be able to reach a state of acceptance, which can provide you with relief and help you tackle your situation in a calmer and more relaxed state of mind. In addition to this, creating a daily worry period teaches you to compartmentalize your worries in order to free up your mind to perform the rest of your day's tasks and responsibilities. Instead of wasting useful time ruminating over your thoughts throughout the day, this strategy enables you to deal with your worries at a convenient time, thereby ensuring you are able to carry out other important activities. When practiced consistently, the technique of designating "worry" time can significantly reduce your tendency to worry and lessen anxiety.

Here are some of the steps you need to follow in order to implement this strategy effectively:

1. Have a daily worry routine for a period of one week. Ideally, you should set your worry periods in the morning or during the day. Do not set your worry time at night right before going to bed, as it may interfere with your sleep.
2. During your allocated worry time, write down all the things that you are worried about. Refrain from trying to find solutions to all of your worries during this period. Writing down the worrisome thought in itself can be a huge source of

relief, and can provide you with a fresh perspective on how to tackle situations that you are worried about.

3. Train yourself to not worry in between your designated worry periods. If you find yourself having worrisome thoughts outside of your allocated worrying time, calmly remind yourself to shelve those thoughts until your next worry time. This can be a little hard to do at first, but with constant practice, it will soon become very easy to switch off your worries until your set worry period comes again.
4. At the end of your "worry" week, take some time to go over the notes that you wrote down during your daily worry periods. This will provide you with a lot of insights concerning your worry habits. For instance, you will notice whether you have any recurrent worries or some which are simply irrational.
5. Once you have completed your worry week, you can set a new one to determine the dynamics of your worrisome thoughts. With regular practice and consistency, you will begin to develop control over your worrisome thoughts and prevent them from interfering with your daily routines and your peace of mind.

Challenge Your Anxious Thoughts

Very often when we engage in constant worrying, it happens simply because we observe the world around us in a way that makes it seem overly cruel and frightening. For instance, we may tend to focus on the worst-case scenario in every situation or believe that our anxieties are reflective of reality. These types of mindsets are typically known as cognitive distortions since they make us perceive reality in an inaccurate way (Grohol, 2019). In order to overcome the problem of incessant worrying thoughts, it is important to become aware of the various types of cognitive distortions that create an untrue perception of reality. Here are 15 of the most common cognitive distortions which people experience:

1. Mental Filtering

This refers to a type of cognitive distortion whereby a person filters out all the positive aspects of a given situation and inflates the negative aspects, which they then focus all their attention on. For example, they may identify an unpleasant situation and focus on it to a point where it completely dominates their thinking.

2. Polarized Thinking

This is a form of thinking which only takes into account two opposing extremes of a particular idea, person or thing without factoring any nuances which may exist. It is also referred to as "black and white" thinking. Polarized thinking often fails to take into account the complexities and grey areas that characterize every individual or situation.

3. Overgeneralization

This is a cognitive distortion whereby an individual makes a conclusion about something, based entirely on very little evidence. This thinking pattern also fails to consider the nuances involved in different situations. So, a person who overgeneralizes might expect a negative situation to repeat itself simply because it happened once.

4. Jumping to Conclusions

An individual who jumps to conclusions assumes they always know what another person is thinking or feeling even without the other party expressing it outright. For instance, they may rush to conclude that someone is against them without bothering to verify whether it is actually true or not.

5. Catastrophizing

Catastrophizing (also known as magnifying) is a cognitive distortion whereby an individual expects the worst-case scenario in any kind of situation. People who engage in catastrophizing may inflate the importance of very insignificant events. For instance, they may believe that they will never be successful in their academic lives simply because they failed in one school test or exam.

6. Personalization

This is a type of cognitive distortion where an individual believes that everything other people say or do is a personal reaction towards them. People who personalize everything tend to feel attacked whenever someone mentions anything in a way that they do not agree with. They also tend to make comparisons between themselves and others in an effort to determine whether they are good enough or better than other people. Personalization is a key trigger for personal insecurity, anxiety, and low self-esteem.

7. Control Fallacies

Control fallacies involve two different, but closely related cognitive distortions. One form of control fallacy entails a belief that one's actions are controlled by external forces. For instance, an individual who engages in this type of cognitive distortion may believe that the reason why they are unable to perform well in school is because of their parent's divorce. On the flip side of this cognitive distortion is the internal control fallacy whereby an individual assumes responsibility for external events that they may not have anything to do with at all. For instance, they may believe that they are the reason why someone is hurt or angry when this is not the case at all. Both of these control fallacies can be very detrimental to one's mental wellness since they lead to overthinking, self-deprecation and self-blame.

8. Fallacy of Fairness

This is a cognitive distortion whereby a person thinks they know what is fair in every situation. So, when something happens contrary to their expectations, they are likely to judge it as unfair to themselves or others. Individuals who engage in this type of thinking are susceptible to feelings of resentment, anger, and helplessness. It is important to realize that life is not always fair, and things may not necessarily end up working out for someone even when they ought to.

9. Blaming

An individual who engages in blaming has a tendency of holding other people responsible for their suffering. In some cases, they may blame themselves for the emotional pain of others even when they have absolutely nothing to do with it. This usually exacerbates the problem of negative thinking and makes them constantly anxious. An individual who engages in this type of thinking ought to realize that nobody has power over our thoughts and emotions apart from ourselves.

10. "Should" Statements

As innocent as they might seem, "should" statements are actually a type of cognitive distortion that can contribute to worry and anxiety. This is because they create an impression of ironclad rules which you are expected to adhere to. Statements such as "I should work out to get the perfect body" or "I should be happy" exert undue pressure on you to act in a certain way in order to achieve certain expectations, which may not be realistic. When these statements are directed inwards, they often lead one to feel guilty or embarrassed in the event that they are unable to meet those expectations. On the other hand, when they are directed at others, they may cause us to be resentful or angry at them for not living up to the exceedingly high standards we have set for them.

11. Emotional Reasoning

This is a cognitive distortion whereby a person uses their emotions as evidence for an external reality or situation. Individuals who engage in emotional reasoning tend to make conclusions that whatever they are feeling is essentially true. Usually, this occurs when their emotions completely override their thinking. It is important to realize that while emotions are very powerful forces, they may not correctly reflect the reality of a particular situation.

12. Fallacy of Change

This is a cognitive distortion which arises out of one's expectation for people to change who they are in order to suit them. This is very common in relationships. A person may wrongly believe that if they pressure or cajole their partner enough, they might change who they are and turn into an idealized or perfect version of themselves.

13. Global Labelling

Global labeling can be thought of as an extreme kind of generalization. Typically, affected people tend to attach a negative universal label to themselves or others if they act in certain ways. For instance, if another person errs against them in any way, they may conclude that the person is a buffoon.

14. Always Being Right

There are some people who are under the impression that they are always right regardless of the situation. The affected people tend to be overly judgmental, and will continually put other people's opinions and actions on trial to prove that their own are absolutely right.

15. Heaven's Reward Fallacy

This is a type of cognitive distortion which is very similar to the fallacy of fairness. A person who falls victim to this kind of distortion wrongly believes that their sacrifices and self-denial will eventually pay off with some kind of grand reward. The problem with this fallacy is that it may lead to anger and resentment when the sacrifices that one makes do not get rewarded as they had hoped.

As you can see, there are plenty of cognitive distortions that can cloud our thinking and contribute to problems of worry and overthinking. In order to overcome worrisome thoughts, therefore, it is important to subject your thinking to scrutiny in order to determine whether it is backed by sound evidence or simply a result of deep-seated cognitive distortions (Grohol, 2019).

Know Which Worries are Solvable vs Unsolvable

Worrying is usually associated with feelings of anxiety and restlessness. However, there are some instances where worrying can actually reduce your anxiety. This is simply because ruminating makes you feel like you're actually working to come up with solutions for your situation. However, there is a huge difference between worrying and problem-solving. Worrying essentially doesn’t provide any solutions because it approaches situations from a position of fear and anxiety. Problem-solving, on the other hand, takes into account facts and evidence when dealing with a problematic situation. Therefore, in order to overcome the problem of worrying too much, you need to distinguish between the worries that are solvable and those that are not.

A solvable worry is one for which there is a remedy or course of action that can be taken. For instance, if you are worried about not making it to an important office meeting due to traffic, you can call your supervisor or manager to inform them about it beforehand. An unsolvable worry, on the other hand, is one that doesn’t have an immediate course of action. For example, worrying about getting sick in the future.

Once you have identified worries that are solvable, you need to start brainstorming on the possible solutions to the problem you are facing. As you do so, try to focus on the things that you can control and make a comprehensive plan of action on how to execute them. If you determine that your worries are not solvable, try and accept the uncertainty about the future, and focus your energies on living in the present. Constantly worrying about the future can distract you from enjoying and appreciating the gifts and privileges that you currently have.

Avoid Getting Caught up in Vague Fears

Very often when we experience vague fears which are not fully understood, we tend to get caught up in them, which leads to worrying and anxiety. This happens because we focus on the worst-case outcome of the situation that we are facing. This, however, is very counterproductive, and only leads to more anxiety and a relentless cycle of unresolvable worrisome thoughts. In order to overcome this tendency to worry over vague fears, it is important for you to investigate them and determine whether such worries are valid or only the result of mental chatter. You can approach this situation by asking yourself, "What is the worst possible outcome that this situation may lead to?" Once you have answered that question to the best of your understanding, try to brainstorm some of the ways in which you can respond to the situation in case those fears materialize. You may end up realizing that the worst-case scenario of the particular situation is not nearly as bad as you imagined. By cross-examining your fears in this manner, therefore, you will be able to get rid of the tendency to worry about fears that are irrational and become more adept at managing your unsolvable worries.

Interrupt the Worry Cycle

If you find that you worry too much, it can be easy to assume that you are doomed to have worrisome thoughts forever. However, there are several simple strategies that you can employ to interrupt your worrying loops and achieve peace of mind. These include exercise and yoga.

Exercise

As we discussed previously, regular exercise can help disrupt your worrisome thoughts, fight stress and reduce anxiety. This is in addition to keeping your body in a healthy condition and enhancing your overall well being. Don't forget, even a little exercise, such as a brisk walk, or going up a flight of stairs will help.

Yoga

The practice of yoga can be very beneficial when it comes to dealing with worrying thoughts. There are various types of yoga, all of which are meant to improve various aspects of our lives. Some of the benefits of yoga include improved blood circulation, an increase in energy and vitality, better cognition and improved flexibility.

Yoga has also been proven to increase the overall health and wellness of people. Practitioners of yoga tend to manifest greater satisfaction in their lives and are less anxious or depressed than those who do not. This is not surprising, considering the fact that all schools of yoga teach and emphasize the need for people to become more aware of the present and live in it. By learning and practicing yoga you can cope with the daily worries of life more effectively and prevent them from interfering with your health and wellness.

Meditation

Meditation is one of the most powerful ways of coping with worry and anxiety. This practice is founded upon the premise that worrying about the past or the future takes one out of the present and leads to anxiety and unhappiness. Meditation is meant to help us live in the present by making us aware of what is happening around us in the moment. People who practice meditation enjoy better health and higher levels of contentment compared to those who do not. By practicing meditation and mindfulness you can disrupt your worrisome thoughts and increase your awareness not only of yourself but of the world around you.

Summary

In this chapter, you have learned about how to overcome the cycle of worry. We have discussed how worrisome thoughts arise, what contributes to them and how we can cope with them in a healthy manner. To recap the main ideas discussed in this chapter, here are the techniques and practices you need to observe in order to get rid of your worries for good:

- Set aside a "worry" period in order to investigate your worrisome thoughts and prevent them from interfering with your productivity.
- Challenge your worrisome thoughts to determine whether they have any validity or are simply the automatic thinking patterns arising from cognitive distortions.
- Become aware of the worries that are solvable and those that are not solvable in order to redirect your energies in a productive way that is geared towards problem-solving, rather than ruminating.
- Disrupt your worry cycles by performing exercises, practicing yoga and meditation.

In the next chapter, we are going to explore the idea of positive thinking and how you can cultivate it to deal with negative thoughts. We will explore some of the ways of identifying negative thinking and the benefits you can derive from thinking positively.

CHAPTER SEVEN:

Being More Positive to Reduce Stress

The power of positive thinking has been a point of discussion for many psychologists and wellness experts. While some people scoff at the benefits of positive thinking, there are many advocates of this practice who consider it a very useful tool for approaching life's challenging situations. If you have been struggling with negative thoughts and worry, applying positive thinking can help you overcome these problems and reclaim your power over your thoughts. So in this chapter, we are going to look at how you can develop a positive attitude in order to reduce stress and anxiety.

What is Positive Thinking?

Well, when most people think about the idea of positive thinking, the impressions that come to mind are those of blissful ignorance in the face of difficult situations. However, this couldn't be further from the truth. Positive thinking does not mean burying your head in the sand and ignoring any difficult situations that you may be faced with. On the contrary, positive thinking is a mindset that approaches challenges with a sense of optimism and confidence. Individuals who are positive thinkers tend to focus on the brighter side of things, even when they meet challenges on the way ("Positive thinking: Stop negative self-talk to reduce stress," 2020a)

Positive thinking is very effective when it comes to alleviating the stress and anxiety that comes with negative thoughts and overthinking. To understand why developing a positive mindset is important, let us briefly look at how positive thinking works.

Positive Thinking and Self Talk

The aim of positive thinking is not to ignore the problems and challenging situations you encounter in life. As a matter of fact, a positive mindset simply refers to the practice of approaching a difficult situation with a winning attitude. So, instead of focusing on the worst-case scenario in any given situation, you pay attention to the proverbial silver lining.

The genesis of any positive mindset is typically the "self-talk", which refers to the stream of thoughts that are constantly running through our minds. These thoughts often stem from logic and reason, although they may also come from our fears, beliefs, and habits that we may have cultivated over the course of our lives. If your stream of thoughts is mostly negative, then you are likely to develop a pessimistic worldview and mindset. On the other hand, if your automatic thoughts are generally positive, you most likely perceive the world through an optimistic state of mind. Developing a positive mindset is not always easy, given the numerous unpleasant situations we often find ourselves in. In essence, it might be very difficult to focus on the brighter side of life when things aren't going the way you hoped. However, there are plenty of benefits that you can enjoy from being a positive thinker, which makes the whole endeavor very worthwhile.

Benefits of Positive Thinking

Here are some of the benefits that you can enjoy from developing a positive mindset and learning to think positively.

Reduced Stress

Positive thinking has been proven to have amazing stress reduction properties. People who practice positive thinking are less likely to suffer from stress and depression. This has to do with the fact that positive thinkers tend to focus their energies on solving an unpleasant situation rather than wallowing in self-pity and helplessness. They are, therefore, able to troubleshoot their stressors faster and more effectively.

Increased Life Span

Research has shown that individuals with a positive mindset tend to live longer than those who constantly think negatively. This is because negative thoughts and emotions usually have a detrimental effect on our health. When they are eliminated, therefore, the physical implications on the body are also reversed, thereby allowing one to enjoy better health.

Better Cognition

Constant negative thinking and overthinking usually impact our cognitive abilities in a negative way. A pessimistic mindset can seriously interfere with your concentration and recall ability. By developing a positive mindset, however, you ease mental and psychological pressure, improve your mental clarity and optimize your cognitive function.

Improved Relationships

Positive thinkers tend to be more open, compassionate and fun to be around. This makes them highly attractive. Therefore, by getting rid of your negative thinking habits, you may become more connected with people and improve the quality of your relationships with your family, friends, and workmates.

Increased Success

Positive people are generally more likely to succeed in their careers as well as personal lives. This is because they tend to see and pursue more opportunities in life compared to their pessimistic counterparts. Positive-minded individuals are also less likely to focus on their failures, as this helps them avoid getting discouraged when things don't go according to plan.

Better Cardiovascular Health

Individuals who practice positive thinking are less likely to suffer from cardiovascular illnesses such as hypertension and stroke. This is because they are able to deal with stress and anxiety in productive ways and prevent them from interfering with their health and personal development.

As you can see, there are numerous advantages that you can enjoy by shifting your perspective and thinking more positively. Apart from safeguarding your health and improving your overall quality of life, thinking positively can greatly empower you to achieve all your goals and aspirations in life. If you have been grappling with negative thoughts and overthinking, developing a positive mindset can provide you with relief from anxiety and stress and enable you to cope better with unpleasant situations. ("Positive thinking: Stop negative self-talk to reduce stress," 2020a)

Perform Random Acts of Kindness

When we get too caught up in our worries and negative thoughts, we become too absorbed in them that we forget other people are facing challenges very similar to our own. To cultivate positive mindedness, it is vital to take the time from our lives and perform acts of kindness towards other people. If you are dealing with negative thoughts and worries, consider stepping outside your daily routine and do something for someone else for a change. This can be as simple as complimenting a random stranger or helping out a friend with a task which they are working on. Performing acts of kindness for other people will help you reconnect with the real world and regain perspective on your own life. This can help you become a more positive-minded person and provide you with opportunities to share your unique talents and gifts with others.

Learn to Accept Criticism in a Positive Way

Human beings, in general, have a strong aversion towards criticism. This is because we tend to take criticism very personally. Whenever someone mentions something critical about us, our minds immediately begin to come up with negative judgments about our character and causes us to become defensive. This makes it very difficult for us to accept criticism in a graceful manner even when it is valid and well-intentioned. However, to become positive-minded people, we need to change this mindset and become more open to criticism.

Very often when we are criticized, we tend to think that there is a fundamental flaw in ourselves that is being exposed for all to see. This can lead to problems such as anxiety and overthinking as we struggle to justify whether or not the criticism was warranted. It is important to realize that criticism of our thoughts or actions is not fundamentally an attack on our character. Therefore, we need to learn how to divorce the two from each other.

When you receive any kind of criticism, instead of reacting to it in a knee-jerk kind of way, take a moment to internalize the criticism and give it some thought. This will prevent you from falling victim to rash reactions such as lashing out at the other person. That reaction might then lead to an escalation or volatile disagreement. Once you have taken the time to mentally digest the criticism, try to look for any positive lessons or points which you can derive from it. Of course, not all criticism will be conveyed politely. The person criticizing you might be unnecessarily brash or insensitive in the way they present their opinion. However, even if they are rude, try to see the positive aspects which you can derive from their criticism. Once you begin to see the criticism in a positive light, thank the other person for their words. They might have presented their criticism in a rude way simply because they are having a bad day. So refrain from the temptation of judging them too harshly. If you realize that the criticism was accurate, make a conscious effort to learn from it since this will help you become a better person.

Summary

This chapter has introduced the concept and benefits of positive thinking. We have looked at the ways in which learning how to evaluate your negative thinking loops can help you change your mindset from a pessimistic worldview to one which sees and focuses on the brighter side of things. In conclusion, here are the big takeaways from this chapter:

- Positive thinking is not the practice of avoiding or ignoring difficult situations, rather, it involves approaching difficult situations with an attitude of optimism and problem solving.
- Developing a positive mindset can be very beneficial in a number of ways including stress reduction, enhanced cognition, and improved overall health.
- In order to achieve a positive mindset, it is crucial to learn how to avoid automatic negative thinking pitfalls that we get caught up in. These include polarizing, labeling, catastrophizing and personalizing.
- One of the best things that you can do to get away from your own negativity is to perform random acts of kindness.

Nevertheless, shifting your mindset from a negative to a positive one is not a simple matter. It requires immense willpower, practice, and dedication. In all likelihood, you will struggle to achieve this during the initial stages of your practice. However, with the right tools and techniques, you will certainly develop a positive mindset that will help you overcome the tendency to worry too much or obsess over negative thoughts.

In the following chapter, we are going to look at how you can cultivate the practice of positive thinking. Some of the topics we will discuss include how to identify areas in your thinking that need improvement, and how a healthy lifestyle can help you develop a positive mindset. By the end of the chapter, you should be fully equipped with the knowhow and skills to navigate any negative thought patterns that you typically experience.

CHAPTER EIGHT:

Cultivating Positive Thinking

In the previous chapter, we looked at how your mindset can impact your life. You will no doubt agree, then, that developing a positive mindset can help you get rid of your tendency to worry and allow you to live a happier and more productive life. As a matter of fact, how we perceive the world and interact with it is to a large extent dependent on our mindset. That is why it is always important to remain positive about every aspect of life. Be that as it may, changing your mindset is not something that happens magically overnight.

Developing positive thinking is a process that takes a lot of time and mental investment to accomplish. This, however, does not mean that you need to be a special kind of person to achieve this. Anyone can cultivate a positive mindset, provided they are committed to changing the way they think and have the right strategies to help them (Hurst, 2014).

In this chapter, we are going to explore some of the useful techniques and methods you can apply when cultivating positive thinking. These highly effective strategies will allow you to orchestrate a paradigm shift in the way you think, and empower yourself to get rid of negative thinking.

Focus on Positive Thinking

Cultivating a positive mindset requires you to redirect your attention from the negative thoughts that you are constantly plagued by, and focus on the positive thoughts about any particular situation. A common example is this perspective is a person's answer to the question "Is the glass half empty or half full?" A positive person will say it is half full. This is easier said than done, considering the fact that we are often inclined to obsess over negative thoughts and downplay any good that may be present. Nevertheless, just as you can develop a bad habit of focusing on negativity, you can likewise reverse this and learn how to think positively.

Identify Areas to Change

The first thing you need to do when learning how to be a more positive-minded individual is to identify areas in your life that need to be changed. Perhaps your negative thought patterns stem from dissatisfaction with your career or an unhealthy relationship. By figuring out the situations that contribute to your negative thinking, you will be able to begin changing this aspect of your life and get rid of the problem. For instance, if negative thoughts arise because you feel unfulfilled at work, you may address this issue with your boss to come up with ways to make the situation more satisfying for you. Likewise, if you are unhappy with your relationship, you can have a mature discussion with your partner to see how you can improve it and make it more fulfilling. Remember, the goal of identifying your triggers for negative thinking and overthinking is to come up with workable solutions to whatever issues you are facing to get rid of the problem of ruminating.

Check Yourself

For you to develop a positive mindset and get rid of the tendency to overthink, you need to become aware of the thoughts that constantly run through your mind during the course of the day. This is a strategy known as “checking yourself”. The aim of this practice is to find out whether you experience more negative thoughts than positive ones. If you realize that most of the thoughts you experience as you go about your day are negative, you need to try and find a way of replacing them with positive thoughts about the same situations.

Be Open to Humor

Having a good laugh undoubtedly has plenty of benefits, which can hardly be overstated. Some of the health benefits of laughter include enhanced blood circulation in the body, the release of muscle tension and triggering of the release of endorphins like serotonin and dopamine, which make us feel good and content. Humor also provides stress relief and can help you get rid of the anxiety you commonly experience when plagued with negative thinking. Poking fun at yourself also helps you perceive life less seriously, and can relieve you of the constant pressures and worries of life, which make you think negatively. By being open to humor, you may come to the realization that some of the problems that you constantly obsess over are not nearly as big as you think. Consequently, this will enable you to develop a better mindset and approach the challenges you encounter in life with a positive attitude.

Adopt and Practice a Healthy Lifestyle

When it comes to developing a positive mindset, maintaining a healthy lifestyle is absolutely vital. This is because the more you take care of your body, the faster you can reverse the physical and mental toll that stressful thoughts and anxiety exact from you. Therefore, you need to adopt and maintain a daily exercise regime to stay fit and improve your overall health and wellness. Set aside some time, ideally 20-40 minutes, 2-3 days per week to perform some physical exercise such as jogging, walking, dancing or stretching. By sticking to good workout habits, you will not only improve your physical health but also your mental state.

In addition to exercise, it is also vital to adopt a healthy diet in order to promote a positive mindset. There are plenty of foods that are known to increase anxiety, and should, therefore, be avoided if you are trying to get rid of negative thinking. These include processed foods, soft drinks, coffee, refined sugars, and dairy. You should also minimize or cut out alcohol completely when trying to cultivate a positive mindset. Some of the foods you can opt for instead include asparagus, almonds, avocado, nuts, kales, and spinach.

By maintaining a regular workout regime and eating healthy, you can build up your physical and mental resilience, which will help you overcome negative thinking patterns and develop a more positive outlook on life.

Surround Yourself with Positive People

Having positive people around you can significantly improve your mindset, and help you become a more positive thinking individual. You need to ensure that the people you spend time with are supportive of you as a person and accept your personality with all the quirks and nuances it comes with. There are several reasons why surrounding yourself with positive-minded people is one of the best things you can do when forging a positive mindset.

It Promotes Authenticity

Positive minded friends and relatives typically desire to see you become the best version of yourself. Therefore, they will support you in your aspirations and goals. They will accept your personal decisions and the manner in which you express yourself. Having positive minded individuals around you will encourage you to embrace yourself. This means you won't need to walk on eggshells to avoid offending them or work too hard to impress them. This can take off a significant amount of mental pressure and make you feel more at ease.

Less Drama in Your Life

Positive-minded people tend to have a very low tolerance for unnecessary drama. They prefer to steer clear of negative energy and focus on being the best version of themselves and connecting with others. By seeking out positive people, therefore, you can avoid meaningless drama, which serves no purpose other than to increase stress, tension, and frustration. In doing so, you will be able to get rid of anxiety and enjoy greater peace of mind.

Provides you With Motivation

Having positive-minded people in your life can also increase your motivation significantly. Positive minded individuals tend to challenge themselves to do or be better. They focus all their energies on building themselves and others up. Having these kinds of people around can provide you with enough motivation to make positive changes in your life and become a better person.

Take Up a New Hobby

Adopting a new hobby can seem like a very challenging task, given the fact that you will have to learn everything from scratch. If you are a career person with very little free time, or constantly busy with family obligations, it can seem impossible to fit your new interest into your already packed schedule. However, starting a new hobby can actually be very beneficial when it comes to cultivating a positive mindset. Taking up a new hobby not only allows you to learn and develop new skills but also allows you to explore your personality more. You might be surprised to discover that you have some latent talents and abilities which you never knew you had. So, when working on improving your positive thinking, try to select a hobby that you are interested in. This can be something like birdwatching, painting, playing a musical instrument, gardening or anything else you feel like you have always wanted to do. Starting a new hobby will enable you to connect with yourself and enjoy a new measure of fulfillment.

Practice Positive Self Talk

Self-talk refers to the internal monologue that is always taking place in your head even as you go about the ordinary activities of your day-to-day life (Holland, 2019). This is usually reflective of your core values, belief-systems, and ideas. Self-talk can be either positive or negative, depending on your personality and experiences. Therefore, if you are a naturally optimistic person, you will likely have positive thoughts and self-talk. On the other hand, if you are a pessimist, your self-talk will mostly be negative. In order to cultivate a positive mindset, you need to shift this internal monologue from negative thoughts to positive ones.

There are plenty of benefits that you can derive from practicing positive self-talk. These include:

- Greater satisfaction with life.
- Improved immune system.
- Better cardiovascular health.
- Stress and anxiety relief.
- Longer lifespan.

When practicing positive self-talk, the key is to identify any negative thoughts that you might be having and replace them with a positive outlook. For instance, instead of saying "I am a failure and will never be good at anything" you can replace that thought by saying "I'm glad I tried my best, I will try to do better next time." By using compassionate words when addressing your negative self-talk, you will be able to get yourself out of the trap of negative thinking and become more accepting of yourself and the situations that are beyond your control ("Positive thinking: Stop negative self-talk to reduce stress," 2020b).

Learn to Laugh at Yourself

As human beings, we tend to be very critical of ourselves. We constantly gauge ourselves against the achievements of other people and set exceedingly high standards for ourselves. When we fail to meet these standards, we may end up being disappointed in ourselves. This disappointment often gives rise to negative feelings of unworthiness and self-blame which can significantly damage our self-esteem. It is important to realize that nobody is perfect, including the people we look up to and who seem to be good at everything. Therefore, we need to get rid of the tendency to expect perfection from ourselves. Learning to laugh at ourselves and our mistakes can help ease the pressure of performing and allow us to become more positive about our lives. It is vital to remember that life is essentially an adventure and that all of us are on the path of self-discovery. Adopting a lighthearted attitude towards our flaws and idiosyncrasies, therefore, will allow us to approach life with perpetual optimism and provide us with a greater appreciation of our lives.

Summary

In this chapter you learned about positive thinking and how to develop this mindset. We have discussed how positive thinking can improve your mindset and enhance your overall health and wellbeing. Granted, this is not something that happens instantaneously. You will need to practice these techniques over a period of time to begin seeing tangible results. However, there is no denying that these tips and techniques will work for you just as they have worked for a lot of people in the past.

To recap the main points of this chapter, here are some of the tips you need to remember when cultivating a positive mindset:

- Developing positive thinking does not happen overnight - it requires diligence and practice.

- Learn how to observe your thoughts consciously to recognize the negative thoughts that you tend to ruminate over most frequently. This will help you to determine which situations trigger negative thinking patterns in you, and how you can change those situations in order to become more positive minded.
- Embrace humor and learn to laugh at yourself and the situations you find yourself in. Taking your life less seriously will reduce the pressure you experience when faced with difficult situations.
- Adopt and maintain a healthy lifestyle which includes regular physical exercises and a healthy diet. This will not only keep your body in good shape but will also provide you with relief from anxiety and stress.
- Surround yourself with positive-minded people who will motivate and encourage you to be the best version of yourself. Find friends who are accepting of the person you are and who constantly challenge you to become the person that you aspire to be.
- Practice positive self-talk by replacing negative thoughts and phrases you may be prone to with positive ones. Always focus on the brighter side of things even when dealing with difficult situations. This will prevent you from falling into the traps of negative thinking cycles, and allow you to be more proactive in finding solutions to the immediate problems you face.

Positive thinking is a concept that goes hand in hand with self-acceptance. As a matter of fact, the practice of positive thinking typically leads to a better understanding of ourselves and allows us to realize and appreciate both our strengths and weaknesses as individuals. Just as it is important to cultivate positive thinking, it is also equally vital to learn how to accept who we are.

In the next chapter, we are going to explore the concept of self-acceptance, why it is crucial when it comes to dealing with negative thoughts, and some of the ways in which you can cultivate a greater acceptance of yourself. I have no doubt in my mind that at the end of the chapter, you will have a greater understanding of self-acceptance and why it is so vital when it comes to combating problems of overthinking, worry and anxiety.

CHAPTER NINE:

The Path to Self Acceptance

Many people confuse self-esteem with self-acceptance. While self-esteem refers to how you see yourself, self-acceptance refers to the feeling of satisfaction you have about yourself regardless of past mistakes and flaws.

How we perceive ourselves is very important to our psychological health as well as to our progress towards our goals and aspirations. People who display high self-worth tend to be highly driven, and they can pursue their goals regardless of the challenges they encounter along the way. On the other hand, people who have a poor sense of self-worth tend to get discouraged easily and are not as resilient when it comes to chasing their ultimate goals in life. They may avoid challenging situations, or find it difficult to persevere when they encounter stressful situations in life (F, 2008).

Individuals who have a poor sense of self-worth tend to perceive themselves negatively and are prone to problems such as anxiety, low self-esteem and a lack of self-confidence. Consequently, they tend to be less successful than their counterparts who have a high sense of self-worth.

In order to truly gain a sense of self-acceptance, it is absolutely vital to accept yourself fully, both the negative as well as the positive aspects of yourself. However, most people find it hard to admit their flaws to themselves, and even once they do, they may still find it difficult to live with these flaws. This often leads to feelings of insecurity, anxiety, and worry which can interfere not only with one's mental health but also hinder them from pursuing the goals that they have set out to achieve in their lives.

Benefits of Self Acceptance

Nevertheless, as difficult as it may be to achieve a sense of self-acceptance, doing so can be very rewarding in a number of ways. Here are some of the benefits that you can enjoy from learning how to accept yourself.

Allows You to Develop Humility

Practicing self-acceptance can help you become a more humble individual. The art of self-acceptance prompts us to acknowledge that we are not in total control of our reality and the world. With a balanced sense of self-acceptance, therefore, you are able to come to the realization that you are simply one piece of a much bigger puzzle known as life. Arriving at this realization allows you to become a more balanced and humble individual.

Enables You to Have a Clear Perspective on Reality

The art of self-acceptance enables you to have an awareness of a reality that is grounded in truth rather than fantasy. By practicing self-acceptance, you can see the world as it is rather than how you wish it would be. This can be very useful in helping you ground yourself and approach situations from a realistic point of view.

Helps You Become Better at Solving Problems

Self-acceptance gives you clarity of thought which you require to thoroughly evaluate your prevailing predicaments and find effective solutions to your most critical issues. When you are realistic about yourself and your abilities, you are more likely to plan and take a path that is likely to have a successful outcome.

Promotes Your Physical, Mental and Emotional Wellbeing

Living in denial about who we are can significantly interfere with the equilibrium of our lives due to the stress and anxiety that come with it. However, when we fully accept ourselves, we end up with increased energy to channel into more productive activities. This helps catapult us towards our life's goals and aspirations.

Improves Your Relationships with Others

Practicing self-acceptance can help us improve how we relate to the people around us. This is because it trains us to be more assertive with our needs, while also acknowledging that other people are different from us and may not share the same beliefs or values that we have. By learning how to accept ourselves, we can connect with people in much more meaningful ways and build relationships that are based on trust, honesty and mutual respect.

Provides You with an Option When Faced with Difficult Situations

Early on in the course of this book, we discussed the importance of being able to distinguish between solvable and unsolvable worries. Solvable worries are essentially those situations where immediate action can or has to be taken. Unsolvable worries are those that are essentially beyond your control. When we engage in ruminating or overthinking, it is often because we are faced with challenging situations for which we do not have an immediate solution. This can lead to feelings of hopelessness, helplessness, and anxiety. Self-acceptance, however, can help us cope better with these challenges. By accepting things that you do not have control over, you can relieve your mind from unproductive thoughts that serve no purpose other than to increase your anxiety and stress.

Enables You to Develop a Better Understanding of Yourself

Our emotions and feelings usually provide us with a lot of information about the things that we value in life. When you suppress or deny your emotions, you can end up feeling alienated from the world and lose sight of who you are. However, by acknowledging and accepting your feelings, you can develop a better understanding of yourself and be able to make decisions that align with your core values and beliefs.

Eliminates the Chances of Uncomfortable Feelings Coming Up Later

Developing an awareness of your feelings and emotions is an essential part of self-acceptance. When you acknowledge your uncomfortable emotions without suppressing or denying them, you are able to resolve them conclusively and promptly, so that they do not emerge later to haunt you.

Allows You to Forgive Yourself

Granted, all of us have done some things in the past, which we are not especially proud of. We may have made some gross errors or mistakes that have impacted our lives in significant ways. Obviously, the past cannot be undone, however, by acknowledging your flaws and past mistakes through self-acceptance, you can forgive yourself for past transgressions and move forward in life honestly and peacefully.

Frees You From the Tendency to Overthink

Very often, we get caught up in loops of overthinking and overanalyzing, simply because we are unable to accept the way things are at present, or we worry about the future, or we can't stop replaying the past in our heads. By practicing self-acceptance, however, we can overthink situations less, thereby conserving our energy and safeguarding our peace of mind.

Allows You to Attain Inner Peace

When you let go of your tendency to idealize, regret or worry about your past or future, you become more in tune with the real world. By accepting yourself for who you are, therefore, you can begin to appreciate the ordinary things in your life a lot more. This will consequently make you more comfortable in who you are and enable you to achieve inner peace and tranquility, even in the face of challenging situations.

A Way of Showing Gratitude to Yourself

Constantly engaging in negative thinking and overthinking can make you very self-critical and overly judgmental of yourself and your actions. This often promotes a victim mentality in us, where we perceive ourselves as less than we are. Practicing self-acceptance, however, allows us to become more compassionate and grateful for ourselves, which can help us become happier and more comfortable with ourselves.

Make You Psychologically Stronger

Whenever we try to avoid the aspects of ourselves that we are ashamed or unapproving of, we gradually lose our confidence and courage. This can be very detrimental to our psychological well being. By accepting yourself wholly, however, you will be able to face your fears and anxieties head-on, thus developing your psychological resilience.

Allows You to Assert Control Over Your Life

The practice of self-acceptance can help you to take control of your thoughts and actions. Whenever you accept a situation that seems very difficult or uncomfortable, you redirect your focus to what you need to do and take actions that are in alignment with your personal values and core beliefs.

Allows You to Discover Your Inherent Gifts and Talents

Practicing self-acceptance can help you to uncover all the talents and gifts that you may have kept under the surface. By recognizing the good in yourself and capitalizing on your assets, you will be able to accomplish new things! The ability to accept yourself fully brings to the forefront all of the parts of you which you have hidden from yourself and others all along. You will be surprised at how impactful these concealed gifts can be, not only to you personally but to other people as well.

How to Practice Self Acceptance

Self-acceptance is typically very challenging for people due to the fact that they constantly engage in self-doubt and self-criticism. The more these doubts and negative thoughts press upon their conscious awareness, the less confident they feel. This can lead to feelings of self-loathing and depression. If you struggle with the problem of poor self-worth, it is absolutely vital for you to nurture in yourself healthy self-acceptance. In order to do so, you must perceive self-acceptance as a skill that you can develop with practice, rather than an innate trait that only exists in a special class of people.

There are several techniques that can help you to develop a sense of self-acceptance and self-worth. Some of these techniques are listed below.

Practice Relaxed Awareness

To develop a strong sense of self-awareness, it is crucial to become aware of your thoughts and emotions. This is easier than you might think. Rather than trying really hard to focus your concentration on specific thoughts, you want to practice relaxed awareness. This refers to a state of awareness of your thoughts and emotions that you achieve when you let go of your preoccupation with attending to specific items or topics. Relaxed awareness can be compared to meditation, in the sense that it allows you to go about your life in an ordinary and normal manner, while operating at a higher level of awareness than most people usually do.

Here is a brief guide on how you can cultivate a state of relaxed awareness and reap the numerous benefits that this state of mind provides:

- Become mindful of your day-to-day actions such as showering, preparing your meals, brushing your teeth, etc. while being relaxed. Avoid trying to focus too much as you do this. Instead, maintain a calm and relaxed state of mind and be present in the moment.
- Acknowledge your uniqueness and develop an appreciation of what you have to offer yourself, the people you know, and the community you live in.
- Try to live in the present and shed off any worries or desires you may have about the past or the future. Focus on what you can actually do or are doing in the short term.
- See each day as a fresh opportunity to learn something new, and bring all your talents and gifts to whatever you do.

Acknowledge What You Notice

When you begin to practice relaxed awareness, you may notice many thoughts, emotions, and feelings running through your mind and body. These include self-deprecating thoughts and fears, as well as pleasant emotions such as contentment and joy. Naturally, you may be inclined to try and suppress some of the thoughts and feelings which you perceive as negative. However, this is counterproductive to your practice of self-acceptance, since these perceived negative thoughts and emotions are an inextricable part of yourself. Instead of trying to avoid them, acknowledge and welcome these negative thoughts just as you do the positive ones. Remember that these negative thoughts present you with an opportunity to learn something about yourself. Just don't dwell on them! This will lead you to a better understanding of your highly complex personality, and allow you to achieve self-acceptance.

Stop Comparing Yourself to Others

As human beings, we have a natural tendency to compare ourselves with other people. We tend to compare the best features of others against the average ones in ourselves. We often rank ourselves using imaginary scorecards. When we perceive ourselves as faring better than others, we feel a sense of validation. On the other hand, when we think that other people are better than us, this can lead to self-esteem and self-confidence issues.

As natural and harmless as it might seem, comparing ourselves to others is actually a very harmful habit that can wreak havoc on our lives and emotional health if not kept in check (Raftlova, 2019). To achieve self-acceptance, it is essential to let go of this habit. This is not always easy to do, considering how entrenched this habit usually is. In most cases, we make these comparisons subconsciously without even being aware of it.

However, by practicing relaxed awareness, you will begin to notice how you get caught up in comparing yourself to others. If you become aware of these thoughts, do not try to suppress or avoid them. Instead, acknowledge them and then let go of them by shifting your focus from them to positive thoughts.

Practice Gratitude

Acknowledging the things you are grateful for in life will make you more appreciative of your situation. It will also give you the energy to face life with a renewed sense of optimism and acceptance. When we focus on the good things we have in our lives, we have no time or space in our minds for negativity.

Learn to Forgive Yourself

Very often, we get caught up in negative thinking loops due to constant self-judgment and self-blame. Forgiving yourself is one of the hardest things to do. Granted, we may have made many mistakes in the past which continue to cast a dark cloud over our lives. However, constantly obsessing over past errors only keeps us stuck in negativity, and hinders our ability to move forward with our lives. Therefore, in order to foster healthy self-acceptance, it is very vital to forgive yourself and let go of the shame, guilt or sorrow of past mistakes.

Cultivating Self Compassion

Becoming more compassionate with yourself is a fundamental step towards achieving self-acceptance and inner peace. Many times, we get stuck in patterns of thinking which involve self-blame and unwarranted self-criticism. This can cause us to have a poor sense of self-worth and rob us of happiness and contentment.

However, by cultivating self-compassion, we can overcome the tendency to beat ourselves down, and we can become more accepting of ourselves. Here are some of the ways in which you can practice self-compassion and attain a balanced state of self-acceptance.

Change Your Mindset

Very often, we experience a poor sense of self-worth because we judge ourselves based on mistakes we may have done in the past. This can be detrimental to our self-esteem and confidence. To heal from past traumas and mistakes, you need to learn to separate your past actions from your current self and realize that your actions in the past do not have to have any bearing on the person you are now unless you want them to.

Spend Time Doing Things That You Love

When you are struggling with feelings of guilt and shame, it is easy to think that you don't deserve anything good in life. However, this couldn't be further from the truth. All of us, regardless of our past actions and mistakes, deserve happiness and fulfillment. Therefore, despite any transgressions of your past, you need to allow yourself to experience happiness by taking time to do things that you love, such as hobbies and interests. This show of self-love will help you to heal and develop a greater appreciation for yourself.

Avoid Making Judgments and Assumptions about Yourself

When you are grappling with negative thoughts about yourself, it is very easy to make blanket judgments and assumptions about your character. For instance, you may think that you are a failure, a bad person or unworthy of love. In doing so, you merely write yourself off and limit your options in terms of what you can do in the future. This is an incorrect mindset, and can significantly hinder you from making progress in life. Therefore, it is important to avoid judging yourself too harshly for your actions, and especially any mistakes in your past. Doing so will help you to acknowledge your actions and move closer to attaining a state of self-acceptance.

Be Mindful

The practice of mindfulness is very useful when it comes to self-compassion. Mindfulness allows you to be in the present moment and enables you to be consciously aware of your thoughts and emotions. By bringing your feelings and thoughts to the forefront of your conscious attention, you can learn to appreciate them and develop an acceptance of yourself.

Try Something New in Life

If you are like most people, you probably have a set of routines that you perform on a daily basis. Routines are very important because they give our lives a sense of stability and comfort. However, when you get stuck in routines, life can end up being lackluster and get predictable and even boring. It is therefore important to step out of your routines every once in a while and get out of your comfort zone. Try to explore other things that challenge you and expand the horizons of your personality. This can help you uncover some talents you didn't know you had.

Letting Go of Guilt

Sometimes guilt is useful, as it links us to our consciousness and prompts us to evaluate our mistakes. Then we can take the right steps towards rectifying any harm we may have caused to ourselves or others. However, too much guilt can be counterproductive to our progress and even detrimental to our personal development. It can keep us stuck in patterns of negative thinking and ruminating about the past. It can prevent us from being able to appreciate the present or be hopeful about the future. If this problem is unresolved, it may lead to negative emotions like depression and anxiety.

If you are grappling with guilt and shame over past mistakes, you need to let go of these in order to become more accepting of yourself. Here are some of the steps that you can take towards this end.

Correct Any Outstanding Wrongs You May Have Made

As we have mentioned, feeling guilty isn't always a negative emotion. It is necessary to accept the consequence of our actions if they have hurt others in a significant way. Feelings of guilt can spur you to right wrongs you may have committed in the past. Therefore, if you feel guilty about a mistake you have made, you can take the initiative to make amends. Granted, it might feel awkward and uncomfortable to reach out to people you have hurt. However, in doing so, you will be able to minimize negative thoughts you may be harboring about whatever happened. Sometimes a genuine apology can be sufficient enough to make amends. It depends on what you feel guilty for doing! If you are not able to directly make amends, think about donating time to an organization that helps others. Do good deeds.

Challenge Your Hindsight Bias

Sometimes we tend to overthink our past mistakes because we validate our hindsight bias too much. It is easy to look back at your past mistakes and make idealizations about how you could have handled the situation better. The truth of the matter, however, is that it is not always possible to predict the outcome of a situation when making decisions in the moment. Even well-meaning intentions can lead to undesirable results. Therefore, when working out your guilt, it is important to challenge your hindsight bias and acknowledge situations where you were acting with noble interests even if the outcome was not what you hoped for.

Challenge the Belief of Over-Responsibility

There are times when we struggle with guilt due to an inflated sense of responsibility. We may wrongly assume that we are responsible for things that happen even when they have absolutely nothing to do with us. If you tend to hold yourself accountable for things that you are not responsible for, you are setting yourself up for stress and misery. It is therefore important to realize that some things are not in your control and you shouldn't hold yourself accountable for them. This will help you overcome the tendency of guilt-tripping yourself, and allow you to be more accommodating of your limitations.

Learning to Forgive Ourselves

The ability to forgive is universally considered to be one of the best virtues anyone can have. This is because it allows you to let go of any feelings of anger or resentment that you have for someone who has wronged you. Some find it easier to forgive than others. However, while forgiving others is something many people are able to do, self-forgiveness can be harder.

Everyone makes errors at one point or another since no one is perfect. It is therefore important to cultivate the art of forgiving yourself and moving past any mistakes you may have made in the course of your life. Learning how to let go of your past transgressions and moving on will help you safeguard your mental wellbeing and allow you to cultivate self-acceptance.

If you struggle with feelings of guilt and regret, here are some useful tips that can help you become more forgiving towards yourself.

Acknowledge the Mistakes You Made

One of the reasons why we get stuck in patterns of regret and guilt is because we fail to acknowledge the mistakes that happened, and the role we played in the way things worked out. This inability to recognize and acknowledge our past mistakes can hinder our ability to learn from these transgressions and move on from them. In order to forgive yourself and begin healing, therefore, you need to honestly admit to your mistakes and acknowledge how it may have hurt someone or yourself. This allows you to take responsibility for your actions and this will minimize the feelings of guilt that you are experiencing.

Try to Figure Out Your Motivation

In order to forgive yourself for any mistakes you may have committed in the past, it is absolutely vital for you to understand why you behaved in the manner you did. Then you can consider why you feel guilty. For instance, you may have done something that goes against your moral convictions. By finding out why you acted in the way you did, you can more easily forgive yourself for your error. This is because understanding the motivations that led to the mistake will help you avoid repeating it in the future.

Learn to Distinguish Between Guilt and Shame

Feeling guilty when you make a mistake that hurts others is completely normal and can spur you to make necessary changes in your life. However, shame is different from guilt. Feeling guilty is an acknowledgment that you know you did wrong, whereas shame is feeling self-reproach about what happened. You can feel ashamed of your actions or feel ashamed because something happened to you. Both of those situations are different from each other, and different from guilt.

Nobody is perfect and everyone makes mistakes, including the most respected people in society. Shame and remorse are natural emotions that allow you to take responsibility for your guilt and move towards better behavior.

Feeling shame or being ashamed because of something that happened to you is different. You may feel shame because what happened is morally repugnant to you or others. You may feel bad because you feel that you contributed to what happened in some way. You may feel ashamed that you are unable to take action to help yourself move beyond what happened. You are not alone. Talk to someone you trust and don't be afraid to seek professional help to access community resources.

Shame is not a very useful emotion since it only serves to undermine your sense of self-worth. Try to avoid wallowing in feelings of shame and self-blame, since this will only keep you stuck in past mistakes and regrets. This will make it difficult for you to accept and forgive yourself.

Strive to be More Empathetic Towards People You May Have Hurt

One of the biggest hurdles of self-forgiveness is that it requires you to have empathy for those who you may have hurt with your mistakes. To really forgive yourself to have to understand how the person that was hurt feels. This can actually increase our compassion for other people. However, when we are focused on self-forgiveness it may make it difficult to relate to other people since we are focused on ourselves. In order to avoid this pitfall, you need to make a conscious effort to empathize with the people who have been negatively affected by your actions. This way you will be forgiving yourself for how you may have really impacted them, and not for how you think you impacted them.

Make a Conscious Decision to Learn from the Experience

Every human being has at some point done or said something which they are not pleased with or proud of. It is normal to feel guilty when we commit a transgression against others. However, getting stuck in a cycle of self-blame and self-hatred can negatively impact your sense of self-worth. This can make it difficult for you to forgive yourself and move forward. Therefore, when dealing with feelings of guilt over a past mistake, focus on the lessons you can draw from the situation. How would you do it differently next time? No matter how badly you may have messed up, you don't need to beat yourself down forever. Recognize your mistake and view it as a learning experience that will help you make better choices in the future.

Summary

As we come to the end of this chapter, there is no doubt that you have learned many very useful strategies for cultivating self-acceptance. This is very important because it is through self-acceptance that we can get rid of negative thoughts that impact our sense of self-worth. By learning how to practice self-acceptance, therefore, we can get rid of negative thinking and ultimately become more positive individuals.

So, to recap the main takeaways of this very instructive chapter, here are some of the points you need to remember when learning how to cultivate self-acceptance:

- Practice mindfulness and relaxed awareness to bring your feelings and thoughts to the forefront of your consciousness. This will help you foster a deeper awareness of yourself and bring you closer to self-acceptance.
- Cultivate gratitude in your life by appreciating the gifts, talents, and blessings you have. Doing so will allow you to realize your own worth and eliminate the tendency to look down on yourself and the situations you find yourself in. Furthermore, practicing gratitude will help you focus on the positive aspects of your life, and improve your self-confidence and sense of self-worth.

- Learn to be more compassionate towards yourself and avoid the tendency to blame yourself for things you have no control over. Practicing self-compassion will make you more in touch with your inner self and help you navigate the complexities of life in a more positive way.
- Learn to forgive yourself and move past the mistakes of your past. Push away feelings like guilt and self-blame which can be major hurdles in your path to self-acceptance.

Achieving self-acceptance is within your grasp. Make conscious efforts to let go of guilt and show yourself and others compassion.

In the closing chapter of this book, we are going to discuss the concept of radical self-love and how you can employ it to fortify yourself against the problems of negative thinking, overthinking and chronic worrying.

CHAPTER TEN:

Practising Radical Self Love

The art of self-love can be very challenging for people to practice, especially when struggling with the challenges of everyday life. It is easy to forget about our own wellbeing when we are struggling to hold down careers and support our families. However, self-love is a very important element of personal growth and self-acceptance. That is why it is vital to practice the art of loving yourself. Self-love is often misunderstood by people who wrongly assume that self-love means being self-absorbed or narcissistic. On the contrary, self-love aims to get in touch with ourselves, our well-being and our happiness to connect with others. Practicing self-love can be very beneficial to ourselves and the people who we interact with (Stenvinkel, 2018).

By practicing self-love, you can challenge the limiting beliefs you may have about yourself, and motivate yourself to work towards your life's goals. The art of self-love also enables you to develop a greater understanding of your strengths as well as your weaknesses. By cultivating a deep love for yourself, you will be less inclined to overlook or gloss over your shortcomings. Instead, you will recognize that you have flaws just like everyone else. Use that knowledge to make yourself a better person.

You should keep in mind that self-love is not a state of mind to be achieved. As a matter of fact, self-love is a process that requires diligence and constant practice. Our self-love grows gradually the more we continue performing acts of kindness, appreciation, and compassion towards ourselves and others.

Here are some of the powerful ways in which you can foster deep self-love for yourself.

Be Someone Who Loves

It can be very challenging to cultivate self-love if you are dealing with thoughts and emotions that are focused on self-criticism and self-blame. When your self-esteem takes a beating from all the challenges you encounter in life, you may even wonder, "What is there to love about me?" The truth of the matter, however, is that everyone, including yourself, has some positive attributes which other people admire.

Instead of trying to love yourself without conviction, you need to first learn how to be someone who loves. Try to focus on what you love about the people you meet, and most importantly, pay attention to the things you love about the ordinary experiences of life. This can include walking to your office on a nice day or having a conversation with a random stranger. Offer loving statements to those that are close to you. By tuning your body and mind to positive emotions, you will begin to find a lot of things to love in your life. This will allow you to be more open to love, and you will be more likely to receive it.

Tap into What it Feels and Looks Like to be Loved

Being loving toward yourself can be easy when things are going well in life. However, when things aren't working out as expected, it is easy to be self-critical. You may get so caught up in your negative thinking that you forget to be compassionate towards yourself.

The truth of the matter, however, is that it is during such times that you need to show yourself the most love. When you are caught up in moments of struggle, you need to think about what someone who loves you intensely would do or say. Chances are, they wouldn't judge you harshly or look down on you. Instead, they would shower you with love, understanding, and compassion. Contemplating your situation in this way will help you get rid of the tendency to self-blame and berate yourself when you are facing a challenging situation. As a result, you will be able to show yourself more kindness and love.

Don't Compare Yourself

As humans, we tend to compare ourselves to those around us in an attempt to gauge how well or poorly we are fairing, or how good or bad we are. Despite the fact that this tendency to compare ourselves to others is natural, doing so can be very negative in a number of ways. Here are some of the ways in which comparing yourself with others negatively affects your life.

- It makes you presume the worst about yourself.
- It robs you of precious time, which you would otherwise be using to do productive things.
- It prevents you from appreciating your own unique talents and gifts.
- It robs you of passion and the drive to pursue your interests and goals.
- It causes you to resent others.
- It robs you of joy and makes it difficult to find fulfillment in life.

As you can see, there is plenty to lose from engaging in constant comparison to others. Therefore, you should endeavor to quit the habit and begin to appreciate the wonderful things you have in life. Here are some of the tips that can help you overcome the tendency to compare yourself to others.

- Become aware of the detrimental effects that these comparisons have on your self-esteem.

- Start acknowledging your personal successes.
- Learn to appreciate the contributions and successes of others instead of being envious of them.
- Learn to be grateful for your uniqueness as well as the innate talents and gifts that you possess.
- Always remember that no one is perfect and that everyone has their own flaws and shortcomings.

Ask Your Support System for Help

Many times when we are dealing with difficult thoughts and feelings, we isolate ourselves from the people who are close to us. We may feel like we are burdening them with our problems when they already have their own to deal with. However, this only serves to alienate us from the people who care about us. Cultivating a strong support system, on the other hand, can help us push through with our goals and navigate stressful situations much more comfortably. People who have strong support systems generally experience higher levels of wellbeing than their counterparts who lack this resource. Furthermore, they are better able to cope with crisis situations in their lives.

A healthy support system can come from close family members, friends, good neighbors, and even pets. It can also come from support groups and mental health professionals. Some of the ways in which support can be provided are in the form of mental, emotional and financial assistance.

Here are some of the things that you should consider when considering the support system in your life:

- How does talking to them make you feel?
- Do they validate your feelings and emotions?
- Do they give advice that is supportive of your wellbeing?
- Do they tell you the truth even if it is difficult to accept?
- Are they happy for you when you triumph?

- Do they motivate you to be a better person?

By asking yourself these questions about the people in your life, you will be able to identify individuals who are supportive of you. This doesn't mean you should write off those who are seemingly less supportive. It only means that you are more likely to gain positive outcomes from spending time with supportive people when you are in need. Know who they are.

Take Concrete Steps to Create Your Desired Life

There are times in life when you come to the realization that the life which you are living is not exactly the one you want. The necessity of changing your life arises out of the desire to align your life with your personal goals and aspirations. It is important to realize that you are fully responsible for creating your desired life and no one else can help you in this regard. So, if you have determined that the life you are living now does not satisfy your desires, you need to take concrete steps to create the life you want for yourself. Here are some of the main techniques that will help you create the positive and fulfilling life that you dream about.

Decide the Kind of Life You Want

The first step is to figure out what you need to change in your life. This doesn't mean you should overhaul everything. Regardless of how you feel about your current life, there are certain aspects of it that are actually good and do not need to be changed. For instance, you may be satisfied by the relationships and friendships that you have, and hence, there is no reason to change them unless you want to "restart your life". Instead, you need to focus on the things that are less appealing to you. For instance, if you are not happy about your current job, evaluate whether you can change it for one that aligns with your goals and desires for personal fulfillment.

Envision Your Desired Life How You Want it To Be

When you begin to envision your life being the way you desire it to be, you will find that things start to fall into place. Having this mindset will act as a motivator for you to make choices that align with your desired life. You must know what you are striving for in order to consciously work towards attaining it.

Do the Things in Life that Make you Happy

When you are trying to create your desired life, you should think about the experiences that make you happy. This includes your work, hobbies, interests, and relationships. Once you have figured out the things that make you content in life, adjust your behavior such that you experience these with more frequency. Doing so will enable you to develop positive habits and give you control over your negative thoughts.

Create and Focus on Your Goals

To create the life that you dream of, you need to be very goal-oriented. This is the time for you to set your goals, and put in the needed work to achieve them. So for example, if you are trying to get into a certain career, work hard to develop the required skills and academic credentials you need.

Don't Worry About What Other People Think

Although it might sound selfish, creating the life that you desire requires you to focus on yourself and ignore what other people may think about you. While everyone is entitled to an opinion, making your decisions based on other people's opinions is setting yourself up for a life of misery. As long as you are not hurting others, do not worry if they approve of the steps you take to improve your life.

Let Go of Fear

Most people neglect to pursue their goals and create the life they want due to fear of the unknown, and fear of failure. The fear of making mistakes and failing is something everyone has experienced at one point or another. Fear of failure is a natural emotion. However, you need to overcome this fear if you are going to make decisions that steer you towards the life you want to create for yourself. Do not worry about not succeeding. Just try to accomplish your objective. If you fail, you can always try again. As long as your heart is in the right place, nothing should discourage you from chasing your dreams.

Surround Yourself with People You Feel Good With

In order to cultivate self-love, it is very important to spend time with people you feel good around. This is because your interactions with people greatly affect your sense of self-worth and confidence. Spending time with people who motivate and encourage you can help you become more accepting of yourself while also challenging you to become a better person. On the other hand, interacting with negative people is likely to make you more pessimistic and negative about yourself. Therefore, you should strive to spend more time with positive people that help you to learn and grow as an individual.

Cultivate Healthy Habits

An essential part of self-love involves taking care of your physical, mental and emotional wellbeing. Therefore, you need to cultivate habits that contribute to positive outcomes in all areas of your life. This includes eating healthy food, exercising to keep your body fit and taking care of your emotional and mental wellbeing. Stop the tendency to do things simply because you "must" or "should" do them. Instead, only do things that empower you and make you feel good about yourself.

*Be Compassionate When Sh*t Happens*

It is very easy for us to beat ourselves down with negative thoughts when unpleasant things happen, or we make mistakes. However, when we experience failure or disappointment, we need to take advantage of this time to shower ourselves with love. Instead of blaming and criticizing yourself when things don't go your way, endeavor to show yourself kindness and compassion. Learn to forgive yourself when you make mistakes and appreciate the good things that you have accomplished. This will help you overcome the feeling of guilt.

Accept What You Cannot Love

Granted, it can be very difficult to love things that seem to go against your personal values and beliefs. However, this does not mean you should simply ignore them or write them off. On the contrary, you need to focus on appreciating them, because doing so allows you to recognize your own uniqueness as a person. This can give you a greater understanding of your own individuality and enable you to be more accepting and loving of yourself.

Have a "Worry-free" Month

One of the most powerful strategies that can help you develop greater self-love is to postpone your worries in favor of positivity. Create a "worry-free" month where you focus on the good things in your life rather than all of the negative worrisome thoughts that serve no purpose other than to drain your energy. By taking some time to enjoy your life without worry, you can increase your energy and develop the clarity of mind and perspective that will help you face your worries when you really need to.

Summary

This final chapter has focussed on fostering self-love and compassion for ourselves. You will no doubt agree that self-love is very desirable. Practicing self-love can significantly help reduce your tendency to ruminate over negative thoughts which erode your personal sense of self-worth. By cultivating self-love, you can overcome the tendency to worry and overthink (Stenvinkel, 2018). Here are the main points you need to remember when trying to cultivate radical self-love:

- Try to focus on the things you love about your everyday experiences, no matter how trivial they may seem.
- Stop the habit of comparing yourself to others and realize that you are a unique individual in your own right. Develop an appreciation for your inherent talents, skills, and gifts.
- Identify your support system and develop a deeper connection with them.
- Clarify your vision of your desired life, and make the necessary changes to live in a way that is more aligned with your vision.
- Spend more time interacting with people who motivate and challenge you to become the best version of yourself.
- Cultivate healthy habits that promote your physical, mental and emotional wellbeing.
- Learn to love yourself even when things do not work out according to your plans and wishes.
- Develop an appreciation for the things which you cannot love and learn to accept them instead of avoiding them.

The practice of self-love will provide you with a deeper understanding and appreciation of your individuality. This can empower you to strive towards your goals and create the life you desire.

FINAL WORDS

As we come to conclude this book, I am confident that the wisdom contained herein provides a clear pathway to eliminating the problem of negative thinking. This problem, as we have learned, is a natural phenomenon that we have inherited as humans over the course of our evolutionary development. It arose out of our need to survive, and provide us with the ability to identify factors that threaten our survival, thereby allowing us to tackle these issues. However, while negative thinking is a natural habit that helps us adapt to our environment, problems arise when we overthink and dwell on negativity. This often interferes with our ability to function and affects our mental and emotional states.

In this book, you have learned techniques to help you clear your mind of negative thinking. You have learned why it is important to identify the source of your negative thinking. By analyzing various cognitive distortions, you can overcome them by ascertaining the validity of your negative thoughts. You also learned about the very effective technique of "name it to tame it" and how you can use this strategy to dissociate yourself from your negative thinking patterns. This will allow you to view them from an objective perspective and reduce their negative impact on your internal state.

Furthermore, we debunked the common misconception about overthinking, which is the belief that overthinking is a permanent problem that cannot be solved. In our exploration of this subject, you have seen how the problem of overthinking arises and the various strategies that can be employed to overcome it. These strategies include reconnecting with the immediate world around you, replacing negative thoughts with positive ones and cultivating a psychological distance between yourself and your negative thoughts. This will help to open your mind to more positivity.

Finally, you learned three main ways you can eliminate your negative thinking patterns forever: cultivate positive thinking, foster self-acceptance, and practice self-love. You now realize the importance of letting go of guilt and forgiving yourself, and how this can help you become more accepting of yourself as a unique individual in the world. We also discussed the concept of radical self-love and how it can help you foster a deeper understanding and appreciation of yourself as an individual. Some of the ways to cultivate self-love include stopping the comparison of yourself to others, becoming goal-oriented, surrounding yourself with positive-minded people and practicing healthy habits in order to safeguard your overall health and wellness. By practicing radical self-love, you can change your overall outlook on life and approach it from a perspective of optimism and confidence. Self-love will also enable you to develop a high sense of self-worth and enhance your self-esteem. When you eliminate negative thinking, you can use the new positivity in your life to create the life you dream of.

I would like to express my confidence in the fact that this book meticulously illustrates the problem of negative thinking and provides brilliant yet simple ways to overcome negative thoughts and worries. All of the strategies and techniques outlined herein have been proven to be very powerful and effective when it comes to overcoming negative thinking. The simple nature of these strategies means that you can implement them in your own life very easily. Negative thinking, although faced by everyone, manifests differently in each individual because we have unique experiences. Therefore, it is ultimately your responsibility to determine how best to practice the techniques we have discussed throughout the course of this book. If you feel like you need additional help or support to deal with your negative thoughts, don't hesitate to reach out to professionals who can guide you.

During the course of this book, I have endeavored to cover this subject matter as comprehensively as possible. However, this is not to say that this book is a conclusive manual on everything regarding the subject of negative thinking. Although you will find the wisdom contained herein very practical and applicable in your real-life, there are also plenty of other resources, both online and offline, that can help you build more knowledge about this subject matter. Take the initiative to explore the subject widely if you want to take what you have learned here to the next level.

In conclusion, what I would like you to take from this book is that negative thinking is not a life sentence. As difficult as it may be to deal with your negative thoughts sometimes, you can use them to help you develop a better understanding of yourself. Therefore, do not feel hopeless or doomed when you experience these uncomfortable negative thoughts. Instead, consider them a challenge to be overcome and a stepping stone towards greater personal growth. With this mindset, you will find it easy to eliminate negative thinking, take control over your thoughts, and shift your focus into positive thinking, self-acceptance and radical self-love.

RESOURCES

Bloom, S. (2015, July 19). 7 Ways to Clear Your Mind of Negative Thoughts. Retrieved February 12, 2020, from https://www.pickthebrain.com/blog/7-ways-clear-mind-negative-thoughts/

Elmer, J. (2019, July 19). 5 Ways to Stop Spiraling Negative Thoughts from Taking Control. Retrieved February 11, 2020, from https://www.healthline.com/health/mental-health/stop-automatic-negative-thoughts#5

F, L. (2008, September 10). The Path to Unconditional Self-Acceptance. Retrieved February 11, 2020, from https://www.psychologytoday.com/us/blog/evolution-the-self/200809/the-path-unconditional-self-acceptance

Grohol, J. P. M. (2019, June 24). 15 Common Cognitive Distortions. Retrieved February 11, 2020, from https://psychcentral.com/lib/15-common-cognitive-distortions/

Holland, K. (2019, January 22). Positive Self-Talk: How Talking to Yourself Is a Good Thing. Retrieved February 11, 2020, from https://www.healthline.com/health/positive-self-talk

Hurst, K. (2014, October 3). 7 Steps To Cultivating A Positive Mindset. Retrieved February 11, 2020, from https://www.thelawofattraction.com/7-steps-to-cultivating-a-positive-mindset/

O'Brien, M. (2019a, December 20). The Four Keys to Overcoming Negative Thinking…for Good. Retrieved February 11, 2020, from https://mrsmindfulness.com/the-four-keys-to-overcoming-negative-thinkingfor-good/

O'Brien, M. (2019b, December 20). The Four Keys to Overcoming Negative Thinking…for Good. Retrieved February 11, 2020, from https://mrsmindfulness.com/the-four-keys-to-overcoming-negative-thinkingfor-good/

Oppong, T. (2020, January 3). Psychologists Explain How To Stop Overthinking Everything. Retrieved February 11, 2020, from https://medium.com/kaizen-habits/psychologists-explain-how-to-stop-overthinking-everything-e527962a393

Positive thinking: Stop negative self-talk to reduce stress. (2020a, January 21). Retrieved February 11, 2020, from https://www.mayoclinic.org/healthy-lifestyle/stress-management/in-depth/positive-thinking/art-20043950

Positive thinking: Stop negative self-talk to reduce stress. (2020b, January 21). Retrieved February 11, 2020, from https://www.mayoclinic.org/healthy-lifestyle/stress-management/in-depth/positive-thinking/art-20043950

Raftlova, B. (2019, September 19). 5 Reasons You Should Stop Comparing Yourself to Others. Retrieved February 11, 2020, from https://www.goalcast.com/2017/03/11/reasons-stop-comparing-yourself-others/

Robinson, L. (2020, February 6). How to Stop Worrying. Retrieved February 11, 2020, from https://www.helpguide.org/articles/anxiety/how-to-stop-worrying.htm

Soleil, V. (2019, August 9). 7 Key Benefits of Positive Thinking. Retrieved February 11, 2020, from https://www.learning-mind.com/7-key-benefits-of-positive-thinking/

Stenvinkel, M. (2018, February 22). Be Good to Yourself: 10 Powerful Ways to Practice Self-Love. Retrieved February 11, 2020, from https://tinybuddha.com/blog/be-good-to-yourself-10-powerful-ways-to-practice-self-love/

Stop Panic Attacks

23 Powerful Relaxation Techniques to End Panic Attacks, Keep Calm and Overcome Phobias. Regain Control of Your Life and Your Peace of Mind

Derick Howell

TABLE OF CONTENTS

INTRODUCTION

Panic attacks are scary, though you don't necessarily have to be in a scary situation to have a panic attack. For example, you could be on a hike, at a restaurant, or asleep in bed, then all of a sudden you feel a strong surge of fear ripple through you. That fear triggers physical symptoms like a pounding heart, sweating shortness of breath, nausea, chest pain, and trembling. This terrifying feeling can last between 5 to 20 minutes, and the worst thing is that you probably didn't see this scary thing before it happened; you were just doing your own thing when you were quickly overcome with these feelings.

There is no known cause for panic attacks, and people of all ages get them. The worst part is that panic attacks come with some pretty intense physical and psychological symptoms. These symptoms are so severe that a person who has a panic attack often ends up in the emergency room, scared for their life. Panic attacks are routinely misdiagnosed by the people who have them, but it isn't because they told a lie or exaggerated; they had very severe chest pains, they couldn't catch their breath, or they started to breathe shallow, short breaths that would leave them gasping for air. It is not surprising that your family members called an ambulance to take you to the hospital the first time they witnessed you having an attack.

While the doctor runs every test and finds that everything is in order, he approaches you with the news that you had a panic attack, which leaves you surprised. You thought you were going to die, and that this was just an overblown anxiety attack. You might even receive a visit from the on-call psychiatrist so they can evaluate you. What you will learn from this psychiatrist is that anxiety attacks are treatable.

There are numerous treatments for panic attacks, including changing your mindset, preventive measures for stopping a panic attack during the event itself, counseling, and other treatments. Anxiety and panic attacks can be cured! In fact, there are six therapeutic methods for treating anxiety attacks. In this book, we will be going over various strategies that can help you to get your life back. I will teach you the five steps of AWARE (acknowledge and accept the panic attack, wait and watch (or work), actions (that make you more comfortable), repeat, and end) This might not make sense to you now, but I will explain this technique and other techniques like it simply and understandably, so you can finally take charge of your panic attacks as soon as possible.

I used to experience panic attacks all the time, especially before a speaking engagement in front of crowds. I've learned how to manage them through the years and experience, and I will be sharing firsthand some of the techniques I've been using to stop those panic attacks. I even wanted to give up my speaking engagements and my job because I was scared of the next panic attack that I was going to have. However, I became determined to learn more about my panic attacks and do my best to get them to stop. I've lived through the heart-stopping panic and the frightening feeling that I was going to die, and plan to teach you the techniques and strategies I have used to cope. I was able to do that, and now I would like to share with you what I learned.

In this book, you will learn how to stop and control your panic attacks, calm yourself down during the most intense attacks, and about some powerful relaxation techniques. I am confident that you can overcome your phobias and cure yourself of panic attacks!

This book is going to give you various strategies that you can use to stop your panic attacks, and I will also tell you about the different therapies that are most effective for dealing. I will even help you with finding a therapist and what questions you can ask them when you go to your first session.

You are not alone in having panic attacks—once you start sharing the fact that you have panic attacks with your friends and family, you might discover that one of them has also had panic attacks. You will find that many men and women from different walks of life have all had panic attack issues. One of the most important things to remember is that you need to reach out to someone in order to ask for help. Reading this book can be a start to reaching out; you may also want to share this book with your family, so they can understand how to help you, and you can even bring this book with you to therapy. While in therapy, you can discuss the techniques within and decide which ones work best for you.

This book isn't meant to be a substitute for medical treatment; it is very important that your doctor clears you of any other potential medical conditions that could be causing your symptoms and experiences. However, once you can confirm that you are having panic attacks, you can start using the strategies in this book to help you through these overwhelming panic attacks. I want you to have the best information possible, so I have included in this book the best therapies and medications that are effective for treating panic attacks.

When you do go to a therapist or a psychiatrist, it is good to know about the medications that they can provide. There are many different categories of medications that can be prescribed for anxiety, and this book will provide you a list of the various types of medications that can be prescribed for anxiety.

There is no set combination of medications that can be prescribed to you. In fact, finding the right medications for you can be a hit or miss ordeal. The psychiatrist will listen to you about the type of anxiety you're feeling; specifically, what your triggers are and how you react to your anxiety. Then the psychiatrist will try to match the best type of medication for your unique reaction to anxiety. The psychiatrist will schedule a follow-up in a month or less to know how you are faring. This is an important check-up because this appointment will be when you can discuss any side effects you are experiencing and how effective the medicine is to your anxiety. During this exam, your psychiatrist may increase your dosage or ask you to try other medications.

This book delivers by giving you a list of medications and describing each category for you, so when you go to a psychiatrist, you are well-informed and can participate in deciding what medication you are going to take.

By reading this book, you can cure your panic attacks and alleviate your symptoms. Panic attacks don't have to go on forever—you can do something to stop them, and this book will help you do just that.

You can find relief now—right this minute. If you are currently experiencing a panic attack, go to Chapters 4 and 5 to find out how you can stop an attack by remaining calm during that intense panic attack. Otherwise, feel free to peruse through this book to gain crucial knowledge for understanding and curing your panic attacks.

CHAPTER ONE:

How Does a Panic Attack Feel?

Panic attacks are not new to society—in the past, people who suffered from panic attacks were called nervous or high strung. At first, panic attacks were thought of as more of a character flaw than a mental illness. Very often, people who suffered from panic attacks were hospitalized or, in some tragic cases, institutionalized. Panic attacks have always been around, but only just recently are we beginning to understand their dynamics.

Panic attacks do not exist in a bubble; everyday women and men all experience panic attacks. For example, a person can get nervous about an upcoming exam or certification, or they could become nervous about a tax audit or an upcoming social event. Does this necessarily mean that you are suffering from panic attacks?

In this chapter, you will learn about three people who suffer from panic attacks. These three people could be anyone that you would cross paths with on the street, at any time. What they have in common is the fact that their panic attacks interfere with their daily living. These three examples are only a tiny slice or cross-section of panic attack examples. The purpose of these examples is to illustrate what a panic attack feels like.

Alice and Her Panic Attack

Alice sat in her car and tried to wait for her heart to stop pounding. She was outside the hospital where her newborn grandson was waiting to meet her. Alice was short of breath and shaking, and she felt that, if she got out of the car, she would surely die. The hospital was huge, and the maternity ward was at the furthermost end of the hospital. How would she be able to get there? She opened the door and stepped out of the car, holding on to the door. Her heart pounded harder and her knees were weak. She tried to take a step but felt dizzy. Immediately, she got back into her car. By now, she was sweating profusely and shivering in the freezing wind. When she reached for her phone to call her son, she dreaded telling him that she couldn't go see her new grandson because of her panic attack. She started to cry—it isn't fair. She put the phone down because she started feeling some massive chest pain, and she feared that she was having a heart attack. She didn't know what to do; she was so scared of dying in her car, but where would she go? To the emergency room?

Alice knew from experience that she wasn't having a heart attack; she was having a panic attack. What would Alice do to get herself to calm down? Alice closed her eyes and gave herself five minutes to calm down, so she could then drive home. She was really looking forward to meeting her new grandson. Though this wasn't the first time this had happened to her, this was the first time her panic attack intervened during an important event.

The twenty minutes passed quickly, and she felt a bit calmer, so she started the car to drive away. Alice tried not to look at the hospital as she drove and she still felt horrible, but the further she got from the hospital, the more she felt the tight band around her chest loosen. What was she going to tell her son about not being able to get out of her car and go see her grandson? Alice sniffled and wiped the tears away, feeling dejected, as this visit was very important to her. Why did she feel this way? She wished that there was something she could do to stop the panic attacks, but who could help her? It would change her life for the better if only she knew what to do.

Bradley and His Panic Attack

Bradley sat in the outer waiting room, waiting to be called for his job interview. He had been preparing for this interview for two weeks; he was well-qualified for the job, and he had even done some outstanding volunteer work in a similar field. Bradley was a great guy, but he had been doing far too many interviews in the past few months. Every interview ended similarly: with him not getting the job.

The cute receptionist told Bradley that it was his turn to be interviewed, and he found himself getting up too fast and feeling dizzy. He closed his eyes and took a deep breath, waiting for the dizziness to go away. The cute receptionist held the door open for him and, in the room, the human resources director and the lead engineer waited for Bradley to take a seat. Bradley felt like there was something stuck in his throat; he swallowed hard, but it didn't go away. He suddenly felt moisture under his armpits and back. Bradley gave a nod to the men before he sat down.

The room felt really hot, and he noticed that his hands were shaking. The men asked their first question, and though Bradley tried to answer, his brain felt empty. Instead, he said something that he had practiced for weeks—a computer-like recitation of his experience. As he talked, he felt a shortness in his breath. The men looked at Bradley strangely, which did nothing to alleviate the pain that was beginning to grow in his chest. It felt like an elephant was standing on his chest. He had to leave the interview as soon as possible, or something really bad would happen, he was sure.

The truth of the matter was that the worst was happening to Bradley right at that minute. Bradley stood and gathered his briefcase, causing the men to stare at him, shocked. The interview ended with Bradley walking out the door, feeling light-headed and faint, though he made it out of the building and into his car. This was interview number 20 that he had just botched up. He sat in his car and tried to calm down but couldn't, as his heart was beating way too fast and he was trembling. He couldn't catch his breath. At that moment, Bradley felt like he was dying. He put his head down on the wheel and prayed.

Lisa and Her Service Dog

Lisa was doing her laundry in the apartment laundry room. She had one load washing and another load in the dryer, and along with her in the laundry room was her service dog. She opened her book and started reading; then, from out of nowhere, she heard an extremely loud sound, startling her. What happened? Within minutes, she was perspiring, her heart beating out of her chest. She started feeling short of breath. Her dog Sandy got close to Lisa's purse, causing Lisa to remember that she had some medication in there. Within minutes of taking the medication, Lisa started feeling better. Sandy stayed close, and

Lisa pet her to calm down. This was what it was like when you had learned what to do when a panic attack happens to you.

Amanda's Story

In her first semester of college, Amanda was the victim of abuse by her high school sweetheart. Jealous that Amanda was making new friends, Josh became increasingly hostile toward Amanda. She did her best to include Josh in her new life, but he was never satisfied. Then, one night, after going to a party on campus, Josh, who was fully inebriated, became violent while dropping Amanda off at her dorm. Fueled by jealousy, Josh began to punch and kick Amanda until she was unconscious. Bystanders who witnessed the violence called the police and an ambulance.

This was a night that Amanda would never forget.

Severe panic attacks often plague a person after they experience a violent or traumatic event. Amanda struggled when she returned to school, and loud noises triggered Amanda's panic attacks. Those panic attacks were a symptom of her Post Traumatic Stress Disorder (PTSD).

Various different situations can cause panic attacks, and there are many degrees to the severity of a panic attack; you don't have to have PTSD to suffer through them.

In order for us, as readers and listeners, to have a better understanding of what it is like to have a severe panic attack, Amanda agreed to answer some questions and have those answers included in this book.

What was it like for you after the attack?

A few days after I got home from the hospital, I didn't feel like myself. I found myself crying for what seemed like no reason, and I felt more depressed than I ever have felt. When it came time to go back to school, I just couldn't go. I stayed in my room and refused to come out. It seemed like I was afraid of everything, even my own shadow.

Did you eventually leave your room?

Yes, my parents convinced me that I had to go back to school because if I didn't go back to school, it would be like Josh took something valuable from me. I went back, but it wasn't easy.

Did you get anxious when you were on campus?

I did more than just get anxious. I had a full-blown panic attack when I crossed the quad to get to my class. Being around a large group of people talking loudly was a trigger for me. I completely lost it in the quad.

What happened?

I started to feel like my heart was going to pop out of my chest because it was beating so hard. I started shaking and I couldn't breathe right. Eventually, I hyperventilated and fainted. It was a humiliating experience.

After this experience, my mother found a therapist for me and I began to work on my panic attack issues. It was really hard for me because I isolated myself from everyone: my parents, my teachers, and even my friends.

How long did this go on?

A few months went by. I grew increasingly isolated and even started to drink and smoke pot on my own. Then, I got tired of always being alone. My friends were doing well in school and getting involved in all sorts of activities, and I was just staying at home feeling more depressed. I even thought about suicide.

Did you have panic attacks during this period?

Yes, I did, every time I had to leave the house. They weren't as severe as the collapse in the quad, but they were serious enough to get in the way of my daily life. My parents insisted I go to school, but just getting up in the morning and dressing for school was an ordeal. I would get paralyzed with panic attacks. When my parents drove me to school, I would feel my heart pounding outside my chest and I had this big fear that I was going to lose control and do something really crazy.

Are you still experiencing panic attacks?

No, I am much better now. Therapy really helped me to get control over the panic attacks.

How did therapy help?

Well, I learned all about the things that triggered my panic attacks, and then my therapist helped me to find ways to cope with my panic attacks. I guess I'll never forget what happened to me, but it isn't as vivid to me anymore. Also, the things that trigger me are getting less and less.

What types of tools did your therapist give you to be able to deal with your panic attacks?

I learned all about being mindful and not pushing myself when I am uncomfortable in a situation. My therapist recommended that I start a journal to explore my feelings, and this helped an awful lot. She also taught me some breathing exercises and ways to cope that I can do when I begin to feel a panic attack coming on.

Do you feel 100% now?

I don't know if I'll ever feel better, but I am a lot more confident now. When I do have bad days—and I do get bad days—I have learned to just take it easy and be kind to myself.

What would you tell others who are experiencing panic attacks?

I would say to do everything you can to learn techniques that will help you with your panic attacks.

Panic Attacks and Their Symptoms

All four of these people suffered from panic attacks but in different ways for various distinct reasons; yet, they all seemed to manifest panic attacks similarly. Just as the reasons for the panic attacks differed, the same goes for the symptoms that happened during an attack or episode. A person can have all the symptoms or only a few.

The duration and intensity of a panic attack can also vary, but the one true thing that people with panic disorder have is that they feel terrible and that they cannot carry on with their usual activities.

The physical symptoms that are most often felt include accelerated heart rate, trembling or shaking, shortness of breath, chest pain, feeling unsteady, and sweating. The psychological feelings can range from a fear of losing control and a fear of dying.

In the next chapter, I will go into more detail about the cause and symptoms of panic attacks. I will also provide you with information that can help you figure out if you are one who is suffering from panic attacks.

Chapter Summary

This chapter detailed four people who struggle with panic attacks, and each person dealt with panic attacks in their own way. In this chapter, we learned that:

- Panic attacks have devastating symptoms that can disrupt a person's daily life.
- Panic attacks can be triggered by trauma or stressful situations.
- Panic attacks can be treated with medication and therapy.

In the next chapter, we will be going over the causes and symptoms of panic attacks—why they happen, physical and psychological symptoms, and panic attack characteristics.

CHAPTER TWO:

Panic Attacks 101

Back when humans were trying to stave off wild animals and other natural threats, anxiety was an important emotion to have. Anxiety demanded that one keep alert and cautious about the world around them, and it was a response to stress or a situation that proved traumatic. Although we are not generally staving off dangerous wild animals on a daily basis, there are still a lot of things to be wary of, including that all-important job interview or meeting your partner's parents for the first time. We will occasionally respond to these situations with fear and almost always with nervousness.

The problem with anxiety is that it can become so extreme that you find yourself *chronically* anxious, or anxious all the time. In this case, you would have so much anxiety that it ends up interfering with your everyday life. If the anxiety becomes this sort of problem, you might have an anxiety disorder. The question is: will you have a panic attack if you have an anxiety disorder?

According to the Anxiety and Depression Association of America (ADAA), a panic attack is an onset of an intense fear that gets in the way of functioning normally. People without an anxiety disorder still feel anxious and nervous, but it does not interfere with their functioning, and they are generally able to endure stressful situations. A person who experiences panic attacks will often feel physically ill in the same situations. This person will have palpitations, a pounding heart, start shaking, have intense perspiration, and other uncomfortable physical and psychological feelings.

Panic attacks will keep people from doing things that have to be done; for example, such an individual may have difficulties going to work because they believe they might have a panic attack while riding an elevator, or they don't go to school because they have had a panic attack every time they took a test.

Is a Panic Attack the Same as an Anxiety Attack?

Although very similar, panic attacks are different from an anxiety attack, with the differences being intensity and timing. When you have an anxiety attack, the anxiety is still manageable and goes away after you get through the stressful situation. You may have the symptoms of a panic attack, like shortness of breath or an accelerated heart rate, but these symptoms go away after the stressful situation is resolved.

A panic attack has some of the same physical symptoms that an anxiety attack has, but these symptoms are more intense and they seem to happen unexpectedly or for reasons you can't explain. Panic attacks are unprovoked and unpredictable; they have more severe symptoms like shortness of breath, dizziness, and even nausea, and some people may even have very severe chest pains during a panic attack. The pain is so acute that these chest pains are often thought to be a heart attack.

Even though panic attacks can be unprovoked or unpredictable, a person can still have triggers that would cause an attack to occur. Bright lights and loud noises can make a person have a panic attack; for example, a person can walk into a situation where everything is calm, then some bright lights start flashing and loud music blares. Unexpectedly, this situation has now caused a panic attack, and they didn't expect to have this attack prior to it happening. Panic attacks also come with the fear of the next panic attack. As the fear is more acute, the person may try to avoid all bright lights in hopes that doing so will help them avoid the next panic attack; in essence, it is not the bright lights that a person fears in this situation, but the next panic attack. The next section will talk more in-depth about this phenomenon.

With an anxiety attack, you would generally know beforehand that the stressful situation is going to cause anxiety—a visit to your dentist can be so stressful that you surmise you will have an anxiety attack when you hear the drilling start and, in this case, it is the dentist that causes the anxiety, not the anxiety attack itself.

Anxiety Attacks vs. Panic Attacks

When you have an anxiety attack, it is still possible to get through the stressful situation. You may want to avoid the situation, but you would go ahead and work your way through it, as the anxiety is manageable. However, with panic attacks, you begin to have what is called **anticipatory anxiety**—worry or fear of having your next panic attack because they are overwhelming and unpredictable, and you believe it impossible to function or endure the next attack. When this happens, you begin to avoid any situation that might cause that panic attack.

Although panic attacks can be diagnosed, clinicians really don't know what causes them. You would think that, since you can recognize the symptoms, you would be able to tell the origins of an anxiety attack. An attack is much more than being stressed about something—you can easily understand why a situation would provoke anxiety, but it may be harder to understand why a person would have a complete physical and psychological meltdown that would render them unfunctional. Researchers have not quite figured out just yet why a mental situation can turn into a severe physical reaction.

What Causes a Panic Attack

Even though clinicians don't know the cause, they still try to isolate what may have triggered the attack, and try to make educated guesses about the situation. For example, a person's genetics and major stress could be the cause of the attack. In some families, you could probably see a direct line of family members with a history of panic attacks so severe that they cannot function. Furthermore, panic attacks are not necessarily learned. Yes, we can learn more about what causes anxiety in ourselves, but the physical symptoms of panic attacks are more than simply learning to be fearful or anxious. At this time, scientists or clinicians know that there is a genetic correlation to panic attacks, but they have not identified the exact gene that causes them.

In one Mayo Clinic article about panic attacks and panic disorder, they state that clinicians may not know the exact cause of panic attacks, but they can predict the type of person that might experience a panic attack. People who are sensitive to stress can be prone to having panic attacks, along with those prone to negative emotions. Although the specific gene has not been identified, scientists have observed that certain changes in brain function may also make a person prone to anxiety attacks.

In the same article, it is pointed out that, as humans, we respond to impending danger with a **fight or flight response**. For example, when a rabid dog comes your way, you wouldn't stick around; you would run. During this reaction, you would experience an elevated heart rate and breathing that speeds up as you react to that life-threatening experience. However, with a panic attack, there isn't always impending, logical danger, despite the severe physical reactions that occur during the instance. In particular, a panic attack can be caused by something other people may hardly notice; for example, a noise or a strange smell could trigger an attack.

A person having a panic attack might not receive any warning that a panic attack is going to happen. You would know that when a rabid dog comes your way, you will have a naturally occurring fight or flight reaction, but what about if you are driving in your car and suddenly have a panic attack? There is nothing in the car that should make you nervous, and you are driving a route that you are very familiar with. Panic attacks can occur at any time and will continue to occur unless the individual can break the ongoing cycle.

Symptoms of a Panic Attack

You might not know when a panic attack will happen, but there are symptoms especially attributed to panic attacks. According to Mayo Clinic, the following is a list of symptoms that typically happen during a panic attack:

- A sense of impending doom or danger
- Chills

- Hot Flashes
- Nausea
- Abdominal cramping
- A sense of impending doom
- Sweating
- Fear of loss of control or death
- Rapid pounding heart rate
- Chest pain
- A feeling of unreality or detachment
- Numbness or tingling sensation
- Dizziness, lightheadedness, or faintness

If these symptoms weren't bad enough, there is also the fear of having another panic attack, as was mentioned in an earlier section. Consequently, you would begin to avoid situations that might cause a panic attack. You may not know exactly when or where you will have your next panic attack, so you begin to anticipate normal situations that *could* trigger you into having an attack.

You would also probably have to deal with unexpected triggers. You might react in panic to flashing lights or loud noises; however, although you learn to fear these situations, not all flashing lights or loud noises will make you have a panic attack.

As stated earlier, panic attacks are severe and unpleasant, generally causing the individual to try to avoid any situation that could cause them to have an attack. More and more the people who suffer from panic attacks withdraw from public life because they are scared of having an attack in public.

Psychological Symptoms and Reactions

We mentioned that panic attacks also have psychological symptoms, and the fear of death is very prominent in people suffering from attacks. Another psychological symptom of a panic attack is the fear of losing control, which can manifest to feelings of going crazy or losing one's mind. When a panic attack happens, you would feel like you have no control over the situation. Not knowing when a panic attack will happen or experiencing intense physical symptoms can make a person feel unsure about their sanity.

In the most severe cases, a person can experience a detachment of self and surroundings, which can cause a person to believe they are observing their life from outside their bodies (Mayo Clinic Staff, n.d.).

Panic Attacks and Other Disorders

There is not necessarily a specific medical test for panic attacks; however, doctors may test you to see if there are any medical reasons for your panic attacks or if you may have panic disorder. For example, if your heartbeat increases or you have chest pain, it could be related to panic attacks or something else, such as heart disease. When a doctor rules out a physical reason, they may send you to be evaluated by a psychologist or therapist. There, you would discuss the circumstances of your panic attacks.

Panic attacks may be part of another disorder that you are being treated for; specifically, you may have a social phobia or depression that may be causing you to experience attacks without warnings. Having depression or social phobia can make you more prone to having panic attacks, though remember that panic attacks can come about on their own without any pre-existing conditions.

If you have experienced a panic attack, there is no doubt that you need to ask for help, as panic attacks can carry severe symptoms with them, such as shortness of breath or chest pains. First, you must rule out a physical reason for these symptoms and, if you don't appear to have a physical reason for these symptoms, then you can explore whether they are caused by panic attacks.

Anticipatory Anxiety

Another way to tell that you are suffering from panic attacks is to evaluate your behavior between the attacks; during these times, you may be experiencing anticipatory anxiety or phobic avoidance, which will be important to notice.

According to Smith et al. (2019), anticipatory anxiety happens in between attacks. Instead of feeling calm and relaxed, you would have a sense of doom and feel tension and anxiety. Characteristics of anticipatory anxiety include the fear of having another panic attack. In this case, you would be constantly worried about having another panic attack, and such thoughts would manifest in the back of your mind.

Phobic avoidance happens when you avoid situations and places that could trigger your panic. This type of avoidance has two distinct characteristics: the first, as mentioned, being the avoidance of places where you think you would have another panic attack. For example, if you have panic attacks at your doctor's office before going through a procedure, you may begin to avoid visits in which procedures would be done. The second characteristic of phobic avoidance is when you avoid places where there is no easy escape; an example of this could be a family party or visiting your in-laws. In these situations, you feel trapped and like there is no escaping the social event. Plus, you would feel that if you had a panic attack, there would be no one there who could offer help.

You might be an anxious person who has a lot of anxiety, but remember that this fact does not necessarily mean you suffer from panic attacks; you might be only having anxiety attacks. When you have a panic attack, you are experiencing overwhelming fear about something, and your symptoms are generally scary and overwhelming.

The Traits of a Panic Attack

Remember that another trait of a panic attack is that they come about suddenly and without any obvious reason. With anxiety, you know the places that make you anxious, but with a panic attack, you would be feeling fine one minute, then experiencing overwhelming symptoms—which could include rapid heartbeat and nausea, for instance—the next.

The Diagnostic and Statistical Manual of Mental Disorders Fifth Edition (DSM-5) states that panic attacks are either unexpected or expected. Specifically, unexpected panic attacks happen without a foreseeable reason, whereas expected panic attacks happen because of triggers or known stressors in your environment, according to Vandergriendt (2019).

An example of having a panic attack and anxiety at the same time is like this: you worry about going to the doctor; you are restless and have a fear of losing control of yourself at the doctor's office. Then, when you arrive at the doctor's office, you feel chest pain, shortness of breath, sweating, chills, or hot flashes, and your heart rate is accelerated. This is a panic attack.

If you remain worried and apprehensive about the situation and those feelings increase when you go to the office, this is an *anxiety* attack. You feel terrible about being at the doctor's, but you can still pull through your visit on your own with relative coherence. It may be uncomfortable (and possibly more so than it would be for most people), but you should be able to stay for the visit and will feel better when it's over.

If you have a panic attack during the visit, you will likely be unable to go through with the visit at all, as your panic attack will require you to have assistance. You will feel the automatic fight or flight response, and you may even run out of the office and not stop running until you are a ways away from the office.

Panic Attack Triggers

Panic attacks are unexpected, but there may be triggers that cause panic attacks. These triggers might not be known to you, which is why the panic attack may seem like it is coming out of nowhere, according to Vandergriendt (2019).

Triggers for your panic attacks can be (but are not limited to) the following:

- A stressful job.
- Driving.
- Social situations.
- Phobias (such as agoraphobia or claustrophobia).
- Memories or reminders of a traumatic experience.
- Some physical situations/events that can cause panic attacks.

- Thyroid problems.
- Withdrawal from drugs or alcohol.
- Reaction to medication and supplements.
- Chronic illnesses such as asthma, irritable bowel syndrome, heart disease, and diabetes.

When you start receiving treatment, you may be able to see patterns in your behavior and begin to recognize your personal triggers.

Risk Factors

There are also risk factors for having a panic attack, as stated by Vandergriendt (2019).

Examples of these risk factors may include the following:

- Having an anxious personality.
- Drugs and alcohol use.
- Genetics—having a close family member with anxiety and/or panic disorder.
- Living with a life-threatening illness or a chronic health condition.
- Experiencing a stressful life event, such as death or divorce.
- Experiencing traumatic events when you were a child or as an adult.
- Ongoing stress and worries, like financial problems or family conflicts.

Learning to Deal with Your Panic Attacks

The good news about panic attacks is that you can receive treatment that will help you understand why you are having panic attacks and when you understand, you can begin to learn how to deal with them and eventually get them to stop happening. Furthermore, you can learn different techniques to battle those panic attacks. The purpose of this book is to help you understand your panic attacks better while learning specific techniques to help you combat them.

When working with a health professional, you can begin to identify triggers and even plan for what you are going to do when you have a panic attack. You can also share this book with your health professional, while your therapist can help you pick which techniques are best for you.

According to Vandergriendt (2019), before working with a mental health professional, your primary care physician (PCP) will want to give you a physical exam, blood test, or electrocardiogram (ECG or EKG). In fact, your PCP may have a questionnaire that will help them distinguish whether you are experiencing a physical or mental reaction during your panic attacks. When you are referred to a mental health practitioner, both you and the therapist will examine what you experience before a panic attack happens. This will help you to identify triggers that could cause you to have a panic attack. Also, your therapist will give you tools to cope with your panic attacks; for example, taking slow breaths or strategies to focus your attention elsewhere.

The Lasting Effects of a Panic Attack

Although very intense, a panic attack usually only lasts about ten minutes; however, the aftereffects of the panic attack can make a serious imprint on an individual's life and their psyche. Ongoing panic attacks can make a person feel like they are losing grip on reality. Intense panic attacks can cause an immense terror that may impact one's self-confidence, and this type of suffering often causes anticipatory anxiety or phobic avoidance.

The good news about panic attacks is that they can be treated with therapy and medication. There are also various techniques that you can use to help you make it through your panic attacks and, ultimately, help alleviate the intensity of your attacks.

Chapter Summary

There are many things to learn about panic attacks—they may occur due to trauma or another mental condition, such as bipolar disorder, social phobia, or depression.

- Mental health practitioners do not know what causes panic attacks.
- There are physical symptoms of panic attacks, such as shortness of breath and chest pain.
- There are psychological symptoms of panic attacks, such as fear of dying or losing control.

In the next chapter, you will learn about various myths and misconceptions about panic attacks.

CHAPTER THREE:

Myths and Misconceptions About Panic Attacks

Now that you are starting to better understand and notice the signs of your panic attacks, it is time to learn about the myths and misconceptions about them. Panic attacks are intense, and you might feel that you will die while having one. Your feelings may move beyond those of humiliation and fearing that you will lose control of your mental facilities. In this chapter, we will learn to recognize some of the things you might have been wondering about in terms of panic attacks and clear up any misconceptions you have.

With any condition, there are many myths and misconceptions that can make things worse; nevertheless, the more you know about panic attacks, the better you will feel. The following sections will detail these myths and misconceptions that people have about panic attacks and panic disorder.

Myth #1: Panic attacks are only a symptom of panic disorder.

Just because you have a panic attack, does not mean that you have panic disorder. A panic attack can still happen as a result of other types of disorders. Here is a list of disorders that can bring about a panic attack:

- Bipolar disorder
- Social anxiety disorder (SAD)
- Obsessive compulsive disorder (OCD)
- Generalized anxiety disorder (GAD)
- Specific phobias
- Irritable bowel syndrome (IBS)
- Various Digestive disorders
- Sleep disorders

Myth #2: Panic attacks are an overreaction to stress and anxiety.

Although feeling anxious due to stress and anxiety can be pretty intense, it isn't the same as having a panic attack. There are two important points to remember about panic attacks:

1. **A panic attack usually occurs without any warnings**. Before participating in therapy, some people who suffer from panic attacks usually have no idea why they had the attack. Unlike with an anxiety attack, when the person is stressed, they are not responding to immediate stress or anxiety; the panic attack just mysteriously happens. With therapy, a person can learn to identify triggers or environments that bring a panic attack to fruition, but it is seldom due to conditions they can control.

2. **People that have panic attacks do not have any control over what is happening**. A panic attack is very severe, and it is nothing like dealing with anxiety. A panic attack is more than having butterflies in your stomach; they are generally so intense that many people who suffer from them land in the emergency room.

Myth #3: Panic attacks can only occur when a person is awake.

Not all panic attacks happen when a person is awake. In fact, there is a name for panic attacks that happen especially at night: **nocturnal panic attacks**. Imagine sleeping, but right in the middle, you are jolted awake by the symptoms of a panic attack—shortness of breath or feeling that your heart is going to burst out of your chest all present during this nocturnal panic attack. Nocturnal attacks do not happen as often as daytime panic attacks, but they do occur.

When a person experiences a nocturnal panic attack, their sleep is disturbed and they often cannot go back to sleep. Nocturnal panic attacks bring with them feelings of fear and disconnection from yourself and your environment, and a nocturnal panic attack will often feel like they are part of a nightmare.

Myth #4: You can die from a panic attack.

The experience of a panic attack can be very intense, with some people experiencing major discomfort such as chest pains, accelerated heart rate, excessive sweating, chest pain, and shortness of breath during episodes. These symptoms often feel like a major physical event, such as a heart attack or something else just as serious happening to our lungs. Many experience symptoms fierce enough for them to have to head straight to the emergency room for treatment. In short, panic attack victims often feel like they are dying, and this fear is often the most prominent feeling during an attack.

However, no matter how intense the symptoms are, you will not die from a panic attack. The procedure in an emergency room is to stabilize and calm you down when you come in for treatment. Some tests may be run to make sure that there is not a physical reason for your panic attack, but once the test comes back and indicates that you are physically healthy, the emergency room doctor will probably talk to you more so they can figure out if there were any other emergency problems that could have caused your panic attack.

There is often no apparent reason that you had a panic attack, and the absence of a reason should be a clue to your doctor. Not having a precondition to panic attacks is one of the major symptoms of an attack, and rest assured that a medical professional will know this.

Overall, there is no reason to fear that you will die from a panic attack.

Myth #5: Panic attacks can make you go insane.

Not having a warning that you are going to have a panic attack might make you feel out of control. Panic attacks usually last for ten minutes, with a peak before subsiding, and especially not knowing outright why you had that panic attack can make you believe you are losing control of yourself and in danger of going insane.

Yes, there might be underlying mental health reasons for having a panic attack, such as having suffered trauma and having problems dealing with that trauma; however, having panic attacks is not an indicator that you will lose control of your mental health.

The fear of completely losing control can become obsessive—you might feel that if you concentrate, you may be able to head off the panic attack. This is you trying to gain some control over what seems to be impossible to control, which is a major frustration that can go even further by making you feel helpless.

In this book, you will be presented with strategies you can use to cope with panic attacks. Panic attacks can make anyone feel humiliated, but there is hope that you will be able to become better at dealing with a panic attack when it happens—or better yet, even before it happens.

Overall, when panic strikes, rest assured that your sanity is intact and that, even if you lose control over yourself, it will only be for a brief period of time.

Myth #6: Panic attacks can be avoided.

When you start working on alleviating your panic attacks, you might discover what is triggering your attacks. This is a process of uncovering your feelings about the trauma you have experienced; however, there are many reasons you might be having panic attacks besides trauma. You could fear something with so much intensity that panic attacks happen every time you come near.

Yes, finding out what triggers your panic attacks goes a long way in alleviating and regaining control over them, but the truth is, even though you know your triggers and fears, panic attacks might still occur.

It is not healthy to think that if you avoid the things that cause you fear, you will avoid panic attacks. Avoiding your fears or staying away from what triggers you can become an impossible task. However, avoiding these things might just make your fears or triggers become even more intense.

The best way to experience a panic attack is to face them head-on and maintain a relaxed state. This book will go more in-depth about the strategies and things you can do to lessen the intensity of your panic attacks, which will also be much healthier ways of dealing with them, in contrast to trying to live a life where you restrict yourself and avoid potentially triggering situations.

Myth #7: There's little you can do about panic attacks.

After having more than one panic attack at a time, you might feel that there is no way out when it comes to having these attacks; however, you can work with a mental health professional to learn how to deal with these attacks and ultimately work to cease them altogether.

For you to begin the process of dealing therapeutically with your panic attacks, it is important that you find a mental health professional who can evaluate you and make a proper diagnosis. With that done, you can start treatment and, once you have your diagnosis, your doctor will likely be able to schedule you for psychotherapy, where you can discuss your panic attacks. Your doctor may also be able to prescribe medications that will help you better deal with your panic attacks and make it easier for you to participate in psychotherapy. Various medications will all target different areas in your brain and serve different purposes, so it is important to work closely with your doctor and decide which ones work best for you, whether that be antidepressants or medication that helps with anxiety.

Remember that no matter what treatment a doctor may prescribe, it is always important to make contact with a mental health professional first before taking medication.

Myth #8: You will be stuck with having panic attacks your whole life.

Although your panic attacks may feel epic, there are things you can do to lessen the intensity of the attack and ultimately stop having them altogether.

Medications and therapies like **cognitive behavioral therapy** (CBT) can go a long way in helping you conquer your panic attacks. In a later section, we will talk more about CBT and its effectiveness.

As it was stated in the previous section, a mental health professional is the first step to conquering your panic attacks; however, in the end, it will always be your motivation to work at therapy that will help you cease them in the end.

CBT therapy can be very successful, but you must put forth the effort to yield those successful results. Coming to terms with having panic attacks might be difficult at first, but the beginning step is to ask for help. When you receive the help you need, you will begin the process of alleviating the intensity of your panic attacks. You can use this book in conjunction with your therapy and the medication prescribed by your mental health professional.

Myth #9: Panic is a gateway to a more serious mental disorder.

Before you go see a mental health professional, you might believe that he or she is going to tell you that you are suffering from another type of disorder, such as bipolar disorder, schizophrenia, or even general anxiety.

The truth is that having panic attacks is a disorder in its own right; it is not any of the disorders mentioned above or any other kind of disorder that you have in mind. It is not a serious mental illness, but simply a condition where you experience panic or fear severely.

Panic attacks can be treated, and you will be able to cut down on the intensity of your panic attacks with a lot of dedicated work in therapy, while also being diligent about taking your medication.

Myth #10: Loved ones cannot help you with your panic attacks.

Panic attacks are very personal, and you might feel so humiliated by them that you don't want to tell anyone about your episodes; however, this does not have to be the case. As you work with your therapist, you might want to include other people in your close circle with the information you are learning in therapy.

It isn't necessary to tell the world, but the more you explain to others, the better you will feel. Perhaps someone you are close to can add some insight into why you are having panic attacks in the first place.

The people who care about you are worried, so perhaps you might consider giving them information that can help them feel involved in assisting you through your therapeutic journey. Yet, if you are a private person, and telling others might disrupt the progress of your therapy, that is all right too. You are always in control of the information you want to reveal to others.

Now that we have busted some of the myths and your preconceived notions about panic attacks, you are ready to start learning some effective strategies to combat panic attacks. Furthermore, this book will be providing powerful techniques and tools that you can use to help deal with your panic attacks.

Chapter Summary

There are many misconceptions about panic attacks, and in this chapter, we discussed ten. Here are three of the main myths that we covered:

- Panic attacks are not the only symptom of panic disorder.
- You can die from a panic attack.
- There's little you can do to lessen the intensity of a panic attack.

These myths and misconceptions might appear scary and intimidating, and can also make panic attacks appear overwhelming, incurable, and uncontrollable. The truth is that panic attacks *are* treatable. You can learn techniques that will help you to deal with your panic attack, including attending therapy and asking your doctor about available medication that can help alleviate your symptoms.

In the next chapter, you will learn how the five steps of AWARE that can help calm you down during an intense panic attack.

CHAPTER FOUR:

How to Feel Calm During an Intense Panic Attack

The possibility of being unable to control a panic attack may seem upsetting to anyone suffering. True, you can study patterns and triggers that happen before a panic attack, but these attacks will still happen no matter how much information you learn unless you know how to combat them.

Don't feel bad because there is something you can do during your panic attacks that will make the situation better. You can learn to be calm and accepting of your panic attacks.

In this chapter, we will discuss the five steps of AWARE:

1. Acknowledge and Accept
2. Wait and Watch (Work)
3. Actions (that make you more comfortable)
4. Repeat
5. End

According to Barends Psychology Practice (n.d.), the first of the five steps of AWARE is to acknowledge and accept what is happening during the panic attack. It is even possible to stop the panic attack with AWARE, but no matter what, the first thing that you still must do is acknowledge and accept your anxiety.

Right before you have a panic attack, you might be experiencing fear; then, the panic attack starts and you are practically bathed in fear. This is okay. It is important to acknowledge the fear and to remind yourself that you are not in any specific danger. The feeling of being in danger is a symptom of a panic attack, but remember that this is just a thought—it is neither true nor relevant. Go with that fear and don't pretend that it is not happening; once you go with the fear, you are ready for the first part of AWARE: Accept.

Accepting Your Panic Attack

When you accept the symptoms of your panic disorder, you are on your way to lessening the intensity of your panic attacks. Remember that you are not in any physical danger, but merely experiencing a fear that can be put back into your control.

Another component to AWARE is that when you are experiencing a panic attack, you are experiencing the worst that is going to happen; nothing else coming your way will be worse than your current situation. Take a moment to ride the panic attack to its ending (Carbonell, 2020).

Resisting the panic attack will only make it worse. If you just acknowledge and accept that a panic attack is happening to you, on the other hand, you will cut down on the intensity of the attack.

Waiting

The next step of AWARE is wait. When you have a panic attack, you probably experience the need to flee or struggle. However, rash action will only make things worse. So often when you have a panic attack, you are reduced to a state in which you cannot think straight and are more prone to do something rash. Moreover, you will make decisions that can just make your circumstance worse.

This is the time to *wait*, as it will lessen your attack's intensity the longer you do so. If you run away from the task or do something to escape the panic attack, you will deprive your subconscious of recognizing that your panic attack has a beginning and an end.

If you take a moment to wait and watch, you will find some relief, and the feelings that you are having at that time will start to die down. In fact, you might even be able to think clearer.

Watch

The next thing you want to do is watch. This is when you take a moment to see how your panic attack is working. It is important to take note of and observe the happenings before your panic attack, as well as during, at this time. By observing these actions, you gain the opportunity to work on a panic diary for taking notes about important details of your panic attacks.

Imagine that, during a panic attack, you wait and watch by writing into your panic diary. This can be a small notebook or an attractive journal that you carry with you at all times. By writing in your panic diary, you gain the chance to calm down and be distracted from the intensity of the panic attack.

When you fill out a panic diary, you are moving from being a victim to an observer. If it is not possible to write in a diary, find another way to become an observer; you can use a smartphone app that will let you record voice memos, or a tablet or other device that you can use to create a panic diary.

Work

You can also add "work" to this step. When you are having an anxiety attack, you may be unable to wait and watch immediately; this is where "work" comes in. For example, you might be driving your car or giving a presentation. Don't freak out and run from this event, but instead, remain engaged in what you are doing and move calmly toward watching and waiting while you are having your panic attack.

I know that this may sound difficult, but let's walk through a scenario. Let's say you are driving your car and you begin to have the symptoms of a panic attack. Your heart feels like it is going to burst through your chest; your breathing starts to come rapidly, and you begin to feel nauseous. When this happens, you are unable to pull to the side of the road because there is no safe place for you to park and wait. You could keep driving, but while in the act, "watch" the panic attack and wait for it to end. Observe how you are feeling, follow the intensity, and know that the panic attack will end, as it will not go on for an infinite amount of time. Remember—you are an observer, not a victim.

Finding Calm During a Panic Attack

What can you do during your panic attack? We've already established that you shouldn't do anything rash; it is important for you to watch and wait.

It is easy to panic and think that your panic attack will never end, but what is it that you already know about panic attacks? Do they indeed last forever? If they did, you would not be reading this book. It is a certainty of life that panic attacks do end.

So, what do you do when a panic attack happens? Well, your job is to make yourself more comfortable with the attack. Carbonell (2020) suggests some techniques that have been helpful to people suffering from panic attacks:

- Belly breathing or diaphragmatic breathing.
- Talking yourself through the attack.
- Getting involved with your present.
- Working with your body.

These techniques are not so hard to do. Belly breathing is as easy as taking a deep breath to fill your belly, then letting the breath back out slowly.

Talking to yourself silently or aloud can reinforce the idea that your panic attack is not going to last forever. You can tell yourself that it is okay to be afraid or that this incident will help you observe your panic attacks' characteristics, so you can learn to be more of an observer than a victim.

Getting involved with your present is important. If you are in the middle of an activity, start concentrating on the present and tasks that you have to accomplish. For example, if you are about to start a presentation, or you are in the middle of the presentation, get involved in your notes or on the slides you are projecting. It's almost like making your world stop spinning so you can carry on with what you are doing—even though you are experiencing a panic attack.

Working towards being aware of your body, can relax the tense areas of your body. Concentrate on the parts of your body that are tense and work to relieve that tension. Loosen up that rigidity in your body and release any tense muscles. Also, don't hold your breath during a panic attack; concentrate on your belly breathing instead.

Overall, you must attend to and take care of yourself, so you feel more comfortable during a panic attack, thus alleviating your symptoms. It can be done. Don't be a victim, but get actively involved in making yourself more comfortable with your situation.

If you need a visual, think of a time you saw a nurse make a patient in her care more comfortable when that patient was sick and worried. To help more with your situation in the long run, work on helping the caregiver inside of you.

Repeat

Sometimes panic attacks have several cycles. You might have just gone through the five steps of AWARE, then another cycle begins again. Don't despair and believe that you have failed—it is just the nature of a panic attack to come in waves. Having a panic attack might feel like waves crashing into you, and if you flail around in the water, you will lose control and expose yourself to the danger of drowning. However, if you keep your wits about you, you can survive the attack waves of a panic attack.

When you find yourself entering a new cycle of an intense panic attack, keep your wits about you and start the AWARE cycle. It might be hard for you to do, but if you acknowledge and accept that you are having a longer panic attack, you will be able to wait and watch (and possibly continue on with your work). Then, you can get into *action* and make yourself more comfortable until the panic attack eventually ends.

End

The final step of awareness is to end the panic attack.

Don't be frightened if you have to start all over two or more times. Remember that you are keeping a panic diary, so you are an observer and not a victim.

Even though you might have several cycles in your panic attack, they do end eventually. Rest assured that your whole life won't become one constant, chronic panic attack. Invest in the five steps of AWARE so the panic attacks become less intense.

It is not your job to make the attack end—your job is to make the five steps of AWARE happen. Let's review the steps of AWARE:

1. Acknowledge and Accept
2. Wait and Watch (and/or Work)
3. Actions (that make you comfortable)
4. Repeat
5. End

When your panic attack ends, you might feel shaken up and uncertain of yourself. As has been reiterated multiple times, panic attacks are very intense, and even if you did the five steps of AWARE, you still lived through yet another episode of panic. At this time, you have some choices in your thinking: you could feel a sense of doom that you can't predict when a panic attack happens. You might even believe that, no matter what you do, you will have to live through a panic attack yet again until whatever you are doing for therapy (be it medications, counseling, CBT) takes effect.

This is your chance to step up and have a positive attitude, like expecting the best. Review your panic diary information, and you will see that, little by little, your reactions to your panic attacks will be improving. Praise yourself for becoming an observer rather than a victim.

Being AWARE

It may never have occurred to you that you could be more aware during a panic attack. People who experience panic attacks often feel a sense of doom in their existence. In fact, sometimes the panic attacks seem like they will only feel worse as time goes on.

Learning and doing the five steps of AWARE can be the answer that will lift you up. Banish that feeling of doom by studying these steps closely and enacting them when a panic attack hits you.

Make sure to work on filling out a panic diary, whether it is in a notebook or on a smart device, as you will be writing down some very important data. This data can be shown to your mental health provider, and both of you can study what is going on when you have your attacks. It can be very helpful to your provider to know what you are experiencing.

There are still even more techniques in this book that can help you. Keep the faith and know that help is on the way.

Chapter Summary

Using the five steps of AWARE will help you remain calm during a panic attack, and staying calm during a panic attack can help lessen the intense symptoms you would experience in a panic attack. The five steps of AWARE are the following:

1. Acknowledge and Accept
2. Wait and Watch (or Work)
3. Actions (That make you more comfortable)
4. Repeat
5. End

These five steps will help you alleviate your panic attacks. Being aware and accepting your panic attacks might be the most difficult thing to do, but it can go a long way in helping you deal with your panic attacks. Often, there is more than one cycle of panic attacks, so it is best to repeat the five steps until your panic attack ends.

In the next chapter, you will learn how to stop your panic attacks.

CHAPTER FIVE:

How to Stop Panic Attacks

Once you have learned the five steps of AWARE and have mastered them, you can look at trying some new techniques that can help stop your panic attacks completely. It is very important to accept and recognize your panic attacks; however, learning to focus on something other than your panic attack can also be beneficial.

In this chapter, you will learn twelve different techniques that you can use to stop your panic attacks. At first, doing some of these things while experiencing a panic attack may be difficult, but with a little practice, implementing them is achievable. You might want to try practicing these techniques and getting good at using them, so when you do have a panic attack, it will be easier to take action.

Teach Yourself to Focus

Although you might feel that it is impossible to do anything but feel terror during a panic attack, it is still possible to do something to quell the attack, despite these feelings. The best thing to do is to teach yourself to focus and act specifically to break your concentration away from the attack.

In the last chapter, we discussed how important it is to accept and recognize that you are having a panic attack. Being able to stop, accept, and recognize that the panic attack can go a long way to actually cutting down the duration of your attack.

It is very important that you don't fight the panic attack or get over-excited. If you are calm and accept that you are having an attack, there is a chance that the symptoms of the panic attack will be less intense than they could be.

Panic Attacks Don't Last Forever

This was mentioned earlier, but to reiterate—if you give recognition to the fact that this panic attack is not going to last forever and that the panic attack will stop at some point in time, you *can* defeat that overwhelming fear that your panic attack will never end. Though panic attacks can be quite overwhelming at times, remember that you are experiencing just a short period of concentrated anxiety.

Physical Symptoms

There may be times that your symptoms feel more physical than mental. Perhaps you just had your first panic attack and you are not sure of its cause. It is good to get a checkup and visit with your doctor to see if there are any physical reasons you might be having intense symptoms like tightening of the chest or excessive sweating and heart palpitations.

Asking for Help

It may also be helpful to talk to your doctor about finding a good psychiatrist or therapist, as they may be able to refer you to other mental health professionals whom they would have a working relationship with. In this way, you will have a team that can work out a unique and effective care plan for you.

Controlling Your Breath

It is possible that your panic attack will take your breath away in its intensity. You may start to breathe rapidly and feel like you can't catch your breath. On occasion, this type of breathing can also make your chest feel tight. When this happens, you can do something that will help you make these symptoms less intense.

Deep breathing and counting slowly to four while you are breathing in and out can be a great help. Continuing to breathe rapidly instead may increase your anxiety and cause extreme tension in your body, eventually resulting in other physical symptoms, like a tight chest or a heavyweight feeling on your chest. Therefore, it is important to concentrate on controlling your breathing.

Breathe deeply, like you are filling up a balloon, and count slowly as you expand your lungs. Breathing in this manner can help you concentrate on something else besides your panic attack. This concentration can then help you get through the panic attack.

Deep breathing is something to focus on, so you can believe internally that you can survive the attack. Moreover, deep breathing can help you feel more in control of the situation and add to your comfort level during a panic attack. Specifically, it is very effective to have something else to focus on during a panic attack.

Medications for Your Panic Attack

We will discuss various other techniques to help you during an attack, but something to consider is taking medications to help quell your attacks. If you're being treated by a psychiatrist or your primary caregiver, you may be prescribed medication to help you get through the intensity of a panic attack. This medication may be prescribed to take regularly in the morning, night, or during the day. Moreover, you may be given medicines to take pro re nata (PRN). A medication that is considered PRN means you would take that medication when you need it.

If you have been prescribed a PRN medication, it is important to have it close by, so when you have a panic attack, you are able to take it. A PRN medication may be able to cut the duration and intensity of the panic attack significantly if you take it properly.

Some PRN medications you may be prescribed include beta-blockers or a benzodiazepine. Propranolol is a popular beta-blocker that is prescribed to help lower a racing heartbeat and decrease blood pressure.

Benzodiazepines like Valium, Xanax, or Klonopin can help calm you down, but you need to be cautious when taking this kind of medication because it is highly addictive. Your body can also gain a tolerance the more of this medication you take. However, benzodiazepines are still very effective in treating anxiety and panic attacks. Remember to use caution when taking this medication, and only take it when it is prescribed by your doctor.

Medications can be great for helping you control your panic attacks, but being careful to choose surroundings that will not trigger your panic attacks is just as important. A more comprehensive list of medications that treat anxiety can be found in Chapter 7.

Bombarding Your Senses

In an ever-changing, fast-paced world, there are a lot of things that can bombard and overload our senses. Loud music is something that everyone has to deal with time and again when going out for a night on the town, or even during a dining experience at a restaurant. Furthermore, there are instances when lights will bombard you. Many popular bars and grills have installed extremely large television screens for their patrons. These television screens may show everything from football games, to popular television shows or special events. Some restaurants have more than one screen on the wall.

When you are bombarded by a lot of stimuli, your brain may react negatively, and it is not unusual for these stimuli to overwhelm your senses and cause a panic attack. Pay attention to warning signs that are posted to warn patrons about flashing lights. Some movies even come with a warning posted at the box office that tells the patron there will be a lot of overwhelming stimuli (flashing lights) during the movie.

If you have panic attacks due to overwhelming stimuli, it is important that you learn to stay away from bright light and sounds. If you can't prevent your exposure and find that bright lights are triggering your panic attack, try to remove yourself from the central area of the noise. If this isn't an option, find a spot in the room where your exposure is limited and do your best to focus on your breathing or any other action that you think can help you get through and/or alleviate the symptoms of your panic attack.

Panic Attacks and Triggers

A "trigger" is something that causes or influences an event or situation to occur—in this case, a panic attack. It is not known for sure what specific events would bring about a panic attack, as we do not conclusively know what causes a panic attack. However, patients have reported that they have panic attacks after being exposed to specific things, such as bright lights, loud noises, enclosed spaces, and crowds. How do you become aware of the triggers that may be causing your panic attacks? One thing you could always do is keep a journal or a diary about the events that trigger your panic attacks.

By keeping a diary about your panic attacks, you might find patterns or indications that certain situations are causing your panic attacks. Until you can work through these situations with your therapist, it is wise to be aware of the things that trigger you. However, do not go to the extreme of staying at home or not participating in an event because you may be exposed to one of your triggers. In therapy, you can work toward desensitizing yourself to the situations that come before you have a panic attack. It is important that you learn about your triggers and actively work toward dealing with them healthily.

Exercising to Release Endorphins

Another healthy way to deal with an anxiety attack is light exercise. Even though there is no way to prepare for a panic attack, exercising is something that will make you feel better.

Exercise is more than just toning your body and burning calories; it helps release endorphins that can improve your mood and relax your body. When you do something as simple as walking, you release these endorphins into your system.

Furthermore, walking can help you deal with a stressful environment. A short walk during a stressful time can help you with regulating your breathing and releasing any nervous tension that has built up when you are stressed.

Walking during a panic attack can help you focus on something other than what is causing the panic. It can also help with alleviating your fight or flight instincts. To summarize, there are many benefits of light exercise when you are having to cope with panic attacks.

Getting exercise is very important for your physical wellbeing, but being mindful can also contribute to reducing the effects of an intensive panic attack. When having a panic attack, it is important to stay focused, even though you are having intense physical reactions. Being mindful can help stop a panic attack.

Being Mindful

Mindfulness is the state of being aware or conscious of what is happening around you. Being mindful will help you deal with the present. Once you are more aware of the present, you can accept that you are having a panic attack, and noticing your bodily sensations, thoughts, and feelings will help you with your recovery.

Niemiec (2017) states that mindfulness is paying attention on purpose. Sometimes, when you have a panic attack, you might get the feeling that you are detached from reality. However, there are exercises you can do while having a panic attack that can bring you back to yourself. Some examples of these exercises include the following:

1. Listen for four distinct sounds and think of why they are all different from each other.
2. Pull your attention to five different things around you and pay attention to why each one is different from the other.
3. Choose three objects and describe to yourself how they are all different, such as in texture, use, and temperature.
4. Focus on one or two different smells around you. What are they and have you smelled them before?
5. Taste something: a candy that you carry in your pocket or purse for example.

Doing exercises such as these will pull your focus away from the panic attack and bring you into the present, which is exactly what you want.

Focusing on One Object

Being mindful is a good way to stay in the present and focus. However, it might be hard, at first, to be mindful without a little bit of practice. One thing you can do to become good at being mindful is to master the art of focusing on one object.

This simple task can really help you while you are having a panic attack. Pick one object near you and focus on it completely. Study that object and determine its qualities to help you focus. What color is the shape? What texture is it? Questions like this can help you tune in to that focus.

You can even carry something with you that you can focus on when you think a trigger or overload of stimuli will appear. A polished rock or crystal can be easy to put in your pocket and will count as a good thing to focus on when a panic attack happens. Doing this might take you out of the chaos that hits when you have an anxiety attack.

When you are having a panic attack, your muscles might tense up. Along with focusing on an object, you can also focus on letting go of the tension in your muscles. Progressive Muscle Relaxation (PMR) might be a good exercise to try while in the midst of a panic attack.

Muscle Relaxation

The key to this exercise is to slow down your breathing and give yourself permission to relax. When you are calm, your breathing will slow down and you can begin to concentrate on your muscle groups and tell yourself mentally to relax. This exercise, or PMR, is simply focusing on each set of muscles in your body and visualizing the muscles relaxing.

There are many different muscle groups that you can focus on—though there may be quite a few groups to remember, some good places to start include focusing on your arms, then your head, neck, shoulders, chest, then hips, and, lastly, your legs and your feet. One by one, tense these muscle groups and feel that tension for 5 seconds, then release your muscles and relax for ten seconds. Do this with your whole body. PMR has a two-fold purpose: first, it gives you something to focus on, and second, you can relax the muscles that have likely become very tense during your panic attack.

Find Your Happy Place

In everyone's experience, there is a place where we are happy and at our best. Perhaps it is a bench in a beautiful park or somewhere at the beach. Each person has their very own happy place.

If it is hard for you to focus on something in the room, close your eyes and bring your happy place into your vision. Take a moment to think about how you feel when you are in this location; think of as many details as you can think of and completely focus on this happy place.

When you think about a calm environment and a place that brings you true happiness, it becomes harder for your panic attack to continue.

Finding a Mantra

A mantra is a word, phrase, or sound that can help you focus (Crawford, 2018). For example, I like to think of the word "happy" when I am stressed. You may have a word or phrase that makes you happy, such as "there's no place like home."

By chanting this mantra, you are taking your mind off the panic attack and thinking and doing something positive for yourself. Another good phrase that you can use during a panic attack is "This too shall pass." This specific mantra not only takes your focus off your panic attack, but it also gives you confidence that what you are going through will end eventually, and that it cannot last forever.

When you find your mantra, try it and see how it helps you regulate your breathing and relax your muscles. This is a good step to stopping your panic attacks, as it not only helps you relax, but a good mantra can also soothe you and help take the anxiety away.

Finding Help During Your Panic Attacks

When you are experiencing a panic attack, it is good to have some help. Perhaps you have a spouse or a friend whom you can tell about these panic attacks. Pick an important person in your life to help you with a panic attack when it occurs.

This person might be like a coach who helps you get through a tough spot by reminding you to do the techniques that can help you when you are having a rough time. For example, you can tell this person to remind you to focus, or you can make this person familiar with muscle relaxation techniques, and they can help you go through that routine.

If you are having a panic attack in a public place, it is still possible to ask for help from the people around you. With your best effort, ask a person to take you to a secluded spot where you can concentrate more on how you can stop your panic attack. Whether in public or in private, it is good to have some help while going through a panic attack.

Panic attacks can be a major intrusion. They can be terrifying and make you feel like the world is crashing down around you. That is why it is important to learn how to stop your panic attacks. You can use one or several things listed in this chapter to help you stop your panic attack when it happens. In particular, it is important for you to believe that you have some input in a situation that initially feels out of control. Memorize these strategies for stopping your panic attacks, so when you do have an attack, you are ready to alleviate it quickly.

Chapter Summary

In this chapter, you learned how to stop panic attacks. Along with using the steps from AWARE, it is important to do things that will help you end the panic attack. The following list outlines the strategies outlined in this chapter that you can take to stop a panic attack:

- Deep breathing.
- Take your medication (if prescribed).
- Limit stimuli.
- Know your triggers.
- Perform light, rhythmic exercise.
- Do mindfulness exercises.
- Focus on something.
- Try muscle relaxation techniques.
- Picture your happy place.
- Repeat a mantra.
- Ask people you trust for help.

Doing these steps along with accepting and recognizing your panic attacks, you will be able to successfully stop your panic attacks from taking over your life.

In the next chapter, you will learn more about some powerful relaxation techniques.

CHAPTER SIX:

Powerful Relaxation Techniques

Going through this book, you are learning new techniques to help you when you are having a panic attack. Some of the techniques presented may get repeated, though it is not because there is a shortage of techniques to employ—it is just that some techniques are worth mentioning twice.

Techniques that help you through your panic attack can be as simple as counting or as complex as mindfulness. Learn as many techniques as possible and don't be afraid to add some techniques of your own.

Practicing these techniques is very important. In order to successfully use these strategies, work on doing them while you are not having a panic attack. Try one at a time and, once you master a technique, move on to the next one until you have a repertoire of techniques you can use when you have a panic attack.

Thoughtful Relaxation Can Make a Difference

When you are having a panic attack, your entire body is tensed up. The fear during a panic attack will put your body on the alert for some kind of danger. Adrenaline is released and your muscles tense. Trying to relax is, thus, *crucial* during a panic attack.

Although you can't anticipate when a panic attack is going to happen, you can prepare for one by learning different techniques. Relaxation during a panic attack is very important. You do more harm than good when you tense up and get very anxious. In fact, the higher the degree of tension in your body, the more intense a panic attack will be.

However, if you learn some relaxation techniques, you can curb the intensity and, hopefully, your reaction to the panic attack will be tamer than if you started out tense before the attack. These relaxation techniques work because they address your body's stress responses, such as an increased heart rate, rapid breathing, and tense muscles.

If you take the time to practice some relaxation techniques, you can be ready for when a panic attack begins.

Breathing Techniques

When you experience a panic attack, your breathing becomes an issue; either you are taking shallow breaths or breathing very fast. Consequently, learning to relax your breathing can go a long way in toning down the intense body reactions you are having during a panic attack.

To get your breathing under control when you are anxious, you might want to follow these steps:

- Ask someone to find you a quiet and comfortable place for you to sit while you are experiencing your panic attack.

- When you are seated at the quiet spot, put one hand on your stomach and the other on your chest, then breathe deeply. For example, you can inhale and imagine your abdomen filling up with air, like a balloon.
- Take a slow and regular breath, in through your nose. Watch and sense your hands as you breathe in. The hand on your chest should remain still while the hand on your stomach will move slightly.
- Breathe out through your mouth slowly.
- Repeat this process at least ten times, or until you begin to feel your anxiety quiet down.

Another breathing technique is to let our thumb and your middle finger pinch your nostrils shut. Lift your middle finger and breathe in, watching the hand on your stomach move. Hold your breath and let your middle finger close your nostril once again. Now it's the thumbs turn to lift up. Exhale the air you are holding through this open nostril. When you are finished with that, start the process again for as long as it takes for you to feel better. This type of breathing is popular in yoga meditation.

Using Thoughts About Your Happy Place

In the last chapter, we talked about finding your happy place during a panic attack and focusing on that place. This technique is successful because it helps to relax your brain and body. The place you are thinking of can be real or imaginary; it just has to be a place that makes you happy and relaxed. Don't make it so complicated that reproducing it in your mind causes anxiety within you.

When you are having a panic attack, it is important for you to slow your relative time as much as possible. When thinking about your happy place, reflect on the details that require you to focus. Remembering that pondering how a place smells, sounds, and feels is a simple way of getting yourself to refocus. You don't necessarily have to remember very specific details about your happy place, such as the exact number of stairs up from the beach to the patio or the color of the walls down to the shade. Just keep it simple.

When you've thought of the details of your happy place, concentrate on being there in your mind. Take slow breaths through your nose and mouth, and focus on your breathing and the details of your happy place. Continue to do this until the panic attack starts to go away.

Positive Thoughts and Their Power

While in the midst of a panic attack, you might be experiencing a lot of negative or anxious thoughts. Sometimes the great intensity of a panic attack makes the sufferer believe they are going to die. Your thoughts might spiral downward into imagining the worst possible outcomes. Therefore, it is important to interrupt these anxious thoughts and stop them from taking over and increasing the harm from your panic attack.

The first thing you can do is become aware that your thoughts are making you anxious. Then, you must interrupt those negative thoughts and place some more positive thinking into your head, so you can stop or interrupt the negative. Some techniques that you might want to try include the following:

- Think of a person you love and remember the details or qualities that make you love that person.
- Think of something you look forward to doing in the future, like going out to a movie or a great restaurant.

- Carry your favorite book with you, so you can take it out to read when you feel a panic attack beginning.
- Turn on the radio or use your smartphone to play music that makes you happy.
- If you were doing something important during the panic attack, try to go back to it and focus completely on what you were doing.

Use these techniques to interrupt the thinking that makes your panic attack worse. It is important for you to shift your attention away from your anxiety and into something positive that can pull you away from the panic attack's intensity.

Using Mindfulness to Live in the Present

As discussed in the last chapter, practicing mindfulness can be very rewarding. Practice being mindful before you have a panic attack, so it can become second nature to you. To practice mindfulness, you need to do the following things (Legg, 2018):

- Take yourself to a quiet and pleasant place to be. Sit down and close your eyes.
- Concentrate on your breathing and how your body feels.
- Shift your focus from your breathing and body, and begin to pay attention to what is around you. Pay attention to what you hear, feel, and smell. Ask yourself, "What is going on around me?"
- Continue to be mindful and switch back and forth from focusing on your body and focusing on what is going on around you until the anxiety begins to fade.

Mindfulness is the best way to bring yourself back to the present. It is also a very important tool to use when you are having a panic attack. Mindfulness is about achieving a calm state and extinguishing the rapid-fire negative thinking that goes on during a panic attack. When you are mindful, you are living in the present, and when you live in the present, there is no past or future to worry about—only the present would mean anything to you.

Releasing Tension

In the last chapter, we discussed how it is important to relax your muscles. Doing PMR is a great way to release tension; however, there is also another technique you can try while you are having a panic attack.

1. Find a comfortable place to be, then close your eyes and focus on your breathing. Inhale slowly through your nose, then exhale through your mouth.
2. Make a tight fist and squeeze your hand as hard as you can.
3. Hold the fist for a few seconds and think of the tension in your hand.
4. Open your hand slowly and notice the tension leaving your hand. Feel your hand getting lighter as you relax.
5. Try this technique on other parts of your body like your legs, shoulders, and feet.

If there is any place on your body that is injured, stay away from it during this muscle relaxation technique. The good thing about this technique is that you can choose how far you take it—if you are having trouble concentrating, try to do as much as you can. Repeat the same areas if you need to. The most important thing is that you are shifting your focus away from the panic attack and experiencing some relaxation.

A Simple Technique

One of the easiest things you can do when you are having a panic attack is count. When the panic attack starts, move yourself to a quiet and safe place. If you are doing something like driving or walking in a crowd, take yourself to the side of the road or somewhere safe to sit. Once you are in that safe place, close your eyes and begin counting to 10. It might be hard to focus on doing it during a panic attack, but be patient with yourself and keep trying to count. Once you have reached 10, try to get to 20 and so on, until your anxiety goes away.

If you can't close your eyes, you can still count. Just keep doing the task and count as much as you can, or count the same numbers over and over. Along with counting, don't forget to breathe.

Other Techniques to Consider

Take care of your stress levels

The techniques covered in this chapter can also be done when you are *not* experiencing a panic attack. There are often times when we feel really stressed. If you take care of that stress with one of these techniques, you may be able to lower your stress levels, and, perhaps, you might even be able to avoid a high enough stress level that would bring about a panic attack.

Avoid the triggers you know about

After a while, you may notice patterns form after having a few panic attacks. If you are in therapy, discuss these patterns. If you are not in therapy, rely on your panic diary for forming conclusions about what can be triggering your attacks.

There is a fine line between avoiding things that trigger you and withdrawing yourself from your usual routine. Be cautious of how you choose to remove yourself from situations that trigger your panic attacks. It can be as simple as choosing seats at a concert that are away from the bright lights and crowds. Sitting on the balcony when possible can take you away from your triggers without preventing you from staying away from the concert.

Make a plan

Pick a friend or a family member to help you when you have a panic attack. Have a plan that is especially for them when you are having a panic attack. For example, you can have them take you to a quiet and secure place. You can also teach this person a deep breathing technique that can help you lower the intensity of your panic attack, and discuss whether or not this person should consider taking you to the ER and under which circumstances. Overall, it is important to have a plan that you can share with a person whom you trust.

Social support

Everyone experiences stressful situations. Don't be afraid to explain to the people in your social circle that you are experiencing panic attacks—you would be surprised to learn how many people actually understand your situation. The more support you have around you, the better the chance that there will be someone around to help you when you are having an episode.

Being proactive

Even though panic attacks happen when you least expect it, you can be proactive and practice the techniques given in this chapter. It can be hard to get through a panic attack, but these techniques might make it easier.

If you think of a technique that has not been mentioned here, by all means, still try it. There are many strategies that have not been mentioned in this chapter that can help you feel better, such as acupressure or listening to nature sounds. Take this chapter as a sample of what is out there for you to try.

Every panic attack is unique, and you might have to try different techniques until you find one that really works. Review these techniques with your therapist and practice them when you can. Don't let a panic attack pull you away from friends and family who can help you; in fact, ask for help whenever possible.

Chapter Summary

In this chapter, you learned about powerful relaxation techniques that you can do during a panic attack. It is important to respond to your body's stress; you can lower your heart rate, stop your rapid breathing, and tense your muscles by doing the techniques described in this chapter.

- It is important for you to keep your breathing under control while having a panic attack.
- Visualize your happy place during a panic attack.
- Interrupt your anxious thought cycle.
- Practice mindfulness.

In the next chapter, you will learn about preventing your panic attacks.

CHAPTER SEVEN:

How to Prevent Panic Attacks

Despite the current research, we still are not sure why panic attacks happen. Is it a brain thing? Does it have to do with stress? Does it have to do with trauma? It is hard to know the answer to these questions because mental health professionals have yet to find the origin behind panic attacks. Just because we don't know the cause of panic attacks doesn't mean that we can't try techniques that will help lessen our chances of a panic attack. In this chapter, we will look at preventative techniques that you can do on your own.

Conquering Stress

The first thing that you must do to help prevent a panic attack is to take care of yourself. Whether it is getting a good night's sleep or eating a balanced diet, it is important that you do everything you can to remain healthy and strong.

Stress is believed to be a factor that can make a panic attack stronger. Even if you have a panic attack, if you are managing your stress well, you can weaken the panic attack's intensity because you are calm, to begin with.

To be able to withdraw stress as a factor, work on the stressors that you have in your life and break them down to smaller nuggets that can't overwhelm you. Get enough sleep and rest, so you can be strong enough to handle your stress.

Learn to practice meditation or do relaxation techniques. These techniques can go a long way in helping you when you are having a stressful day. Keeping a journal about your challenges can also help with stress. By writing about your stressors, you can work out a better plan for dealing with them.

Strategies to Relieve Stress

Regular exercise can also help you work off some of that stress. Even if it is only 15-20 minutes a day, any type of physical activity can help you release some of the stress that is manifesting itself.

As mentioned in the previous section, another thing you can do to deal with stress is to get enough sleep. If you are staying up late and waking up early, you will feel a deficit of rest that will weaken your ability to deal with challenges. Sleep is *so* important to your wellbeing; in fact, if you are having trouble getting a good night's rest, it might be good to schedule an appointment with your primary care physician to talk about your inability to sleep.

Overall, being able to be well-rested and calm about your challenges will help you avoid severe panic attacks.

A Healthy Diet Will Do You Good

While preventing panic attacks, you need to consider your diet. The food you eat is important—a diet rich in whole grains, vegetables, and fruit can help you feel full and well-fed. Processed foods won't go a long way in satisfying your appetite, nor will a diet that is mainly carbohydrates. The problem is that you may have a drop in your blood sugar, which would make you feel weak. Another important thing to note about nutrition is that you should be eating three solid meals a day, along with snacks. Your body needs to be nourished. If you are feeling jittery or massively hungry, you might be more prone to panic attacks. Maintaining a healthy and nourishing eating routine can help make you feel better.

It is also wise to drink enough water to stay hydrated, and have limited access to or avoiding caffeine altogether. Your body needs to stay hydrated to function well. Also, the over-consumption of alcohol is another thing to watch while maintaining a good diet. Alcohol can spike your blood levels and create havoc for your body.

Harvard Study About Preventing Panic Attacks with Good Nutrition

An article published in the Harvard Health blog by Naidoo (2019) about nutritional strategies and anxiety described that when mice were tested, researchers found that diets low in magnesium tended to increase their anxiety. Conversely, diets high in magnesium can promote calmness, which can include: leafy greens like spinach and nuts seeds, Swiss chard, whole grains, and legumes.

Here are some foods that have been shown to be very helpful in preventing anxiety:

- Foods rich in zinc have been linked to lowering anxiety: oysters, egg yolks, beef, cashews, and liver.

- A 2011 study showed that omega-3s can help reduce anxiety: fatty fish like Alaskan salmon.
- The Chinese government approved the use of asparagus extract due to its anti-anxiety properties. This approval came after a research study done by Hilmire et al. (2015; Naidoo, 2016).
- Foods rich in B vitamins like almonds and avocados have an impact on anxiety.

Good antioxidant levels are thought to help fight anxiety. A 2010 study done by Carlsen et al. revealed this information. Foods that are high in antioxidants are:

- **Beans:** Pinto, black beans, and red kidney beans
- **Fruits:** apples, black plums, prunes, and sweet cherries
- **Berries:** blackberries, blueberries, cranberries, strawberries, raspberries
- **Vegetables:** broccoli, spinach, kale, and artichokes
- **Nuts:** pecans, walnuts
- **Spices:** ginger, turmeric

With all the data showing that certain foods can help curb anxiety, it makes sense to strive for good nutrition when trying to prevent panic attacks.

Making Panic Attacks Less Intense

Is there a way to make your panic attacks less intense? As discussed, feeling like you are having a heart attack or thinking you will die are some reactions you could have to an intense panic attack. The good news is that there are things you can do for your panic attacks.

Panic attacks can come about very quickly, and it may seem like the symptoms are only going to get worse, but the truth is that, just as your panic attacks have beginnings, they also have ends. The worst thing you can do is get caught up with the intensity of your symptoms. Yes, it is natural to be overwhelmed and scared during an episode, but if you can focus on things other than your panic attack, you might have a better time.

Moreover, it may also be wise to surrender to your panic attack and just let it take its course while remembering that it won't last forever. Also, try telling yourself that the symptoms are only part of your panic attack and not a medical condition (only after your health provider has cleared you from having any medical issues)

After your panic attack, instead of obsessing about its intensity, take the time to learn more about panic attacks in general, so you can erase your fear of the unknown.

Breathing and Your Panic Attacks

A common symptom of a panic attack is shortness of breath and hyperventilation. The way to overcome this is to remember to use breathing techniques during the attack. Learn how to slow your breathing down, as taking a deep breath of air while counting to ten is a good way to combat your shortness of breath. If you need more than ten seconds, continue counting. By taking deliberate breaths, you can help yourself calm down and reduce the intensity of your panic attack.

As discussed in an earlier chapter, it is effective for you to place your hand on your stomach, so you can feel your abdomen expand when taking in a breath, and how your abdomen lowers when you expel your breath. Concentrating and focusing on something else other than the shortness of your breath can really help with that aspect of a panic attack.

Cutting Down on the Intensity of Your Panic Attack

You may feel fear and apprehension when a panic attack starts; however, you can work at not feeling overwhelmed. Changing your focus from the panic attack to something or someone else can be a great tactic for alleviating an intense panic attack.

One thing you could also do is call one of your panic attack confidants on the phone who can help you during the episode. You can also try counting to 100, or any other mental action that will distract you from your panic attack.

Manage Your Time to Relieve Stress

Break down tasks into manageable pieces and set deadlines to reach them. Don't commit to more work than you can handle. It is also good to manage your personal life in a way that gives you a structured schedule with downtime and relaxation periods. Try to set boundaries with coworkers and people in your personal life, as it is important for you to have periods of calm as often as possible.

If you are frazzled by work and your personal life, you will leave yourself open to a meltdown and possibly a severe panic attack.

What *Not* to Do

One thing that you don't want to do is have any negative self-talk, like telling yourself that you are going to die or that something terrible is going to happen to you. Try to remember positive affirmations that can replace your negative thoughts, such as "Even though I feel scared, I accept myself," "I will get through this," or "I am strong".

Self Care is Important

Even though your symptoms are extreme, there are things that you can do for yourself. It is very important that you take care of yourself, which might include lifestyle changes that can help you reduce your feelings of anxiety and stress.

As discussed before, this is the time to learn relaxation techniques, how to meditate, or try practicing yoga. Include these techniques in your daily life, so they can begin to make a difference for you.

Exercising can also help to reduce your stress and anxiety levels. Just 20 minutes every day or three times a week can be beneficial. Taking a short walk or working out in a swimming pool are also two exercise activities that can cut down on your stress.

The more you practice these activities, the more likely you will be to use these techniques when you are having a panic attack. It might be awkward to start dancing or riding away on a bicycle during an attack, but you might find that, as the symptoms lose their intensity, you might be capable of doing something unorthodox to get through your panic attacks.

Self-care is all about what makes you feel better. Don't be afraid to take up a new hobby that promotes your calmness; for example, putting together puzzles or making quilts can go a long way in supporting calmness. You can also explore spirituality as a way to bring calm into your life. These things can really help you with taking care of yourself, and they can make a difference in the way you feel every day.

While working towards vanquishing your panic attacks with self-care, you might think of keeping track of the techniques that are effective. Starting a panic diary, personal journal, or a mood and anxiety spreadsheet can be a visual reminder of what is successful for you during a panic attack, and what you need to work on in the future.

Working with Your Mental Health Providers

When working with your mental health specialist, they will design a treatment plan that is unique to you. First, they will clear you of having any other medical issues that may be causing the symptoms of your panic attack. For example, they will make sure that your heart doesn't have any issues or that you don't have asthma that might be the other reason for your shortness of breath.

As mentioned in an earlier chapter, your psychiatrist may decide to give you medication that you can take during the panic attack to calm down. Your therapist will also help you decide which strategies to use during the panic attack.

If your panic attacks are increasing, do not be afraid to tell your mental health providers. Psychiatrists and therapists will always be open to trying something different to help you. The goal is all about your wellbeing—if you believe that your mental health providers are not with you 100%, discuss your treatment concerns with them. Overall, the more you communicate with the people you have chosen to help you, the better.

Medications That Can Help

After a therapist evaluates you, they may suggest that you see a psychiatrist for medication. The following sections will break down various medications often used to treat anxiety.

Selective serotonin reuptake inhibitors (SSRIs) have a low risk of side effects; they are antidepressants and are usually the first choice your mental health provider will suggest. They are used because they help maintain a balance of serotonin in your brain. Low serotonin levels have been correlated with constant depressive feelings, so balancing serotonin can help with negative thought processes.

Serotonin and norepinephrine reuptake inhibitors (SNRIs) are another category of antidepressants that may be prescribed to you.

Designer antidepressants are another class of antidepressants that can target serotonin and neurotransmitter that can give you more energy, alertness, motivation, and attention.

Tricyclic antidepressants are an older set of antidepressants that may take longer to work than SSRIs.

Miscellaneous tranquilizers are being used because they are new and have a much lessened addictive side effect.

Benzodiazepines are a **central nervous system depressant**. It is often used as a short-term medication, as they can be addictive; however, they are effective in reducing the intensity of a panic attack. Benzodiazepines are not recommended for patients who have substance abuse issues or a history of being addicted to drugs and alcohol.

MAO inhibitors are an older type of antidepressant that allows critical neurotransmitters to remain available in the brain to regulate mood effectively. These inhibitors are rarely used because they have serious side effects, including headaches, nausea, and drowsiness.

Beta blockers are used to treat hypertension, but it has also been known to reduce anxiety. These medications help with the physical symptoms of anxiety, like shaking, trembling, rapid heartbeat, and blushing.

Atypical antipsychotics are not often prescribed for anxiety, but these medications target other neurotransmitters that SSRIs do not target, such as dopamine and noradrenaline. Prescribed at a lower dose, these medications are sometimes used in addition to SSRIs.

A psychiatrist will work with you and your therapist to find the right medications for your unique situation. In some cases, it is a hit-or-miss situation when trying to find an effective medication; therefore, it is imperative that you stay honest with your psychiatrist when searching for the right medications or combination of that will help you. Be sure to tell your psychiatrist of any medical issues or side-effects that you may be experiencing.

A complete list of medications that can be used to treat anxiety

The following is a list of the various medications that doctors may prescribe to treat anxiety. Keep in mind that you should only take these with a proper diagnosis and prescription from your doctor; make sure to work with them to figure out which medication will suit you and your situation best.

Selective serotonin reuptake inhibitors (SSRIs): Luvox (Fluvoxamine), Celexa (Citalopram), Zoloft (Sertraline), Lexapro (Escitalopram), Paxil (Paroxetine), Paxil (Paroxetine), Prozac (Fluoxetine)

Serotonin/norepinephrine reuptake inhibitors (SNRIs): Cymbalta (Duloxetine), Effexor (Venlafaxine), Pristiq (Desvenlafaxine),

Serotonin-2 antagonists reuptake inhibitors (SARIs): Desyrel (Trazodone), Serzone (Nefazodone)

Noradrenergic antidepressants (NaSSAs): Remeron (Mirtazapine)

Norepinephrine reuptake inhibitor (NRI): Wellbutrin (Bupropion)

Tricyclic antidepressants: Tofranil, Elavil, Adapin, Pamelor, Anafranil

MAO inhibitors: Nardil, Parnate, Marplan

Benzodiazepines: Ativan (lorazepam), Centrax (prazepam), Klonopin (clonazepam), Librium (chlordiazepoxide), Serax (oxazepam), Valium (diazepam), Xanax (alprazolam)

Tranquilizers that are not Benzodiazepines: Buspar (buspirone), Vistaril (hydroxyzine)

***Beta Blockers**:* Inderal (propranolol), Tenormin (atenolol)

***Atypical Antipsychotics**:* Risperdal (risperidone), Abilify (aripiprazole), Zyprexa (olanzapine), Seroquel (quetiapine), Geodon (ziprasidone)

***Mood Stabilizers**:* Depakote (valproic acid), Eskalith (lithium), Lamictal (lamotrigine), Neurontin (gabapentin)

***Other**:* Tegretol (carbamazepine), Topamax (topiramate)

Panic Attacks at Work

Unfortunately, panic attacks can't be scheduled to only happen during your personal time. There is a chance that you will have a panic attack at work. In particular, it is important that you work out a plan for what to do when you have a panic attack in this situation.

Although you may want to keep your panic attacks to yourself, it might help if you tell a supervisor or human resource staff about your panic attacks. Telling a coworker too might also be beneficial, and explaining that you have panic attacks and what you do when you have one can free up some of the stress that you have about your panic attacks happening in the workplace.

If you are having panic attacks at work, you might want to look for patterns, indicators, or triggers before the panic attack happens. If you find that there are consistent triggers in your workplace, don't quit your job just yet; remember that there are therapies like exposure therapy and CBT that can help you deal with these triggers. It *is* possible to counter the triggers that spin you into a panic attack.

Ask for Help

Discuss the difficulties you have at work with your therapist. In addition, choose a therapist who understands that you might have to contact them outside of your appointment. There are therapists who are open to receiving texts and emergency phone calls who help you through panic attacks at work.

If it isn't possible to call your therapist during this time, choose a family member, like your spouse or a sibling whom you are close to. Remember that another technique is to have an object that calms you; for example, you can choose a smooth rock or small object to keep in your pocket or purse that can make you happy and promote calmness.

Designated Safe-Spaces

You can also scout out optimal places to be when your panic attack begins. This might seem odd to you, but think about it—would you rather have a panic attack in your cubicle or outside in a peaceful place? When your panic attack starts, you can leave the office to go to your safe place. Places that you might designate as your safe place at work can be, but are not limited to: your car, a private office, a bathroom stall, or a quiet area located outside of your office.

Planning what you will do at work when a panic attack occurs is important for reducing your stress levels. You might feel mortified when thinking about the possibility of having a panic attack at the office and in front of your coworkers, but having a plan will make you feel better about being at work.

Making a Solid Plan

One thing you can take into consideration when planning is how you will leave the office and make it to your safe place. Will you tell anyone where you are going? Will you ask a coworker to come with you, so they can help? Will you stay put at your desk and do some breathing techniques to calm down enough to leave your desk and go to your safe place? Will you call your therapist or text your supervisor to let them know what is going on? Can you ask a coworker to take you home? These are some of the questions that you should think about when making a plan for when you have a panic attack at work.

Another thing to consider is writing down your plan for panic attacks at work. You can make a printable document to tape to or keep in your desk, or you can keep it digitally in your phone or on your work computer. Whatever you do, make sure that it is easy to get to when a panic attack happens (Rauch, 2016).

Overall, there are various things you can do that will help you overcome panic attacks. Don't hesitate to take care of yourself and build up your morale. Remember—panic attacks are manageable and, in some cases, completely curable.

Chapter Summary

It is possible to do things that might prevent your panic attacks, and taking care of yourself in your daily life can really make a difference. It is also important to work on techniques that will help you to avoid having a panic attack. Some of the things you can do include the following:

- Good nutrition and a good night's sleep.
- A positive outlook.

- Therapy.
- Exercise.
- Appropriate medications.
- A system for handling stress at work.

In the next chapter, you will learn about overcoming your fear of panic attacks and phobias.

CHAPTER EIGHT:

Overcoming Your Fear of Panic Attacks and Phobias

The duration of a panic attack can be as short as ten minutes, but their effects can stay with you for hours or even days after the attack. You might find that you are anxious and uneasy after an initial panic attack and the fear of having another panic attack soon after can be difficult to shake.

This uneasiness can cause you to anticipate a panic attack every hour of every day. You may begin to avoid any environments and situations that precipitate your anxiety attacks; for example, you might stop going to the mall or to the park because you had anxiety attacks in those places.

Staying away from the places that you think triggers your panic attack is not the only thing you might consider doing after an attack—you might start changing your behavior entirely because you believe that certain behaviors are causing you to have a panic attack. A common behavioral change is not going to family functions or gatherings because you have had panic attacks when surrounded by your family or in-laws.

Being Frightened and Isolating Yourself

A cycle of fear and avoidance can start once you stop going to places and start changing your behavior. Doing so creates a cycle of fear and avoidance that can negatively affect your daily functioning. It is true that you might be able to stop some of your anxiety attacks by staying home or avoiding certain people, but these tactics are usually only good for the short term.

Although panic attacks may leave you helpless, there are things you can do that don't include avoidance or isolation. You can—and as we've been doing with this book—educate yourself about panic attacks. Beyond what we've gone over so far, there may be someone in your family or friend circles who also deal with panic attacks, and there exist support groups for people who have panic attacks. These groups will help you learn about our current understanding and the practical side of panic attacks.

You can also head to the library or the internet to learn more about panic attacks. There is a lot of information out there; However, make sure you pick a reference or a website that is legitimate. You can apply the journalistic three sources rule—if you can find three references containing the same information, then there is a good chance that you are dealing with genuine fact and not mere speculation.

Accepting Panic Attacks

As we learned in chapter 4, accepting your panic attacks can help with the intensity of the panic attack. It's a hard reality to live with, but you can make peace with knowing that you are prone to these kinds of episodes. Just remember that you have the power to do something about them and that it is important to reach out and get help.

When possible, change your response to your panic attacks and do something positive after an attack that empowers you. Vow to learn routines and behaviors that will support you and make you stronger. Become an observer of your panic attack and not a victim when it happens, and do the same positive things after each panic attack. Don't let the panic attack win—stand firm and resolve to conquer your panic attacks. Keep practicing the techniques you are learning in therapy, your support group, or from this book.

Furthermore, it is important that you prepare for when you have a panic attack. For example, always have your panic attack journal at the ready, so you can jot down what is happening before, during, and after an attack. Try rehearsing what you are going to ask of the people you have chosen to help you during a panic attack, and become familiar with the things you are going to do during an episode, so when it happens, you can do what you need to do during the attack.

How to Deal with Specific Phobias

Sometimes, the root of the problem with panic attacks is that you have a specific phobia of a person, place, or thing. Perhaps something traumatic happened to you, and you developed a phobia after the fact. Phobias can be a major trigger for panic attacks.

For example, if you were attacked by a rabid dog and survived, you might always be scared of any dog that crosses your path. You may, in fact, go out of your way to completely avoid any dogs in general, including changing your walking route, avoiding a friend's house if they own a dog, and never owning a dog yourself.

Specific phobias have the best prognosis of any anxiety disorder. If you work hard in therapy, you may be able to cure any anxiety you have toward your phobia. There is strong evidence that CBT can cure the anxiety attacks that are linked to phobias.

One of the main tenets of cognitive behavioral therapy is desensitizing you to the object that you fear; sticking with the earlier example about fear of dogs, your therapist might take you to an animal shelter to be around dogs that are locked in their kennels. The belief is that once you are desensitized towards your phobia, the panic attacks will cease.

Although it is not exactly certain why people have panic attacks, mental health professionals have suggested that the main cause of panic attacks are certain phobias. The good news is that if a phobia is the reason for your panic attack, you have a good prognosis for treating your panic attack.

Cognitive Behavioral Therapy

Cognitive behavioral therapy, or **CBT**, has been found to be effective at curing phobias. Perhaps there is a certain behavior that you have to work through or negative self-talk that reinforces the fear you have toward your object of anxiety. CBT will help you sort out these actions.

One practice, which is an extension of CBT, is **exposure therapy**, and it is a technique that is especially effective in treating anxiety attacks. Exposure therapy is a behavioral therapy that helps people with problematic fears. When a therapist uses exposure therapy to treat panic disorder, they systematically expose the patient to the events or environments that trigger their panic attacks. The therapist would create a safe environment for you to experience stressful situations.

Exposure Therapy

Exposure therapy is appropriate for people who have panic attacks due to a traumatic memory or a phobia. If you avoid these situations, you will probably isolate yourself unhealthily, which isn't good. The fear and avoiding isolation can amplify your fears, making it hard for you to lead a regular and stress-free life. For example, if you have a fear of bumblebees, you may go from simply avoiding places with beehives to not going outside at all.

Developed in the early 1900s, exposure therapy was used by behaviorists like Ivan Pavlov and John Watson. Pavlov is most famous for his classical conditioning of dogs, during an experiment in which he trained dogs to salivate when he rang a bell.

Behaviorist Joseph Wolpe developed a systematic desensitization technique in 1958, where he used relaxation training, anxiety hierarchy, and exposure to lessen a patient's sensitivity to situations that the patient dreaded or was afraid of. In the 1970s, more was done to develop exposure therapy.

The types of exposure therapy are as follows:

Imaginal Exposure: A patient is asked to deal with their fears by picturing the situation in their mind. By picturing a crowded mall, a person with the fear of being in crowds can systematically work through their anxiety.

In Vivo Exposure: A patient is exposed to real-life situations that would cause them fear and stress. For example, a patient who has a fear of dogs might go to the nearest rescue shelter and view the dogs while they are in their pens.

Virtual Reality Exposure: This is where virtual reality is used to treat a patient's fear. The situation is fabricated to feel like the real thing; for example, a person afraid of heights may experience a virtual reality simulation of climbing down a tall building.

Aside from these forms of exposure therapy, there are other, more specific exposure therapy techniques:

Systematic Desensitization: This technique implements relaxation training and the development of an anxiety hierarchy, in which you rank your fears or phobias on a simple scale of 1-10. Learned relaxation techniques offset stress and anxiety.

Graded Exposure: This technique uses the concept of desensitization to help quell a patient's anxiety.

Flooding: A patient is exposed in vivo or imaginal to his anxiety-evoking events for a prolonged time. This therapy is done until the anxiety is diminished significantly (Exposure Therapy, 2015).

***Prolonged Exposure* (PE)**: This is similar to flooding, but psychoeducation and cognitive processing are used. This is an effective treatment for trauma-related issues.

***Exposure and Response Prevention* (ERP)**: This form of therapy decreases the link between compulsions and obsessions. A therapist will provoke an obsession in the patient, then ask them not to engage themselves in their compulsions or behavioral rituals. This option is good for patients who are working to rid themselves of any obsessions and compulsions.

Exposure Therapy and Its Successes

A clinician who treats patients with exposure therapy regards anxiety as a false alarm to a person, place, or thing. This anxiety is overblown and not appropriate to the feared object, and the proportion of the patient's fear is not in line with the reaction of others.

The more a patient removes or avoids the object of fear from their vicinity, the less chance they will have to discover the inappropriateness of his response to anxiety. A person might understand in their mind that being afraid of their object of fear is ridiculous or overblown, but deep in their mind, they would still harbor an intense fear. In kind, this intense fear quite often leads to panic attacks.

An example of how a therapist may manage treatment during exposure therapy is as follows:

1. Provides ongoing assessments of the patient's fears.
2. There is a tailored education about the anxiety that the patient is experiencing.
3. Provides strategies, such as mindfulness, and encourages the patient to practice these strategies when dealing with their phobia(s).
4. Graded exposure to the object of fear.
5. A program of cognitive interventions that will identify and challenge faulty or negative thinking.

Cognitive restructuring and medication are also used as supplemental techniques for helping patients undergoing exposure therapy.

The following section outlines an example of graded therapy. In this case, the patient is afraid of lizards.

1. The patient will be required to look at pictures of lizards.
2. The patient will then be required to touch the picture of lizards.
3. Next, they will be told to look at live lizards on the internet.
4. The patient will then touch a fake lizard.
5. The patient will touch the glass or top of a container that is displaying live lizards.
6. The patient will then imagine what it is like to touch a lizard.
7. Finally, the patient will touch a live lizard.

Exposure therapy can be very difficult for a person with panic attacks; however, it is important to stick with the therapy as long as possible for it to take effect. Research has shown that exposure therapy can be very effective, so it is important to participate as well as possible when in this form of therapy.

Chapter Summary

Fear and phobias are major components of panic attacks. The sooner you deal with them, the better your ability to prevent future panic attacks. It is possible to overcome your fears about panic attacks by educating yourself, changing your responses, and practicing acceptance of your panic attacks.

Exposure therapy helps to desensitize you to your phobias. You will go through several steps to reach a point where you are not at the mercy of your phobias, including:

- Looking at pictures of your phobia.
- Touching pictures of your phobia.
- Looking at your phobia “live.”
- Touching a fake item of your phobia.

- Touching your phobia through a glass case.
- Imagining how it would feel to touch your phobia.
- Actually touching your phobia.

CHAPTER NINE:

Cognitive Behavioral Therapy and EMDR Therapy: Treatment without Medication

When you are ready to start healing yourself, it is time to look into some therapeutic options. Indeed, science may fully understand what causes panic attacks, but that does not mean that specific types of helpful therapy don't exist.

Some of these therapies include:

- Panic-focused psychodynamic psychotherapy (PFPP)
- Cognitive behavioral therapy (CBT)
- Eye Movement Desensitization and Reprocessing (EMDR)

The course of therapy that we will describe in chapter 9 is cognitive behavioral therapy (CBT), which is a form of therapy that has proven to be effective in treating panic attacks. It is known to be goal-oriented with quick results, as you will likely see. The success of CBT and quick results is a reason that therapists prefer it to treat patients suffering from panic attacks.

Cognitive Behavioral Therapy

Cognitive behavioral therapy (CBT) is psychotherapy used by therapists who treat various psychological disorders, ranging from anxiety to bipolar disorder. CBT is a psychotherapy that focuses on a person's thoughts, feelings, perceptions, and how they act upon those feelings. Therapists who use CBT believe that your thoughts, perceptions, and feelings influence your behavior (Star, 2019).

A tenet of CBT is that you might not be able to change what is going on in your life, but you *can* change the way you perceive your life.

When you see a therapist for your panic attacks with CBT, they will help you become more aware of your conscious thoughts. For example, a therapist will weed out the negative or faulty thought processes that have appeared and become bad habits in your daily life.

CBT has proven to be effective in patients who suffer from a major depressive disorder, post-traumatic stress disorder (PTSD), addiction, and general phobias. CBT has proven very successful, and many therapists have also used it to treat patients with irritable bowel syndrome (IBS), chronic fatigue (Star), and fibromyalgia.

Mainly, CBT offers you the chance to exchange your negative thoughts and actions into more positive thoughts and actions.

Dealing with Negative Thoughts

When you have a panic attack, you are dealing with self-deprecating beliefs and negative thoughts. It can also happen that, in your daily life, you have many negative thoughts. Being afraid and having negative thinking can all link back to panic attacks. The primary goal of CBT is to help patients overcome negative thinking and replace it with positive thoughts and healthier actions.

There are not only mental components to panic attacks, but physical components as well. The somatic symptoms of a panic attack may include chest pains, shortness of breath, rapid heartbeat, and heavy sweating. These symptoms can all overwhelm a person who is having a panic attack; therefore, a person who regularly suffers from panic attacks may develop distressing thoughts and fears of going crazy, dying, and/or losing control (Star, 2019).

The result of a panic attack is that a person may become terrified of the triggers that appeared before their panic attack. For example, if you generally have a panic attack when you go to the dentist, merely being within the dentist's office waiting room before they work on your teeth would probably cause you to go into a panic attack. From that moment on, you would have a remarkable fear of going to the dentist's office, so you would cease to go all together, even if you develop a major toothache and your gums swell. In this case, the disruption to your life is that you would rather go through immense physical pain than go to visit a professional specially trained to alleviate your tooth and gums pain.

The longer you avoid the dentist's office, the more scared you would become, which is a typical result for anyone who stays away from the things they fear.

When you begin CBT, you might not be able to control when you have a panic attack, but you can learn some brilliant coping mechanisms that could help you to deal with your panic attacks.

The Processes of CBT

There are certain processes that you will go through when you participate in cognitive behavioral therapy. According to Star (2019), they are the following:

1. Notice and take charge of your negative thoughts—first, you will identify your negative cognitions or thinking patterns.
2. Participate in activities and exercises that will help you notice your negative thoughts much easier. When you are involved in these activities, you will learn healthier thought processes, and you might even have homework that could help you identify your faulty thinking.
3. You will be asked to do writing exercises. By writing down your thinking, you can evaluate and recognize your faulty thinking. Once you have isolated this kind of thinking, you can replace it with healthier thinking that does not bring you down or trigger your panic attacks. For these exercises, you can make a journal specific to what you are writing; for example, different journals for your thoughts and feelings, some affirmations you have come up with, what you feel gratitude for, or a journal for documenting and describing your panic attacks.
4. You will be working on behavioral changes and skill-building. In this stage, you will learn how to reconfigure your maladaptive behaviors while building and using healthy coping strategies (Star, 2019). At this stage, you

will focus on learning skills that can help you manage your stress and anxiety, along with skills to help you make it through your panic attacks. You will probably be told to rehearse these new skills in therapy and be encouraged to practice them daily, beyond therapy.

5. Desensitization is a frequently used CBT technique that will help you to gradually learn to cope with anxiety-producing stimuli. Furthermore, you will learn to manage any anxious feelings you may have. Your therapist will slowly introduce you to more anxiety-inducing affairs, and you will continue to work through your feelings of panic and fear.
6. Learning to remain calm during a panic attack will be taught to you in therapy. CBT helps you reduce the symptoms of your particular panic attacks. There may sometimes be other treatment options, like medication, that your therapist will recommend along with working through CBT. The main goal for your therapist is to help develop a plan for treatment that is best for you.

EMDR Therapy

An effective treatment for panic attacks is **Eye Movement Desensitization and Reprocessing** (**EMDR**). According to Gotter (2019), this therapy is an interactive psychotherapy technique used to relieve psychological stress.

EMDR is a therapy that helps you become less emotionally upset by diverting your attention. When your attention is diverted, you will be more likely to be less emotional. The whole point of this therapy is to diminish the impact that these emotionally upsetting memories may carry. EMDR is a good therapy for those patients who may find it difficult to talk about their traumatic past.

EMDR is used to treat the following disorders:

- Depression.
- Anxiety.
- Panic attacks and panic disorder.
- Eating disorders.
- Addiction.

How Does EMDR Help Patients?

Patients being treated with EMDR have to commit to at least 12 separate therapy sessions, which is broken down into eight phases. These phases are the following:

Phase 1: History and treatment planning

This is the phase in which your therapist learns more about the trauma and painful memories that you are dealing with. In this session, you may also want to talk about the things you know trigger your panic attacks or suspected triggers. Your therapist will then decide what treatment you should receive.

Phase 2: Preparation

During this phase, your therapist will work with you to decide on strategies you can use before or during your panic attacks. Your therapist will most likely teach you stress management techniques, like mindfulness and deep breathing in this stage.

Phase 3: Assessment

During this phase, your therapist will decide on specific memories that they will be working on with you, along with all the components associated with those memories. Specifically, they will be trying to deduce the physical sensations that you feel when you focus on an event.

Phases 4-7: Treatment

Gotter (2019) explains that this phase of the treatment is when your therapist will actually begin with your treatment. During your session, you will be asked to focus on a negative image, thought, or memory.

While you are doing this, your therapist will simultaneously ask you to do specific eye movements. Gotter says that "the bilateral stimulation may also include taps or other movements mix in, depending on your case."

After you do bilateral stimulation, you will be asked to make your mind blank and recall your thoughts and feelings. When you recall these thoughts, your therapist might ask you to refocus on the memory or have you start thinking about another traumatic memory.

If the traumatic memory is too much for you, your therapist will bring you back into the present before they would have you recall another traumatic memory. While working through the phases of EMDR, the upsetting thoughts and feelings associated with your traumatic memory should also start to fade.

Phase 8: Evaluation

In this phase, you and your therapist will be talking about the progress you are making in EMDR therapy. For example, are the traumatic memories still painful, or have the feelings associated with that memory begun to fade?

Various studies done on the effects of EMDR have displayed the practice as positive with significant changes in their patients. In this case, EMDR would be another option for you when seeking treatment for your panic attacks.

Chapter Summary

It is possible to receive treatment for your panic attacks that doesn't include medication. CBT and EMDR are two of the most common therapies to treat panic attacks. The CBT process includes:

- Recognizing and replacing negative thoughts.
- Writing exercises.
- Skill building and behavioral changes.
- Desensitization.
- Relaxation techniques.

In the next chapter, you will learn more about getting help for panic attacks.

CHAPTER TEN:

Getting Help for Panic Attacks

Panic attacks can be quite overwhelming, and having random attacks can disrupt your life. Consequently, it is imperative that you do something to help your attacks to either go away or become less intense.

So far in this book, we have discussed strategies such as exposure therapy and cognitive behavioral therapy that are both excellent in helping you cease or lessen your panic attacks. In this chapter, we will be looking at some more therapeutic options that you can do to decrease the intensity of your panic attacks or end them altogether.

Therapy requires a lot of commitment and hard work, but if done correctly, the results can be very effective. The key is to find the right kind of therapy for your unique needs.

Cognitive Behavior Modification

Sometimes we find ourselves engaging in a lot of negative self-talk. Clinicians believe that negative self- talk may contribute to or be the catalyst for your panic attacks. Psychologist Donald Meichenbaum developed **cognitive**

behavior modification, or **CBM**, to focus on identifying dysfunctional self-talk. When you identify behaviors and patterns that may hinder your recovery, you can make significant progress to leading a better life. Meichenbaum believed that behaviors have outcomes that manifest themselves due to our own self-verbalizations. This is why it is so important to have positive thoughts. When you reduce your negative self-talk and change to positive thoughts, you may see an improvement or complete cessation of your panic attacks.

Rational Emotive Behavior Therapy

Albert Ellis developed **rational emotive behavior** (**REBT**). REBT is a cognitive behavior technique known to be effective in the treatment of panic disorders (Ankrom, 2019). Ellis, thus, developed a therapy that helps patients to identify and dispute negative thoughts or "irrational beliefs." For example, telling yourself constantly that you don't measure up to regular people can be a thought that causes deep psychological problems. By identifying that this statement or thought is not true, and why it isn't true, you can begin to reduce the frequency and intensity of your panic attacks.

Being in therapy and using the REBT technique can work to change your brain, so you cope better with your panic attacks or cease having them altogether.

Panic-focused Psychodynamic Therapy

Panic-focused psychodynamic therapy (**PFPP**) is a type of panic disorder therapy based on specific psychoanalytic concepts. This therapy emphasizes the theory that people are defined by early human experiences, and that unconscious motives and psychological conflicts are at the core of your current behavior (Ankrom, 2019).

PFPP therapists make the assumption that the unconscious mind hides painful emotions and defense mechanisms that may be keeping our painful emotions hidden; therefore, PFPP therapy helps bring emotions that we have hidden in our subconscious into the forefront of our mind, so we can better deal with these emotions. When this is done, your panic disorder symptoms can either be alleviated or eliminated.

Group Therapy

Sometimes, going about it alone in therapy can be too much. If this is the case, perhaps group therapy would work better for you. **Group therapy** is often made up of people who are experiencing the same or similar problems that you are having. It is based on the principle that you can learn from one another about techniques that will help you to diminish or stop your panic attacks.

Some benefits of group therapy include:

- A minimization of the shame and stigma by sharing experiences with other people who have similar symptoms and challenges.
- Other group members can provide you with inspiration and reinforcement by modeling the healthy actions that you are learning in group therapy.
- Group therapy can naturally provide an "exposure environment" for you to learn how to diminish your fear of having panic symptoms in social situations.

Overall, you should feel completely safe when attending a group therapy session. The group that you join can have anywhere between 2-10 or more people in attendance. There is often a therapist or counselor that leads the group. In some instances, the group is run by an experienced person, and topics are brought up and discussed by the group. The therapist or group leader will encourage you and the others to talk about your panic attacks and ultimately your fears in a safe space.

Couples and Family Therapy

Even though having a panic attack is a singular experience, you are not alone—friends and family members are also affected by your panic attacks, and the people who love you will be concerned about the intense symptoms of your panic attacks. It is hard to see someone you love going through something as overwhelming as panic episodes.

Some patients have found that going to **couples** or **family therapy** can address issues that had begun forming in the minds of their family members, significant others, and/or friends. Family therapy addresses topics such as your dependency needs caused by your panic attacks; questions and concerns that your family and friends have about giving you support; and general communication and education about your panic attacks.

Couples and family therapy can help to improve your environment. Moreover, therapy can help you with eliminating certain cues or triggers that might be caused by the discord that exists in your family or friend circle. However, it may be necessary for you to also go to individual therapy as well as couples or family therapy in order to work out the issues that cause your panic attacks. In particular, it is important for you to pick a therapy that addresses your unique needs.

Reasons to Participate in Therapy

Panic attacks affect about 6 million adults in the United States, which counts for 2.7% of the population. Panic attacks are more likely to occur in women than in men according to the Anxiety and Depression Association of America (n.d.).

It might be hard to go to a therapist for help with your panic attacks. You may believe that your panic attacks are untreatable, but this isn't true. Many people find relief from their panic attacks when they start attending therapy. It is true that going to therapy and doing all the things that your therapist asks of you can be very hard, but the alternative is to endure infinite and random panic attacks that are so intense that they regularly interfere with your daily life.

The following list brings to light various reasons why people avoid getting help for their panic attacks ("Panic and Panic Disorder," 2019):

- They are more prone to alcohol or drug abuse.
- They have already become financially dependent on others.
- They have experienced a decline in health.
- They have attempted suicide.
- They have become homebound due to the development of **agoraphobia** (fear of going outside and avoidance of things that may cause panic or anxiety in the individual).

Another important reason for going to therapy is that a therapist can help reassure you that you are not "going crazy."

Ten Ways to Find a Good Therapist

The most important thing to do when deciding to ask for help is to find a good therapist, but how do you find a good therapist? Here are five strategies you can use to find a good therapist.

1. Ask your family doctor if they work with any psychiatrists or therapists. Furthermore, you can ask them who they would go to if they were having severe panic attacks. Your family doctor works with other health care professionals, so they would be a good person to ask.

2. Friends and family may surprise you with how much they know about mental health; in fact, you may find that some of your friends or family are in therapy or have friends who go to therapy. Consequently, they may be able to give you contact information for a therapist who would work well for you.

3. Ask if your place of employment has an Employee Assistance Program (EAP), and the place to find out would be your human resource department. EAP services may be provided at work or be outsourced. Counseling might also be an employee benefit that you could take advantage of.

4. Your insurance company will most likely have a list of psychiatrists and therapists who are covered by your insurance. If you need help selecting a therapist from their list, ask to be assigned to a caseworker or nurse provided by your insurance for help.

5. A search for "therapist" and "panic attacks" on the internet may also be an effective strategy for finding a good mental health professional. Many mental health professionals have websites or blogs that can also help you get to know them

better. Listings on the internet often have the areas of treatment that they offer, so choose a professional who has experience with panic attacks and has good therapy results for your case.

In the past, if you lived in a small or rural town, it was almost impossible to find a mental health practitioner; however, many therapists are now also on Skype, Facetime, or have a general telephone. This is good if you live in a small town with limited resources, or if you are too busy to travel to a therapist's office. In fact, sometimes a combination of phone therapy and face-to-face contact is good for helping with social phobias that you have developed due to panic attacks.

While doing your search, get at least three references from each source that you can ask. The more mental health professionals you contact, the better your chances of finding a therapist or doctor who will be the perfect fit.

Questions for Your Therapist

Going to a therapist may be a new experience for you. You may have doubts and anxiety about working with a therapist and discussing your panic attacks. Specifically, it is important to go prepared for your first appointments. Here are some questions that you might want to ask or discuss with a mental health professional:

- What can I do about the intensity of my symptoms? Can you help me with some relaxation techniques?
- My symptoms are very intense. What is going on in my brain and body that causes such strong symptoms?
- Is it possible to learn how to stop a panic attack?
- Could there be any physical conditions that are causing my panic attacks?

- Is there anything I should avoid, like certain foods, beverages, or medications?
- I would like to explore factors in my environment or personal relationships that could be triggering my panic attacks. Can you help me with this?
- Do you work with any psychiatrists that could help me with my medication needs? Can you refer me to someone whom you trust?
- What kinds of therapies do you offer? Specifically, are you familiar with any forms of therapy that have been successful in ceasing or alleviating panic attacks?
- What types of therapy would you suggest for me?

These are all great starting points and questions for when you are interviewing a therapist and deciding who might be a good fit for you. You can decide which questions fit your situation best and go from there.

Going to a Psychiatrist.

After a therapist evaluates you, they may suggest that you see a psychiatrist for medication. Some medications used to manage the symptoms of panic attacks have been discussed in chapter 7.

A psychiatrist will examine you and work with your therapist to find the right medications for your unique situation. Be sure to tell your psychiatrist of any medical issues or side effects that you are prone to experience, and if you have any allergies to a specific medication.

Although you might be overwhelmed by your panic attacks, it is important that you ask for help. There are many different forms of therapy that can successfully treat your panic disorder.

There also exist various medications that can help with your therapy as well.

We may not know exactly what causes a panic attack, but there are proven methods that can help you deal with the intensity of your panic attacks and, ultimately, along the many avenues of help that are available, you can finally eradicate your panic attacks once and for all.

Chapter Summary

In this chapter, you learned that there are six common types of therapy to treat panic attacks. These types are: CBT, CBM, REBT, panic-focused psychodynamic therapy, group therapy, and couples and family therapy.

There are also several different ways for you to find a therapist. These methods include the following:

- Asking your PCP doctor for a referral.
- Asking friends and family about any therapists they know.
- Going through your insurance company.

FINAL WORDS

If you've ever experienced a panic attack, you know that having an attack can feel like your world has just blown up. Your body has symptoms that are so severe, you may think that you are dying. It is one thing to have a single panic attack, but to have several at rando—well, this can make life quite hard to lead. Having a panic attack with no intervention can scare you so much that you drop out of activities and live in fear that you will have another attack; in fact, there are two known conditions when it comes to panic attacks: anticipatory anxiety and phobic avoidance. These two symptoms of a panic attack can take you out of the game quite literally. Leaving the house because you fear there will be a trigger is very real to a person who suffers from these types of attacks.

Although panic attacks can be overwhelming and intense, there is a way out. There are many forms of therapies and strategies that can help you if you suffer from episodes. The techniques in this book, if done diligently, can go a long way toward making your panic attacks less intense and, in some cases, stop altogether. In this book, we explored the definition of a panic attack, myths and misconceptions, how to stop panic attacks, powerful relaxation techniques, ways to prevent panic attacks, and how to get help.

The central theme of this book has been to give the message that panic attacks can be stopped. It takes hard work in therapy and on your own, but there are ways to stop your attacks.

It is important to believe that you can conquer your panic attacks. In this book, we myth-busted misconceptions about panic attacks, and you discovered that you can't die from a panic attack and that panic attacks won't make you insane.

Panic attacks are not a joke—they may come at you big and take no prisoners. However, you can always follow the techniques outlined in this book to make the fight fair; for example, being calm and accepting the panic attack is one place to start. You may believe that the only way through a panic attack is to "panic" and become agitated, but it doesn't have to be this way. You can be firm and follow the five steps of AWARE: acknowledge and accept; wait and watch (or work); actions (that make you more comfortable); repeat the above steps; and finally, end. If you learn to do these five steps, you will be well on your way to making it through your panic attacks.

The hardest part about panic attacks is that there is no known hard and fast cause for them. It gets confusing because if we don't know what causes a panic attack, how can we treat them? How can we make them stop happening? Despite not knowing the cause of panic attacks, mental health providers have developed successful ways for treating them. I discussed these strategies in this book and stand behind them.

When you manage to do the five steps of AWARE, don't stop there. Get out in front of the panic attack and do the steps you learned in chapter 5. Know your triggers and limit your stimuli to prevent a panic attack from happening. When you start to panic, relax and do some deep breathing or relax your muscles, one group at a time, so you can release the tension that has developed across your body. Visualize your happy place and be strict about your negative thoughts—work on not having them. Completely kick them out of your mind and, above all, practice mindfulness and live in the present—not the future or the past. These techniques work because they address your stress responses, including any increased heart rate, tense muscles, and rapid breathing.

Relaxing and taking care of the stressors in your life is also important. It is not enough to know your triggers because you must also make sure you are not overwhelmed or stressed out. You have to be proactive and eat the right foods, get enough sleep, and manage your time, so you don't become overburdened.

The most important thing you can do if you are having a panic attack is to reach out for help. Your first step was reading this book, and your next step will be to do the strategies we have discussed. Beyond that, you might want to find a therapist or let your friends and family know how they can help you. Have a plan for when you have a panic attack and assign a person who will be with you at work or home to help you when you are having an episode. Reaching out to a therapist is also important. With the six common types of therapies, you can rest assured that you will be able to find a treatment that will be effective for you.

Don't be afraid of sharing with others the difficulty that you are having due to your panic attacks. Couple and family therapy can really help connect with the people who care about you. Although you may feel alone when you are suffering from panic attacks, remember that you are not. The people in your life are going through these attacks with you, and it is the most natural thing in the world for them to want to support and help you. Don't be afraid to reach out and include them in your treatment plans.

My greatest wish is that this book will help or has helped you find your way out of having panic attacks. Good luck, and don't lose faith!

APPENDIX

For your convenience, I have gathered together the 23 relaxation techniques mentioned in the book.

The first of the five steps of AWARE is to acknowledge and accept what is happening during a panic attack. It is even possible to stop the panic attack with the five steps of AWARE. The first thing that you must do is acknowledge and accept your anxiety ("How to Stop Panic Attacks," n.d.) The first of the five steps of AWARE is to acknowledge and accept what is happening during a panic attack. It is even possible to stop the panic attack with the five steps of AWARE. The first thing that you must do is acknowledge and accept your anxiety ("How to Stop Panic Attacks, n.d.)

The next step of AWARE is *wait*. When you have a panic attack, you probably experience the need to flee or struggle; however, rash action will only make things worse. Often, when you have a panic attack, you are reduced to a state in which you cannot think straight; therefore, you are more prone to do something rash. Moreover, you make decisions that may just make your circumstances worse.

The next thing you want to do is *watch*. This is the time to try to understand how your panic attack works. What was happening before you had the attack and what is happening during the attack are both important aspects to observe. By observing these actions, you have the opportunity to start a panic diary that can help you notice important parts of the panic attack.

You can also add “work” to this step. When you are having a panic attack, you might not be able to wait and watch immediately—this is where “work” comes in. For example, say you are driving your car or giving a presentation. Don’t freak out and run from this event, but instead, remain engaged in what you are doing and calmly move toward watching and waiting while you are having your panic attack.

So, what do you do when a panic attack happens? Well, your job is to make yourself more comfortable with the attack. Some techniques that have been helpful to people who have panic attacks include:

- Belly breathing or diaphragmatic breathing.
- Talking yourself through the attack.
- Getting involved with your present.
- Working with your body.

When you find yourself entering a new cycle of an intense panic attack, keep your wits about you and start the AWARE cycle all over again. It might be hard for you to do, but if you acknowledge and accept that you are having a longer panic attack, you will be able to wait and watch (and possibly continue on with the work aspect). Then, you can get into *action* and make yourself more comfortable until the panic attack eventually ends.

The final step of aware is to *end* the panic attack.

Although you might think it is impossible to do anything during a panic attack but feel terror, it is possible to do something to quell the attack. The best thing to do is teach yourself to focus and do things that will break your concentration away from the attack.

1. Teach yourself to focus

It is very important that you don't fight the panic attack or get over-excited. If you are calm and accept that you are having an attack, there is a chance that the symptoms of the attack will not be as intense as they could be.

2. Asking for help

It may be helpful to talk to your doctor about finding a good psychiatrist or therapist, as they may be able to refer you to mental health professionals that they have a working relationship with. In this way, you will have a team that can work out a care plan that is unique and effective to you.

3. Controlling your breath

Deep breathing and counting slowly to four while you are breathing in and out can be a great help. If you continue to breathe rapidly, it may increase your anxiety and cause extreme tension in your body, resulting in other physical symptoms like a tight or heavy feeling in your chest. Therefore, it is important to concentrate on controlling your breathing.

If you breathe deeply, like you are filling up a balloon, your breath can help fill your lungs slowly and steadily (Crawford, 2018). Counting slowly as you expand your lungs or abdomen can help you concentrate on something else besides your panic attack, and this concentration can consequently help you to get through your panic attack.

4. Medications for your panic attack

There are various other techniques that can help you during an attack, but something to consider is taking medications to help quell your episodes. If you're treated by a psychiatrist or your primary caregiver, you may be prescribed medication to help you get through the intensity of a panic attack. This medication may be prescribed to take regularly in the morning, night, or during the day. Moreover, you may be given medicines to take PRN, which means that you would take this medication when you need it.

5. Avoid bombarding your senses

If you have panic attacks due to overwhelming stimuli, it is important that you learn to stay away from bright light and sounds when possible. If you can't prevent your exposure and find that bright lights are triggering your panic attack, try to remove yourself from the central area of the lights. If that isn't an option, find a spot in the room where your exposure is limited and try to focus on your breathing or any other action that you believe can help lessen the intensity of your panic attack.

6. Panic attacks and triggers

How do you become aware of the triggers that may be causing your panic attacks? One thing you can do is keep a journal or a diary about the events that trigger your panic attacks.

By keeping a diary about your panic attacks, you might notice patterns or indications that certain situations are causing your panic attacks. Until you can work through these situations with your therapist, it is wise to be aware of the things that may be triggering you; however, do not go to the extreme of staying at home or not participating in something that is healthy for you just because your participation may expose you to something that triggers you. In therapy, you can work toward desensitizing yourself to situations that come before you have a panic attack. It is important that you learn your triggers and work actively toward dealing with them healthily.

7. Exercising to release endorphins

Another healthy way to deal with a panic attack is light exercise. Even though there really is no way to prepare for a panic attack, exercising is something that can still make you feel better.

Exercise is more than just toning your body and burning calories—it helps release endorphins in your body that can improve your mood and relax your body (Crawford, 2018).

When you do something as simple as walking, you release the endorphins into your system. Even walking can help you deal with a stressful environment. A short walk during a stressful time can help you regulate your breathing and release any nervous tension that has built up in you when stressed.

Walking during a panic attack can help you focus on something other than what is causing the panic. It can also help with the powerful feelings of fight or flight. In sum, there are many benefits of light exercise when you are having to cope with panic attacks.

8. Being mindful

Mindfulness is the state of being conscious of what is happening around you. Being mindful can aid you in dealing with the present—not the past or future. It is great to use for achieving awareness of the present moment, accepting that you are having a panic attack, and becoming aware of your bodily sensations, thoughts, and feelings.

A therapist might tell you that mindfulness is paying attention on purpose (Niemiec, 2017). Sometimes, when you have a panic attack, you might get the feeling that you are detached from reality; however, there are exercises you can do while having a panic attack that can bring you back to yourself. Some examples of these exercises are the following:

- Listen for four distinct sounds and think of why they are all different from each other.
- Pull your attention to five different things around you and consider why each one is different from the other.
- Choose three objects and describe to yourself how they are different. Reasons can include different textures, uses, and temperatures.
- Focus on one or two different smells around you. What are they and have you smelled them before?
- Taste something: a candy that you carry in your pocket or purse, for example.

Doing exercises such as these will pull your focus away from the panic attack and bring you back to the present (Legg, 2018).

9. Focusing on one object

Being mindful is a good way to stay in the present and focus; however, it might be hard at first to be mindful without a bit of practice. One thing you can do to become good at being mindful is to master the art of focusing on one object.

This simple task can really help you while you are having a panic attack. Just pick one object near you and focus on it completely. Study that object and determine its qualities to help you focus. What color is the shape? What texture is it? Questions like this can help you tune into that focus.

10. Muscle relaxation

The key to this exercise is to slow down your breathing and give yourself permission to relax. When you are calm, your breathing slows down and you can concentrate on your muscle groups and tell yourself mentally to relax. This exercise, or PMR, is simply focusing on each set of muscles in your body and visualizing the muscles relaxing.

There are many different muscle groups that you can focus on; there is a lot to remember, but you can start with your arms, then your head, neck, shoulders, chest, hips, then, lastly, your legs and your feet. One by one, you would tense these muscle groups, feel the tension for 5 seconds, then release these muscles and relax for ten seconds. Do this with your whole body. This has a two-fold purpose—first, it gives you something to focus on; and second, you would relax the muscles that have become very tense during your panic attack.

11. Find your happy place

In everyone's experience, there is a place where we are happy and at our best. Perhaps it is a bench in a beautiful park or somewhere at the beach. Each person has their very own happy place.

If it is hard for you to focus on something in the room, close your eyes and bring into your vision the place where you are most happy. Take a moment to think about how you feel when you are in this happy place—consider as many details as you can and completely focus on your place of choice.

When you are having a panic attack, it is important for you to slow down time as much as possible. When you are thinking of your happy place, think of details that require you to focus. Remembering how a place smells, sounds, and feels, as this is a simple way of getting yourself to focus. You don't necessarily have to remember details, like how many stairs up there are from the beach to the patio or the exact color of the walls in your happy place. Just keep it simple.

When you've thought of the details of your happy place, concentrate on being there in your mind. Take slow breaths through your nose and mouth, and focus on your breathing and the details of your place of choice. Continue to do this until the panic attack starts to go away (Legg, 2018).

12. Finding a mantra

A mantra is a word, phrase, or sound that can help you focus (Crawford, 2018). For example, I like to think of the word "happy" when I am stressed. You may have a word or phrase that makes you happy, such as "there's no place like home."

By chanting this mantra, you are taking your mind off the panic attack and toward something positive for yourself. Another good phrase to use during a panic attack is "This too shall pass." This specific mantra not only takes your focus off your panic attack, but it also gives you confidence that what you are going through will end, and that it can't last forever.

When you find your mantra, try it and see how it helps you regulate your breathing and relax your muscles. This is a good step to alleviating your panic attacks, as it not only helps you relax, but a good mantra can also soothe and help you take the anxiety away.

13. Finding help during your panic attacks

When you are experiencing a panic attack, it is good to have some help. Perhaps you have a spouse or a friend whom you can tell about your panic attacks. Pick an important person in your life to help you with the panic attack when it happens.

This person could act like a coach who helps you get through a tough spot by reminding you to do the techniques that best help you when you are having a panic attack.

14. Breathing techniques

- Ask someone to find you a quiet and comfortable place for you to sit while you are experiencing your panic attack.
- When you are seated in a quiet spot, put one hand on your stomach and the other on your chest, then breathe deeply. You can inhale and imagine your abdomen filling up with air like a balloon.
- Take a slow and regular breath in through your nose. Watch and sense your hands as you breathe in. The hand on your chest should remain still, while the hand on your stomach would move slightly.
- Breathe out through your mouth slowly.
- Repeat this process at least ten times, or until you begin to feel your anxiety quiet down.

Another breathing technique you can use is to let your thumb and middle finger pinch your nostrils shut. Lift your middle finger and breath in while watching the hand on your stomach move. Hold your breath and let your middle finger close your nostril once again. Next, it's the thumbs turn to lift up. Exhale the air you are holding through this open nostril. When this is finished, start the process again for as long as it takes for you to feel better. This type of breathing is popular during yoga meditation.

15. Positive thoughts and their power

The first thing you can do is to become aware that your thoughts are making you anxious. Then, you must interrupt these negative thoughts and place some good ones in your head to stop or interrupt the negative thinking. Some techniques that you might try include the following:

- Think of a person you love and remember the details or qualities that make you love that person.
- Think of something you look forward to doing in the future, like going out to a movie or a great restaurant.
- Carry your favorite book with you, so you can take it out to read when you feel a panic attack beginning.
- Turn on the radio or use your smartphone to play music that can make you happy.
- If you were doing something important during the panic attack, try to go back to it and completely focus on what you were doing.

Use these techniques to interrupt the thinking that makes your panic attack worse. It is important for you to shift your attention away from your anxiety and into something positive that can pull you away from the intensity of your panic attack.

16. Using mindfulness to live in the present

As discussed in the last chapter practicing mindfulness can be very rewarding. Practice being mindful before you have a panic attack so that it becomes second nature to you. To practice mindfulness, you need to do the following things:

- Take yourself to a quiet and pleasant place. Sit down and close your eyes.
- Concentrate on your breathing and how your body feels.

- Shift your focus from your breathing and your body and pay attention to what is around you. Consider what you are hearing, feeling, and smelling. Ask yourself, "What is going on around me?"
- Continue to be mindful and switch back and forth from focusing on your body to what is going on around you until the anxiety begins to fade.

Mindfulness is the best way to bring yourself back to the present. It is also an important tool to use when you are having a panic attack. Mindfulness is about achieving a calm state and extinguishing the rapid-fire negative thinking that goes on during a panic attack. When you are mindful, you are living in the present, and when you live in the present, there is no past or future to worry about.

17. Releasing tension

Doing Progressive Muscle Relaxation (PMR) is a good way to release tension; however, here is another technique you can try while you are having a panic attack (Legg, 2018).

- Find a comfortable place to be, then close your eyes and focus on your breathing. Inhale slowly through your nose, then exhale through your mouth.
- Make a tight fist and squeeze your hand as hard as you can.
- Hold the fist for a few seconds, think of the tension in your hand.
- Open your hand slowly and notice the tension leaving your hand. Feel your hand getting lighter as you relax.
- Try this technique on other parts of your body, like your legs, shoulders, and feet.

18. A simple technique: counting

One of the easiest things to do when you are having a panic attack is to count. When the panic attack starts, make sure that you move yourself to a quiet and safe place to be. If you are doing something like driving or walking in a crowd, take yourself to the side of the road or somewhere safe to sit. Once you are in a safe place, close your eyes and begin counting to ten. It might seem hard to do during your episode, but be patient and keep trying to count to ten. Once you have reached ten, try to get to twenty and so on, until your anxiety goes away.

If you can't close your eyes, you can still count. Continue with the task and count as far as you can, or count the same numbers over and over. Along with counting, don't forget to breathe.

19. Make a plan

Pick a friend or a family member to help you when you have a panic attack and have a plan especially for them to follow. For example, you can have them take you to a quiet and secure place when an episode occurs. You can also teach this person a technique that would help you lower the intensity of your panic attack, such as deep breathing. You can also discuss whether or not this person should consider taking you to the ER. Overall, it is important to have a plan that you can share with a person that you trust.

20. Breathing and your panic attacks

A common symptom of a panic attack is shortness of breath and thoughts of hyperventilating. The way to overcome this is to remember to use your breathing techniques while you are having a panic attack. Learn how to slow your breathing down; in fact, taking a deep breath of air while counting to ten, then counting to ten again when you let out your breath is a good way to combat your shortness of breath. By taking deliberate breaths, you can really help yourself calm down and reduce the intensity of your panic attack (Star, 2020).

21. Cutting down on the intensity of your panic attack

You can call someone on the phone who is prepared to help you when a panic attack episode occurs. You can also try counting to 100 or doing another mental action that can distract you from your panic attack.

22. Manage your time to relieve stress

Break down tasks into manageable pieces and set deadlines to reach them. Don't overcommit to more work than you can handle. It is also good to manage your personal life with a structured schedule that includes downtime or relaxation periods. Don't be afraid to set boundaries with coworkers and people in your personal life, as it is important for you to feel periods of calm as often as possible.

RESOURCES

American Psychiatric Association. (2013). *Diagnostic and Statistical Manual of Mental Disorders* (5th edition). American Psychiatric Association.

Ankrom, S. (2019). Psychotherapy for treating panic disorder. *Verywell Mind.* https://www.verywellmind.com/psychotherapy-for-the-treatment-of-panic-disorder-2584312

Anxiety and Depression Association of America. (n.d.). Facts and Statistics. *Anxiety and Depression Association of America*. https://adaa.org/about-adaa/press-room/facts-statistics

Carbonell, D. (2020). A breathing exercise to calm panic attacks. *Anxiety Coach.* https://www.anxietycoach.com/breathingexercise.html

Carbonell, D. (2020). The key to overcoming panic attacks. *Anxiety Coach.* https://www.anxietycoach.com/overcoming-panic-attacks.html

Carlsen, M. H., Halvorsen, B. L., Holte, K. Bøhn, S. K., Dragland, S., Sampson, L., Willey, C., Senoo, H., Umezono, Y., Sanada, C., Barikmo, I., Berhe, N., Willett, W. C., Phillips, K. M., Jacobs, D. R. Jr., & Blomhoff, R. (2010). The total antioxidant content of more than 3100 foods, beveages, spices, herbs and supplements used worldwide. *Nutrition Journal, 9*, 3. https://doi.org/10.1186/1475-2891-9-3

Cirino, E. (2018). Anxiety exercises to help you relax. *Healthline.* https://www.healthline.com/health/anxiety-exercises

Crawford, J. (2018). How can you stop a panic attack? *Medical News Today.* https://www.medicalnewstoday.com/articles/321510

Elliot, C. H., & Smith, L. L. (2010). *Overcoming anxiety for dummies* (2nd edition). Wiley Publishing Inc.

Exposure therapy. (2015). GoodTherapy. https://www.goodtherapy.org/learn-about-therapy/types/exposure-therapy

Gotter, A. (2018). 11 ways to stop a panic attack. *Healthline.* https://www.healthline.com/health/how-to-stop-a-panic-attack

Gotter, A. (2019). EMDR therapy: What you need to know. *Healthline*. https://www.healthline.com/health/emdr-therapy

Healthline Editorial Team. (2018). Everything you need to know about stress. *Healthline*. https://www.healthline.com/health/stress

Hilmire, M. R., DeVylder, J. E., & Forestell, C. A. (2015). Fermented foods, neuroticism, and social anxiety: An interaction model. *Psychiatry Research, 228*(2), 203-8. https://doi.org/10.1016/j.psychres.2015.04.023

Holmes, L. (2017). Panic attack myths we need to stop believing. *Huffington Post*. https://www.huffingtonpost.ca/entry/panic-attack-myths_n_6509750

How can I prevent panic attacks? (2019). WebMD. https://www.webmd.com/anxiety-panic/how-prevent-panic-attacks#1

How do you feel scared? (n.d.). This Way Up. https://thiswayup.org.au/how-do-you-feel/scared/

How to stop panic attacks? (n.d.). Barends Psychology Practice. https://barendspsychology.com/how-to-stop-panic-attacks/

Katie's story: Recovering from panic attacks, anxiety, and depression. (n.d.). Mental Health Foundation. https://www.mentalhealth.org.uk/stories/katies-story-recovering-panic-attacks-anxiety-and-depression

Mayo Clinic Staff. (n.d.). Panic attacks and panic disorder. *Mayo Clinic*. https://www.mayoclinic.org/diseases-conditions/panic-attacks/symptoms-causes/syc-20376021

Miller, T. (2017). 9 people describe what it feels like to have a panic attack. *Self*. https://www.self.com/story/9-people-describe-what-it-feels-like-to-have-a-panic-attack

Naidoo, U. (2019). Nutritional strategies to ease anxiety. *Harvard Health Publishing*. https://www.health.harvard.edu/blog/nutritional-strategies-to-ease-anxiety-201604139441

Niemiec, R. M. (2017). 3 definitions of mindfulness that might surprise you. *Psychology Today*. https://www.psychologytoday.com/us/blog/what-matters-most/201711/3-definitions-mindfulness-might-surprise-you

Panic and panic attacks. (2019). GoodTherapy. https://www.goodtherapy.org/learn-about-therapy/issues/panic

Rauch, J. (2016). How to handle a panic attack at work: The complete guide. *The Talkspace Voice*. https://www.talkspace.com/blog/how-to-handle-a-panic-attack-at-work-the-complete-guide/

Smith, M., Segal, R., & Segal, J. (2019). Therapy for anxiety disorders. *HelpGuide*. https://www.helpguide.org/articles/anxiety/therapy-for-anxiety-disorders.htm

Star, K. (2019). Cognitive behavioral therapy for panic disorder. *Verywell Mind*. https://www.verywellmind.com/cognitive-behavioral-therapy-2584290

Star, K. (2019). EMDR for panic attacks and anxiety. *Verywell Mind*. https://www.verywellmind.com/emdr-for-panic-disorder-2584292

Star, K. (2016). 7 common myths about panic attacks. *Verywell Mind*. https://www.verywellmind.com/common-myths-about-panic-attacks-2584405

The key to calm: 10 relaxation techniques for panic attacks. (n.d.). Dignity Health. https://www.dignityhealth.org/articles/the-key-to-calm-10-relaxation-techniques-for-panic-attacks

Vandergriendt, C. (2019). What's the difference between a panic attack and an anxiety attack? *Healthline*. https://www.healthline.com/health/panic-attack-vs-anxiety-attack

Ways to stop a panic attack. (2019). WebMD. https://www.webmd.com/anxiety-panic/ss/slideshow-ways-to-stop-panic-attack

Overcome Social Anxiety

Proven Solutions and Treatments That Cure Social Disorders, Phobias, People-Pleasing, and Shyness. Drastically Improve Your Self Esteem, Build Confidence, and Just Be Yourself

Derick Howell

TABLE OF CONTENTS

INTRODUCTION

Have you ever prepared so much for a presentation only to get there and just freeze up or stutter through your talk? You've probably also felt that mild uneasiness that comes with talking to strangers, right? It may be normal to feel a bit nervous in social situations, but if your everyday interactions are causing you fear, embarrassment, self-consciousness, and significant anxiety, then you have what is called social anxiety – a disorder that can ruin your life if you don't overcome it.

There are differing degrees of social anxiety, but, all in all, it can make us act awkwardly in any social situation. Social anxiety disorder is a mental health condition that makes people feel irrational anxiety whenever they interact socially. For these people, interaction with others is very fearful; they are mostly scared or anxious about being evaluated or judged negatively. If not kept in check, it can create fear in almost every area of one's life, amongst other things. It also causes low self-esteem, depression, negative thoughts, heightened sensitivity to criticism, and poor social skills.

Social anxiety is very prevalent. Some people have even concluded that it is just the way they are, and they can't do anything about it, but that is not correct. The difference between those who overcome social anxiety and those who live with it is that the former did something about it, and the other chose to resign to their fate.

In a broad sense, it is okay to be shy; most of us can be shy to varying degrees. But if your level of shyness is high enough to deter you from living your best life, then it is abnormal, and something needs to be done about it. Because if you think of it, nothing that is within your power to change should hamper your progress in life. Nothing within your control should stop you from living your best life.

Social anxiety can cause you to blow a career opportunity, ruin that presentation you've prepared so much for, or freeze up on a date and go home wondering what went wrong. If you have ever been in any of these situations, you are not alone. Millions of Americans are with you on this. The good news is you can do something about it, and reading this book is taking a step in the right direction.

There are various treatments and steps, as well as lifestyle and mindset changes you can take to get over your fear of social interactions. Social anxiety is a thing of the mind, and that is where we must go if we wish to overcome it. While therapies that work to adjust the mindset, such as Cognitive Behavioral Therapy (CBT), have proven to be effective against social anxiety, lifestyle changes such as reducing stress, exercising more, participating in social events, getting enough sleep, and eating healthier are also good ways of handling social anxiety. In the course of this book, we will take an in-depth look into the different ways that can help you reclaim your life from the chilly grip of social anxiety.

I know these methods will prove effective for you, because as a professional speaker and an anxiety coach who has helped several people with social anxiety, and after having suffered from it myself, I can say that I know what works (and what doesn't). I have presented on the topic multiple times and written several pieces to help people with a social anxiety disorder. I am particularly passionate about this subject because it nearly robbed me of my dreams, and when I successfully moved past it, I was on the right path again. That freedom I felt after breaking free is my motivation, and I hope that before you flip the last page of this book, you too will experience that freedom.

Why should you aim for this freedom? You should do so for everything. The benefits are so numerous, and I can attest to that from firsthand experience. When you eventually rid yourself of social anxiety disorder, you will finally get the chance to:

- Be yourself
- Socialize more
- Gain more friends
- Be more comfortable in public
- Increase your self-esteem
- Experience freedom from excruciating thoughts
- Experience freedom from extreme sensitivity
- And more...

How do I know this? I used to experience terrible fear whenever I would go on stage to talk, or when meeting new people, or countless other social settings - but the tips in this book have been the most beneficial for me, and that has helped me get over my fears and anxiety. Now, I am a well-established speaker and writer who has managed to make a name for myself. I have also succeeded in building successful relationships that have kept my emotional and business life in good shape. I socialize very well and enjoy life. You're probably wondering if I also have good self-esteem? You sure can bet on that.

However, don't be fooled. I did not achieve these dramatic results by simply being extraordinary. It is not just me, as millions of Americans are waking up to reality and ridding themselves of this burden. I've watched people under my mentorship go from extremely timid and shy to daring and outgoing. You can be next!

What am I promising to you? After reading this book, you will overcome social anxiety (that, I am sure of). I will not hold back anything from you as I will dole out every step, system, and hack that has worked for me and countless others, and I will provide you with actionable steps to help you get over your social anxiety in no time.

You can start facing your fears and getting over your social anxiety as soon as you start reading this book. With every single minute, you are held up with social anxiety; you let opportunities pass you by. Remember that the future belongs to those who act now. All it takes is for you to read this book, follow the action steps outlined within, and you will see drastic changes unfold in your life.

Continue reading to find out the secrets that have helped me and countless others get over the worst of social anxiety. Don't just read this book; make a decision to follow every step I have included. Two people might read this book and experience differing impacts. The hungrier you are for results, the faster you will get them with this book.

CHAPTER ONE:

What is Social Anxiety?

The term social anxiety is often confused with shyness, but they are two totally different things. The nervousness and uncomfortable feeling that comes with a social event is social anxiety. In this section, I will give you a detailed explanation of what social anxiety is. My aim of doing this is to help you understand what social anxiety is, the different ways it can affect you, why it affects you, when it happens, what triggers it, and what it feels like when it is happening. I believe that when you have understood these aspects, then you can be better prepared to handle the anxiety more effectively. So, let's explore together.

So, What Really Is Social Anxiety?

Social anxiety is the extreme fear of having a negative evaluation by other people. People with this disorder are always on edge when they are around people because they fear that they might embarrass themselves. The fear is stemming from the fact that they just don't feel good enough about themselves. As if that was not enough, they still fear that they may be judged for showing signs that suggest they are anxious, such as sweating, trembling, or blushing. The problem can easily snowball.

To escape this maze of anxiety, people with social anxiety often keep to themselves and avoid social gatherings. But the problem with this decision is that social gatherings are inescapable. Think of the classroom, job interviews, group conversions, parties, balls, events, beaches, cinemas… they all scream “social gathering.” So if you must avoid “social gatherings” you are indirectly avoiding life.

This reminds me of when I was in school. I would refuse to raise my hand to answer a question in class, even when I knew the answer. The few times I tried, it didn't end well, as I made such a mess of myself that I could not even look my mates in the eyes after class. So I decided, I'm just going to stay silent in class. Do you know what that cost me? It caused me to not have a good relationship with any of my teachers because I doubt they ever noticed me in class. Less bright students went on to build lasting relationships with those professors, and sometimes it even showed in their grades. Not that the professors were biased, but being close to a professor will inspire you to work harder and score better grades to impress them.

Occurrence

If you have experienced the symptoms of this disorder, don’t think it is just you. It is not just you. According to the 2017 statistics from the National Institute of Mental Health, about 7% of people in the United States have suffered social anxiety over the last year. And of the rest, another 12% will suffer social anxiety at some point in their lives.

Types of Social Anxiety Disorder

According to the Diagnostic and Statistical Manual of Mental Disorders (DSM-5), there are two categories of SAD. These categories are Generalized Social Anxiety and Performance-Only Social Anxiety. Before now, it was known as generalized SAD and specific SAD. The specific was replaced with “performance-only” since the "specific" was originally referring to when a patient suffers anxiety when performing.

Let’s take a brief look at the two categories:

Generalized Social Anxiety

This refers to the category of people who experience fear and anxiety in both performance and social settings. This disorder is considered to be more serious than performance-only SAD because it is not selective, and it is experienced more frequently. According to the DSM-5, sufferers of Generalized social anxiety experience fear and anxiety when:

1. Exposed to unfamiliar people and prone to scrutiny
2. Scared of possible humiliation

In mild cases, people with generalized social anxiety can be comfortable with their close friends and families.

Performance-Only Social Anxiety

As the name suggests, people with this disorder will only feel fear and anxiety when they are in a performance situation. To demonstrate this, one can experience no anxiety in social gatherings but become anxious when it is time to perform before a group of people. Performance can be an art or a speech.

If you have this form of SAD, don't celebrate yet; it can still hold you back in its right. This form of SAD can greatly hamper your hopes of progressing in your career or other performance-based achievements.

Aside from when they feel their anxiety, there are other differences between the two categories of SAD. The differences are in their method of treatment, response to treatment, physical symptoms during an attack, and the age they were when they first experienced anxiety.

You need to know the type of disorder you have before progressing to the cure section of this book. This is an ideal time for you to conduct a self-check and be completely truthful to yourself on where and when you get anxious, so you can know how to properly apply the techniques and steps I will be sharing with you in the latter chapters of this book. It is usually best to adapt treatment methods that are tailored for a specific condition to get the appropriate result.

Knowing If You Have Social Anxiety Disorder

At first, some people make the mistake of thinking their symptoms are a result of a non-psychiatric medical condition. Start by eliminating this line of thought. You can do this by ensuring that you are not suffering from anxiety for other medical reasons such as hyperthyroidism, endocrine problems, certain heart problems, or low blood sugar. You can have a health care provider evaluate your condition.

Can it Lead to Other Complications?

Social anxiety disorder, just like other serious health conditions, can have complications. The most common one is its persistence throughout a person's lifetime. If you don't do anything about it, it can stay with you throughout your life. Most people erroneously believe that when they grow older, they will outgrow their anxiety. I hate to break it to you... but it doesn't work that way. Rather, it gathers momentum as you grow older.

Negative self-talk and trouble being assertive are also some signs of extreme social anxiety.

In some severe cases, the sufferer might choose to drop out of school, or quit work, or go into isolation. If this happens, and it is not checked, depression, and even suicidal thoughts, may follow. Unchecked social anxiety has even driven some to cut their lives short.

More specific complications that could arise are:

Comorbidity

Comorbidity is a concept in medicine in which other conditions coexist with the condition in focus. Social anxiety is also comorbid. Statistics tell us 66% of patients suffering from SAD are also suffering from other related mental illnesses. Some of the common illnesses it coexists with are clinical depression, anxiety disorders, and avoidant personality disorder. Experts say SAD patients are likely to develop clinical depression because they lack personal relationships and keep to themselves most of the time. A publication from the National Center for Biotechnology Information has found that people with SAD are 1.49 to 3.5 times more likely to have clinical depression, too.

Substance Abuse

Since depression and anxiety are often too much for people with SAD, they may start seeking something to let them "self medicate," that they believe will help their condition. That is where substance abuse comes in. Statistics have it that 20% of people with SAD are also alcohol dependent.

And how well do they fare when they start depending on substances? They become even worse. It has been discovered that socially anxious people who depend on substances are less likely to try group-based treatments.

Key Insight

Some socially anxious people are aware that their anxiety is misplaced; they know it is uncalled for. Sometimes, they even demand an answer from themselves as to why they are allowing such a minute issue to bother them so much. But then, their anxious feelings persist and continue escalating. So, knowing you are socially anxious isn't total freedom, but it's a good step in the right direction. You will need to seek a real solution like the ones discussed in this book to set yourself free. No matter how chronic your social anxiety is, it is curable, and there is hope for you.

What Social Anxiety Is Not

Social anxiety is often confused with many other things. Below, we'll look at some of the things we experience (that may make us believe we have social anxiety) to give us a better understanding of what it is.

It is not "Stage Fright"

We all know that stage fright is a very common phenomenon among humans. Most people will feel nervous if they must stand before a crowd and speak. If that is what you are feeling, it is normal. You are getting that feeling because you are not used to the crowd. You could try enrolling in a speech club that would give you the opportunity to try to talk to a group of people.

Also, most people can feel slightly nervous when attending a social event or taking part in a competition. I will not classify that as a social anxiety disorder. It becomes SAD when you experience excessive fear and anxiety with everyday social events. You are more self-conscious, and you fear embarrassment even when nothing is embarrassing about you.

A person that experiences stage fright will feel comfortable with everyday tasks, such as eating outside or filling out forms in the presence of people, but you may have SAD when these trivial events cause you anxiety.

It is not a Panic Disorder

Due to the nature of social anxiety, people tend to confuse it with panic disorders. Even though they are both in the five major anxiety disorders that are listed in the DSM-5, they still differ in many ways.

The difference is that socially anxious people do not experience panic attacks. What they may experience are anxiety attacks. People with a panic disorder may not realize that it is panic that they are feeling. But people with social anxiety understand that what they are experiencing are fear and anxiety. A person with a panic disorder may even need to visit the hospital after an attack because they may think there is something physically wrong with them, but it is not so for people with social anxiety.

Diagnosis

Sometimes, it can be difficult to tell for sure whether what you have is SAD or not. The best way to know is to check with a doctor or healthcare professional. They can carry out a physical evaluation and basic psychiatric examination. In the physical examination phase, the doctor aims to see if there could be any other physical causes for the way you are feeling. If they ascertain that there is no physical explanation for your condition, they may recommend a psychiatric examination. A psychiatrist or a psychologist will ask you for the symptoms you have experienced, when you experienced them, how often you experience them, and for how long you've been having the symptoms. Some of them will require you to fill out a questionnaire to help with your evaluation.

With SAD, your examiner will always want to find out if the anxiety you feel is so intense that it can interfere with your daily life. Because, as I said earlier, mild anxiety can be normal. He will check if your anxiety can interfere with your career, relationships, or other social concepts.

The mental practitioner is not quick to label you with SAD. He must go through due process. In fact, in the U.S and some other countries, the symptoms you describe must agree with the criteria stated in the Diagnostic and Statistical Manual (DSM) for social anxiety.

Unlike other categories of medical conditions, mental conditions cannot be verified in a lab test. So it will be judged based on some predetermined criteria. In the case of SAD, the criteria are published in a handbook known as the Diagnostic and Statistical Manual of Mental Disorders. It is published by the American Psychiatric Association (APA).

SAD Diagnostic Criteria

Now let's look at the criteria as outlined in the Diagnostic and Statistical Manual of Mental Disorders:

- The patient fears any social situation that can make him the focal point, such as public speaking, eating outside, or meeting new people.
- The patient has a marked fear of humiliating or embarrassing himself or getting rejected by people because of his actions or his symptoms of anxiety.
- The patient experiences fear or anxiety that is not proportional to the threat.
- The patient has experienced this condition for 6 months or longer.
- Due to the fear, the patient experiences significant distress or impairment in certain areas of his life, such as career, school, or relationship.
- The fear or anxiety being felt by the patient is not due to the effect of other drugs or medications. The anxiety is not caused by other mental or physical health conditions.
- And if the patient only experiences these fears when they are performing before people, then it is not generalized, it is of the "performance only" category.

Can it be cured?

This condition can be cured using psychotherapy and medication. Let’s look at the options available to you.

Psychotherapy

We have established that the anxiety and fear you feel whenever you get those attacks are not real. But you will never see it like that. Those people you think don’t like you? The truth is that they do. These incorrect assumptions you hold about yourself are not true. To help you see these things for what they are, psychological treatments will use several established techniques that will expose the truth about your problems. It is not going to happen all of a sudden; it will be a gradual process. But when it is done, you will be able to cope with those symptoms and overcome them eventually.

One very important therapy that has proven very effective against social anxiety is Cognitive Behavioral Therapy (CBT). I will show you how you can use this therapy to overcome social anxiety later in this book. Other therapies, such as interpersonal therapy and family therapy, can also be used for handling social anxiety.

CBT is particularly helpful because it will help to keep track of your thought patterns that are responsible for your symptoms. It takes attention away from what other people think about you to what you think about yourself. This is important because it is the way you think about yourself that gives you the symptoms you feel. With CBT, you will learn to identify and modify those negative thoughts that have held you down for a long while now.

Medications

In severe cases of SAD, medication can also be used. Several medications exist for this condition, but the most common is the selective serotonin reuptake inhibitors (SSRIs). They are widely used because people consider it the safest and most effective.

Examples of medications that are based on selective serotonin reuptake inhibitors (SSRIs) are

- Paroxetine (Paxil, Paxil CR)
- Fluvoxamine (Luvox, Luvox CR)
- Sertraline (Zoloft)
- Fluoxetine (Prozac, Sarafem)

This medication can have some side effects on some people. The most common side effects are:

- Headaches
- Nausea
- Insomnia
- Sexual dysfunction

Apart from selective serotonin reuptake inhibitors (SSRIs), other medications that can also be used are Benzodiazepines and beta-blockers.

Benzodiazepines

These are primarily anti-anxiety medications. Common examples are alprazolam (Xanax) and clonazepam (Klonopin). However, due to the addictive nature of these medications, courses are usually kept short to avoid dependence.

The side effects of benzodiazepines may include:

- Confusion
- Loss of balance
- Lightheadedness
- Drowsiness
- Memory loss

Beta-blockers

We know how adrenaline is meant to help us deal with an emergency. In people with social anxiety, it can cause undue anxiety even when there is no emergency. Beta-blockers numb the stimulating effects of adrenaline. But this treatment is not continuous. It is only used for specific situations, such as when you might want to make a presentation.

The suggestions I have provided here are only for informational purposes and shouldn't be substituted for professional medical advice and treatment. Always seek the advice of a therapist or your physician for the medication to use. Never delay or disregard seeking medical advice from a professional because of the information I have provided here.

Now that we have seen social anxiety for what it really is, the next step is to know why people get socially anxious, knowing the root cause will put us in a better position to deal with your SAD accordingly.

In this chapter, you have learned what social anxiety is all about, the meaning, types, criteria for diagnosing the disorder, and possible treatment for it. This aims at introducing you to the concept of Social Anxiety Disorder (SAD). In the next chapter, I will be discussing why people get anxious and the causes of anxiety.

CHAPTER TWO:

Why Do People Get Socially Anxious?

In the first chapter of this book, we took a general look at the subject matter; what is social anxiety? In this chapter, we will be focusing on how, when, and why it affects you. I will be answering some of the common questions you might have on the SAD. Most of the questions you've been secretly asking yourself are answered here, just in case you are not sure if you have a social anxiety disorder. I will leave no stone unturned since I am writing from the abundance of my experience and knowledge. Now, shall we?

When Does It Happen?

Different people with social anxiety disorders may indeed feel it in varying ways, but some certain situations are more likely to trigger it. The following situations are ones that people with this disorder tend to dread the most. And yes, your guess is right, they are all bits of social settings. They include:

- Speaking in public.
- Conversing with strangers.
- Going on dates.
- Making and maintaining eye contact with other people.
- Entering and staying in crowded rooms
- Using restrooms outside.
- Meeting with important people.

- Attending and fielding questions in interviews.
- Partying and being friends.
- Eating in the presence of other people.
- Getting introduced to strangers.
- Being teased.
- Being criticized.
- Going to public places such as school and work.
- Being watched while executing a task.
- Starting conversations with people.
- Declining people's requests.
- Reading aloud.
- Sending texts.

What Does It Feel Like?

Now that we know some of the common triggers, let's look at the most common ways it manifests itself.

1. Feeling Isolated

Look at this statement from an anonymous social anxiety patient

"[Social anxiety] makes me feel as if I am the only one suffering that way, and everyone else is just fine with going out and having a good time together. It makes me feel that no one like me, so why would they want to talk to me? When they do talk to me, I always feel they are trying to find an excuse to get away and go talk to someone else."

From this statement, we can sense a feeling of isolation. It tells you that nobody likes you and nobody wants to be your friend. It makes you feel people don't like you, and they are avoiding you.

2. Erroneous Beliefs

We can see that this condition lies to you. It also paints other people's lives as beds of roses, and only you have to cope with a thorny bed. But in reality, everyone has their fair share of life issues to deal with. But you likely won't see it like that. Instead, you will see yourself as an unfortunate one.

3. It Freezes Your Reasoning

Another patient narrates his experience by saying:

> *"Internal' feelings that] include a shakiness in my voice, [and] brain fog that stops me from thinking straight," but also to "physical feelings [that] include an upset stomach, loss of appetite, sweaty hands, muscle stiffness."*

This statement captures most of the common symptoms you will find in people with SAD, especially when they are in the midst of people.

What Effects Does it Have on You?

1. Isolation and Depression

Life is more fun and fulfilling when spent with friends, family, and even strangers. But when you let social anxiety close your eyes from seeing this, you just spiral down towards depression. When you experience a problem, you will blow it out of proportion since you will never share it with someone who might help you see it another way.

2. Difficulty with employment and school

People with this disorder always try to choose a path that can help them avoid as many people as possible. The result is a drastic drop in the opportunities available to you. Your intelligence level may be such that you will thrive well in the noble professions such as medicine, engineering, or law, but since you dread interaction, you will not live up to your true potential.

3. Gateway for other sickness

You might not know it yet because maybe you have not gotten to that stage, but social anxiety can open the flood gate for other individual ailments such as substance abuse and life impairment. Because once you slide into depression and do not have any way of socializing, the next thing might be to result in substance abuse, extreme pornography consumption, masturbation, or game addiction. The result is impairment for life.

4. Relationship and family difficulties

The problem here is that people with SAD will convince themselves that nobody wants them, and they will lock out every person who cares about them, and this can spell doom for their relationships. They dread and avoid personal relationships.

5. Low Self-Esteem

People with social anxiety are usually trapped in that feeling of not being good enough. This thought pattern can have destabilizing effects because it will affect the productivity of the sufferer in whatever they do. they will condemn themselves to believe they are second class citizens, and it will show in every aspect of life.

6. Heightened Sensitivity to Criticism

People with social anxiety can easily misinterpret situations, and that makes them easily offended. They can misinterpret constructive criticism that is intended for their own good into something offensive.

Why Do People Get Socially Anxious?

The reason you feel socially anxious might stem from why you became socially anxious in the first place. For example, if you got your anxiety from your first role in that ill-fated drama in high school, then it is very likely that you will get socially anxious whenever you are the center of attention.

This means that two socially anxious people might have different reasons for avoiding a similar situation. But the common reasons fall into the following list:

- Being judged by others in social situations

- Being embarrassed or humiliated
- Accidentally offending someone
- Being the center of attention

What Are You Avoiding?

People with social anxiety disorder have this behavioral problem of avoiding anxiety-provoking situations. As one that is socially anxious, if you anticipate going to a social event, maybe going to a party, you may find yourself getting anxious and decide not to go. Immediately after you choose not to go, you begin to feel your anxiety decreasing and feel more comfortable.

The comfort you feel from the reduction of anxiety after you decide not to go out will only reinforce your avoidance. Now your reward for avoidance is the short-term comfort you feel. This comfort will maintain your fear of negative social situations even when you don't experience embarrassment. For instance, you are lost and trying to find your way, and then you see someone approaching you. You felt so anxious talking to the person and decided not to, and immediately, your anxiety drops. The increase in your anxiety has a lesson attached to it. To either stop talking to people or don't ask for help, in order to feel less anxious. But how long are you going to avoid it?

A crucial element of Cognitive Behavioral Therapy (CBT) is about helping an individual with a social anxiety disorder practice sustainable social situations and to stay in them long enough to learn that nothing bad will happen if they have to speak to a stranger or ask for help. Once this is realized, the anxiety will subside. They also get to learn that being in social situations is something they can do, and their willingness to confront their fears is empowering. After that realization, they will start seeing themselves as the kind of person that can do virtually anything.

What Are the Likely Causes?

According to experts, social anxiety disorders can be traced back to both genetic and environmental causes. All of the cases discussed below are not agreed upon by all, as researchers have differing views on them.

1. Genetic causes:

It has been observed that the condition can run in families. If that's the case, some researchers think that genetic links could be a cause of social anxiety, although it is still being researched. This research is attempting to establish just how much of it is hereditary and how much is acquired by individuals.

If your parents or siblings have it, you have a higher risk. I am adding this extra detail so that you can look out for symptoms in your young ones. When detected early, it is easier to manage and cure. If any of your first-degree relatives have SAD, you are 2 to 6 times more likely to suffer from the disorder. (Cuncic 2019)

Several studies have come up with varying heritability rates for SAD, but all of them seem to agree around it falling between 30% to 40%. From this statistic, we can conclude that 1 of every 3 SAD cases can be traced back to genetics. (Concic 2019)

However, scientists have not been able to name the particular genetic makeup that causes SAD. But they have found the chromosomes that are linked with other anxiety disorders like panic attacks and agoraphobia.

2. Certain chemicals in the body

With the discovery that wrong levels of serotonin, a brain chemical, an individual may experience heightened sensitivity, scientists are trying to see if there are chemicals in the body that can increase the chances of a social anxiety disorder (SAD).

3. Neurotransmitters

Neurotransmitters are the chemical medium through which your brain transmits signals from one cell to another. If there is an imbalance in the levels of this chemical, you can lead to social anxiety disorder.

The common neurotransmitters that have been traced back to anxiety are:

- Norepinephrine
- Dopamine
- Serotonin
- Gamma-aminobutyric acid (GABA)

Psychologists have tested people with a social anxiety disorder, and they discovered that most of them have imbalances in the levels of these neurotransmitters. If we understand how these chemicals interact to bring about anxiety, it could help us in deciding the best medication route to take when attempting to cure the disorder.

4. Brain structure

Then again, some researchers are of the opinion that the amygdala can influence fear response and in some cases, lead to excessive reactions.

Medical researchers are using a technique known as neuroimaging to develop an image of the brain, much the same way x-rays create an image of the inside of our body. They are using this technique to compare blood flow in different areas of the brain that are involved in anxiety, in both phobics and normal people while they are addressing a group of people.

Four areas of the brain are actively involved in anxiety:

i. The brain stem: This part of the brain controls heart rate and breathing. You know how different this can be in socially anxious people.

ii. The limbic system: This part of the brain controls mood and anxiety levels. So if it is faulty, you can experience mood swings and high anxiety levels.

iii. The prefrontal cortex: This part of the brain is responsible for assessing a threat and giving feedback to the brain. If it blows perceived threats out of proportion, you may respond with anxiety.

iv. The motor cortex: This part of the brain is responsible for controlling your muscles.

Using the neuroimaging technique, as we discussed above, scientists studied blood flow in the brain and found some differences with the phobics group when they were addressing a crowd. There was a study in which they used type Positron Emission Tomography (PET), a type of neuroimaging techniques. In the study, they showed that the amygdala, which is a part of the limbic system that controls fear, experienced more blood flow in people with SAD when they were addressing a crowd. (Tillfors et al., 2001).

When they did the same study for people without SAD, they discovered that the cerebral cortex, which was associated with thought, got more blood flow.

1. Weather and demographics:

Some researchers also believe that your location can increase your chances of having SAD. These researchers claim that people in the Mediterranean countries are less likely to have social anxiety disorder when compared to people in Scandinavian countries. They say that warmer weather and higher population density reduce avoidance of social gatherings. And when one goes out often and interacts with people, his chances of suffering from SAD are greatly reduced.

2. Cultural or Societal Factors:

There are still some researchers who believe that cultural factors play a role in reducing social anxiety rates. For instance, if someone is from a culture that encourages communal living, like in traditional

African settings, they will have a lesser chance of suffering social anxiety.

On the contrary, if you grew up in a society that emphasizes collectivistic orientation, like Korea and Japan, you have a higher probability of developing social anxiety. For instance, these cultures have a syndrome known as taijin kyofusho. A syndrome centered around the fear of making other people around you uncomfortable (Nagakami et al, 2019).

If you are scared of making people uncomfortable, then that can degenerate into social anxiety. These cultures also emphasize how you fit in.

Risk Factors

Risk factors are the things that can increase your chances of succumbing to social anxiety disorder. In most cases, this disorder starts between early and mid-teenage age, but it can also start earlier than that. At that point, some triggers can heighten the risk of getting the disorder.

Some of the factors are discussed below:

Gender: It has been established that the disorder is more predominant among the female population than the male.

Upbringing: It is also believed that if you grew up witnessing traces of social anxiety with people around you, you could also develop the disorder. So if your parents avoided social gatherings, and they were too protective with you, you can develop the disorder too.

Psychologists believe that fearful and socially anxious parents can transfer both verbal and non-verbal cues that can trigger social anxiety. So if your mum is someone that cares too much about what people will say about her or you, you might grow up being anxious about what people think about you.

Also, as a child, if you were not allowed to go out and socialize very often, you can grow up without developing appropriate social skills. And if any of your parents were particularly critical, overprotective, or rejecting, you can also end up being socially anxious.

Hurtful Childhood Experiences: As a child, if you suffered bullying and rejection from people around you, you might have grown up thinking you are not good enough, and that is why you got picked on. If not checked, you might grow up with this mindset and you will start avoiding people in general. Other extreme experiences such as rape and parental conflicts, can also increase a child's chances of having SAD.

One's Personality: Some people are naturally withdrawn and shy. These people are more prone to social anxiety disorder when compared with their bold and daring counterparts.

A demanding ordeal might also trigger it: For instance, if your dream is to be a performer, and on your first day of mounting the stage, you performed very badly and got booed off stage, you might dread having that experience again, and withdraw yourself from public appearance.

Having a feature that attracts attention: This is one of the most common causes of social anxiety. Common examples are facial disfigurement, speech impediments such as stuttering, and health conditions such as Parkinson's disease. Features like these may keep them on edge, and so they have a higher level of self-consciousness. This heightened self-consciousness can culminate into social anxiety, especially if the bearer gets insulted for such a feature.

As you have seen in this discourse, there is no particular single cause for SAD. What we have are a bunch of factors that could combine to cause it. When we start looking at the solutions later in this book, we will look at why it is important to find out the root cause of SAD during treatment.

What Are the Physical Symptoms?

People with SAD are too conscious of other people's assessments of them, and oftentimes, they believe the assessment is negative. The following physical symptoms will often manifest. For example, if you are giving a speech and you stutter just once, you might think that everyone in the room picked it up on it, but it's far more likely that they didn't. You will then tell yourself that you are a terrible public speaker, and these people know it. This thought pattern will make you stutter more, sweat, or tremble.

The common physical symptoms are:

- Blushing
- Difficulty talking
- Stammering
- Shaking or trembling
- Increased heart rate
- Fast pace of breathing
- Sweating
- Mind going blank
- Lightheadedness
- Difficulty concentrating
- Urge to use the toilet
- Dizziness
- Muscle tension
- Vomiting
- Nausea or stomach upset
- Urge to escape or leave
- Stumbling and falling when walking past a group of people. This happens when you become worried about the way you walk.
- Crying
- Dry mouth and throat
- Clammy and cold hands
- Diarrhea

- Heart palpitations
- Feelings of unreality (derealization)
- Feelings of detachment from oneself (depersonalization)
- Paresthesias (tingling)
- Red face
- Hot flashes
- Shortness of breath

What Are the Behavioral Symptoms?

In terms of behavior, a person with social anxiety has gone beyond shyness, and also has convinced himself that he is no good. To avoid being embarrassed for his perceived flaws, he chooses to avoid situations altogether.

The common behavioral symptoms are:

- Avoiding the situation altogether
- Avoiding similar sorts of situations
- Leaving prematurely
- Focusing on yourself
- Trying not to draw attention to yourself
- Keeping quiet
- Not looking at other people

What are the emotional symptoms?

The dominant emotional symptoms of those with social anxiety are:

- Anxiety and nervousness
- High levels of inexplicable fear
- Automatic negative emotional cycles
- In some severe but rare cases, people can even develop dysmorphia for any part of their body (mostly the face), and they will start considering themselves irrationally and negatively.

Out of all the emotional symptoms stated above, incessant and intense anxiety (fear) is the most prevalent one.

Some Negative Beliefs and Maladaptive Behavior That Can Increase Social Anxiety

People with social anxiety have some negative beliefs. These negative beliefs are more pronounced whenever there is an upcoming social situation or event. To them, these thoughts are meant to protect them from the various threats they perceive. Psychologists, Asta Klimaite, John Clarke, and Kathryn Smerling, reported some of these thoughts patterns as stated below:

"I am probably going to embarrass myself."

"I might not blend in with the rest."

"Nobody will like me."

"The people there will hate me."

"I might even pass out."

"My nervousness will show, and people will notice."

"I will not be able to say anything because I won't know what to say."

"I am not going to offer anything."

"People will not like to befriend me."

"I might even say something stupid."

"I have problems."

Something all of the statements above have in common is that they all have to do with low self-esteem. These statements are born of an inner lack of confidence. When you feel like you are unworthy, you will likely also feel you don't have anything to offer. You will then tell yourself that since you don't have anything to offer, you are not likable and that means you don't deserve social interaction like everyone else.

To be sure that the statements above don't play out as prophesied, a person in this situation will choose to bypass the social gathering. When they do this, it has immediate benefits because it allows them to escape the symptoms they dread so much. But what about the long-term demerits? The demerits of not living your life to the fullest and limiting yourself.

In this chapter, you have learned why people get anxious in social situations, the different causes of the anxious feeling, and the symptoms of anxiety (both physical and behavioral). In the next chapter, I will be giving you tips on how to deal with SAD. The tips are to help you cope and live a better life.

CHAPTER THREE:

Tips for Dealing with Social Anxiety

By this point, you should have a good idea if you have social anxiety. Feeling too anxious and inhibited when meeting people, speaking in front of people, using public restrooms or locker rooms, and eating in public are some of the common signs of social anxiety.

A lot of people with this issue will choose to ignore the signs and avoid social situations instead of facing the facts and seeking help. Like I mentioned earlier, they may even choose to use drugs and alcohol to self-medicate. However, self-medicating isn't the way out, as it can lead to an increased risk for depression, alcohol abuse, and loneliness.

To an extent, social anxiety affects a lot of people, and the good news here is that something can be done about it. In this chapter, I will be giving you some tips on how to cope with anxiety and make your life easier, happier, and more fulfilling. Let's take a look at some of those helpful tips:

Learn to Face Your Fears

As humans, it is very natural to avoid scary emotions. No one would want to walk into what already seems like a painful experience blindly. Usually, this is about you hiding from possible challenges that contribute to your joy and overall growth. You can't always hide away from this fear; it will still strike back no matter how hard you try to suppress it. It is even more likely to strike back when you need emotional equanimity the most.

If you learn how to face your fears, you will have better control of your decisions and your life. One effective way to learn how to face your fears is by facing the social situations which you are always scared of. A lot of people with social anxiety will rather avoid situations, but avoidance will only keep fueling your social anxiety.

Of course, avoiding some nerve-wracking situations can make you feel better, but it's all in the short-term. In the long run, it will prevent you from being comfortable in social situations, and you still won't know how to cope with it. For a fact, the more you keep avoiding your fears, the more those fears become frightening.

Avoiding your fears can also stop you from reaching goals you've set for yourself, and prevent you from doing the things you love to do. For example, because you are scared to speak in a group, you'd rather hide your great ideas. Because you are scared of making new friends, you'd rather be quiet and lose people who would've helped you get out of a particular situation. There are so many examples where your fear will make you lose what you should have gained.

Though it may seem somehow impossible to overcome your fear of social situations, there is still hope, and you can take it one step at a time. What you need to do is to start with situations that you can manage, and slowly work your way up to the more challenging ones. In no time, you will gain some coping skills and boost your confidence as you gradually move through the anxiety ladder.

Let's take socializing with people as an example. If it makes you feel very anxious, a way to gradually face your fears is to attend a party with a close friend – someone you are already very accustomed to. At the very least, you won't be alone or feel uncomfortable since you have a close friend around. If you continue this way, you will eventually get comfortable with this step, and then you can proceed and try introducing yourself to a stranger you meet at the party.

Another way people avoid their fears is by always being on social media or burying their nose in their phone. We live in a smart world where everything (and everyone) is always connected. So, when we experience fear of social situations, we can easily utilize our smartphones by hiding behind the phone to chat with people, know what is going on in people's lives without asking them face-to-face, and make new friends online, just to avoid social interactions. This can only do you more harm than good despite giving short-term satisfaction.

According to a 2016 study of young adults and smartphones, there were "significant positive correlations" between the overuse of smartphones and an occurrence of social anxiety.

Another 2017 study revealed that out of the 182 young adults who were smartphone users, people that showed addiction to technology displayed social anxiety, low self-esteem, and isolation.

The evolution of the world has made smartphones give us a sense of connection. According to Isaac Vaghefi, an assistant professor of management information systems at Binghamton University, New York, smartphones are a tool that gives us that immediate, short, and quick satisfaction, and it can be very triggering.

In the end, you will realize that hiding behind your smartphone can only delay you in addressing your fear of social situations. At first, you will see that facing your fears is actually scarier and can be counterintuitive, but it is always better to face your fears through a gradual process.

According to researchers, a crucial approach in the treatment of fear that stems from social anxiety is an intentional exposure to social mishaps. The goal here is to disrupt the person's supposed standards and social norms deliberately, just to break the cycle of further use of avoidance strategies and fearful anticipations.

As a result of this, people are compelled to reassess the perceived threat of a social situation after realizing that the social mishaps don't usually lead to the feared irreparable, long-lasting, and undesirable consequences. To put it simply, by intentionally approaching social situations, you will learn that a small number of slips shouldn't lead to exclusions and rejection by social groups. We are all human, and make mistakes on occasions, too; no one is above making mistakes.

For you to effectively work your way right up a society anxiety ladder, try out the tips below:

- Take it one step at a time, and don't face your biggest fear immediately. Moving too fast in climbing the ladder is never a good idea, as you may feel too embarrassed and decide to hide yourself more. Instead, take it slow, don't force things, and don't take too much since it is a gradual process.
- Exercise patience. To fully overcome social anxiety, you will need to be patient because it takes enough practice and time to master your emotions. You shouldn't give up after one or two tries and say you have done your best, the results may not be visible at that time, but will definitely be seen later.
- Learn to stay calm with the skills you have learned. You can stay calm by focusing on your breathing, taking in deep breaths, and challenging any form of negative norms.

Keep Away Negative Coping Strategies

Some psychological symptoms come from the negative mental and emotional states linked with social anxiety. This can worsen your social anxiety and makes you feel more isolated. Sometimes, you may find it so tempting to take drugs or drink alcohol to help you feel at ease and comfortable, but to be honest, these can only increase your level of anxiety.

Research revealed that social anxiety isn't limited to just inner feelings like shakiness in one's voice or having a brain fog that hinders one from thinking straight, but also has physical feelings like a loss of appetite, stomach upset, muscle stiffness, sweaty hands, and feeling faint. When people like this find themselves in social situations they can't avoid, probably a school event where a lot of people will be in attendance, they try to dampen the symptoms of their social anxiety by using some negative coping strategies. For example, smoking cigarettes or drinking alcohol.

While you may feel good after a few puffs and maybe even less worried, smoking too much will most likely make the anxiety get worse. The same thing with drinking alcohol, drinking too much of it will increase your level of anxiety. Too much alcohol intake could cause a bad mood, increased level of anxiety, and disrupted sleep patterns.

The Anxiety and Depression Association of America (ADAA) reported that about 20% of people that have social anxiety also have an alcohol use disorder. It was also revealed that the findings are associated with adults and adolescents struggling with social anxiety.

A very helpful tip that can keep your anxiety in check and help stay clear of the potential chance to worsen your anxiety symptoms is to avoid any negative strategy you have set aside to help you get by. Avoid drinking alcohol, no matter how promising the initial relaxation it gives you. It might feel comforting, but will definitely hurt you in the long run.

On the other hand, leading a healthy lifestyle, eating well, exercising regularly, and avoiding alcohol can help you cope with social anxiety.

Change your Perspective

Changing your perspective is another great tip that will help you deal with your social anxiety. By changing your understanding of the stress you are going through, you will be able to deal with anxiety better.

The major problem I see in people with SAD is that they see all stress as bad and damaging. They dread being in social situations and the thought of it alone triggers stress. If only they get to change their perspectives, and look at things from a different point of view, they wouldn't see stress as damaging. In 2013, Jeremy Jamieson, an assistant professor of psychology at the University of Rochester, New

York, conducted a study with his colleagues. In the study, it was realized that when an individual suffers from social anxiety or not, and knows how his or her body reacts to some stressors (e.g., public speaking), he will experience a little stress even in uncomfortable social situations. Meaning, they won't need to feel stressed from the social situation.

When we hear of "killer stress," our mind races, and we picture being stressed out. What it means is that our body is just preparing itself to tackle a demanding situation. It is putting together the necessary resources, delivering oxygen to the brain, and pumping blood to the major muscle groups. When we understand that there shouldn't be a cause for alarm, we will feel more at ease. Research has suggested that a coping tool that helps with negative thoughts and worries is by embracing the "yes, but" technique. This technique is all about you challenging your negative thoughts and offset them with a positive one.

For example, if you are thinking about a social situation and beginning to experience anxiety, say: "Yes, I will be attending a social gathering today where many people will be in attendance," and go ahead and add… "But, I am also an amazing person with great attributes; there will be so much to talk about when I meet people."

To switch things up for negative thoughts, one needs to counter his or her fear with positive thoughts and likely positive affirmation. This will help you reaffirm yourself and know you are making the right decision. Like I said earlier, dealing with social anxiety comes with you facing your fear, and having positive affirmations helps you do this.

Be Confident

Confidence is so magical that when you have it in abundance, it will open doors for you. It is one priceless thing that a lot of people wouldn't mind spending money for – yet it is something we all can develop. A lot of adults are crippled by shyness and social phobias; they lack the confidence to face people or be heard and seen.

Confidence is something that can be learned, just the way you would learn to ride a bike or acquire a skill: you get better at it with lots of practice. Try to act more confidently in your appearance, the way you talk, and the way you act, and you will see how positively people will react. I am not saying you should ridicule yourself, be a clown, or make a spectacle of yourself just to be seen as confident. What I mean is being more firm in whatever you do. At first, it will definitely feel terrifying, and you might want to take a step back; but you shouldn't because it only gets better each time. Practice makes perfect!

Gaining confidence doesn't happen overnight; it requires conscious effort from you just the way developing other skills require effort. By avoiding social interactions, your social anxiety will still be as it is, but when you choose to face your fears and stop avoiding them, you become ready to fight your social anxiety.

Do Something Nice for Someone

Doing something nice for someone is one good way of being in control of social situations and helps distract you from any concerns or negative thoughts you have. When I say doing something nice, you don't need to buy an extravagant gift or do more than you can afford, but a simple act of kindness will do the trick for counteracting your social anxiety.

Research has suggested that being kind can have a positive effect on one's mood. A 2017 study revealed that doing something nice for someone will activate the area in the brain that is linked to motivation and the reward cycle (Cohut, 2017).

Another 2015 study that was published in the journal *Motivation and Emotion* suggested that acting selflessly can help people with social anxiety feel more at ease when in social situations. In that same study, people who were actively involved in showing kindness to each other later on felt the need to be less avoidant of social situations. The act of kindness can be helping a stranger cross the street or helping a neighbor mow his lawn (Trew & Alden, 2015).

According to Jennifer Trew, who is one of the study authors from Simon Fraser University in Burnaby, Canada, being kind is something that will help you counter those negative social expectations by encouraging the positive expectations and perceptions of one's social environment. Kindness can reduce the level of your social anxiety and make you feel less likely to stay away from social situations.

A report from Medical News Today (MNT) published in August 2019 showed the importance of replacing negative links with positive ones in order to reduce social anxiety. For instance, by replacing bad experiences with good ones. In a bid to do this, some people were interviewed, and someone had this to say:

"People have a negative narrative in their head because that narrative comes from memories of awkward or embarrassing moments that override everything else, so if you one good interaction, you can use that momentum in the same way to get yourself another, and another. Before you know it, you have a library of positive references, and you naturally find that negative self-talk diminishing."

In the end, it all boils down to having a better mental environment.

Take a Breath

A lot of changes take place when your body is experiencing anxiety. Some of the physical symptoms linked to anxiety are dizziness, pounding chest, increased heart rate, and muscle tension. By taking a minute to slow down, your breath can position you better and be in control of your body. When it comes to breathing techniques, there are several of them that are effective in helping you calm and relax your body. I will be focusing more on the diaphragmatic breathing as a relaxation technique, later in this book.

For now, we are focusing on how to take a breath. You can start by taking a seat, be comfortable, and try to take the biggest breath you have ever taken for that day and hold it. Count from 1 to 4, then exhale slowly and push out as much air as possible. Again, take another deep breath by filling your stomach with air, and continue doing so until you realize that your breath is beginning to slow down to its normal rate.

Finally, to deal with social anxiety effectively, you need to identify those situations you avoid. Start by making a list of these types of situations, or situations that make you feel anxious just thinking about, for example, eating outside. You are in fear that people might observe how you eat or ease yourself and decide to avoid such situations — same thing with speaking in front of a group or saying hello to a stranger.

So, ask yourself, what situations provoke your anxiety, and what do you avoid? Make a list of them and know what you are dealing with. In the next chapter, I will be going deeper by showing you ways in which you can overcome anxiety.

In this chapter, I provided some useful tips you can use to deal with SAD. Using the tips requires us to make some changes in our lives. In the next chapter, I will be explaining what it means to overcome anxiety and the different ways to do so.

CHAPTER FOUR:

Overcoming Social Anxiety

Your palms are sweaty, your mind is racing, and you are finding it so difficult to bring words out of your mouth, no matter how hard you try… we've all experienced this feeling at one time or another, but some of us experience it worse, and more often than others – it all points to social anxiety.

No one wants to be embarrassed or look stupid around people, but the extreme end of this spectrum of thinking causes people to avoid social situations just to be "socially safe." But, have you asked yourself why you keep avoiding social situations so much? Your life isn't on the line, and you won't be losing anything. Yet, you keep avoiding it.

I can easily recall the same discomfort you feel when you're in public. Conversely, it can be difficult to remember physical pain with the same detail, for example, when you hit your leg on the table so badly a few days ago. So it's no surprise that research revealed humans feel social pain much more than they feel physical pain, and social pain can be relived over and over again.

In a paper by the German Socio-Economic Panel Study (SOEP) titled "Perceived Job Insecurity and Well-Being Revisited: Towards Conceptual Clarity," it was revealed that the fear associated with losing one's job is more painful than when the job is actually lost.

Most of the advice we get on how to overcome social anxiety is usually a dead end. We may have been told to just "suppress the feelings" when it comes. But what happens when the feelings are suppressed? Our ability to experience positive feelings is on the low but not the negative feelings. So what do we do then the negative feelings start creeping out?

I've rounded up some of the best strategies, from ancient stoics, mindfulness experts, and neuroscientists, to help people deal with their negative feelings associated with their anxiety disorder. The good news is that it's not that hard to do. You only need to study it, practice it, and get better at it. Now, let's move on to how you can overcome your social anxiety:

Challenge Your Negative Thoughts

Sometimes, finding relief or getting a lasting solution for social anxiety may seem impossible, but there are a lot of things that can help you. First, you need to challenge your negative thoughts. If you have social anxiety, then you should be familiar with some negative beliefs and thoughts which normally give birth to your fear and anxiety. Some of these negative thoughts can be:

- "I might make a mess of myself."
- "I don't want to be seen as a fool."
- "I might be at a loss for words and won't know what to say."
- "My hands might start trembling, and I'll end up embarrassing myself."

If you go with these negative thoughts by choosing to avoid the situation, you can only experience short-term relief, but you keep allowing the social anxiety to own you. But when you choose to challenge these thoughts, you are fighting to gain back control of your life, and your symptoms of anxiety will spiral down in no time.

To effectively challenge your negative thoughts, follow the tips below:

• Identify the negative thoughts that fuel your anxiety. For instance, if you are in a class and you are so scared that you will get called upon by your teacher to answer a question, the underlying negative thought can be "If I get called upon, I am going to embarrass myself and everyone will laugh at me."

• Evaluate and challenge negative thoughts. You can start by asking yourself questions. Questions like, "Why do I think I will embarrass myself?" or "Even if I fail to answer the question, am I not in the school to learn?" By logically evaluating your negative thoughts, you can now replace the thoughts with more positive and realistic ways you view social situations, which usually trigger your anxiety.

Thinking about why you think and feel the way you do can be terrifying at first, but at least when you understand the reasons that fuel your fear and anxiety, you can decrease the chances of it interrupting your life.

There are some unhelpful thinking styles you might be inculcating in yourself. It won't do you any good, but it will fuel your anxiety. Below are some of the unhelpful thinking styles. Take a look at them, and honestly determine if you are engaging in any of them. If you are, now is a good time to call it quits.

- Personalizing. This is when you assume people focus on you in a negative way, or what happens with others concerns you.
- Mind reading. You assume people know what you are thinking, and they see you the same way you see yourself (negative).
- Catastrophizing. By blowing things beyond proportion. You think it is a terrible thing for people to see you nervous.
- Fortune telling. You start predicting the future by assuming the worst will happen to you, or things will go horribly. This will only create anxiety within you.

Focus Less on Yourself and More on Others

It is quite difficult to put a stop to the countless thoughts that run through your mind when you are in situations that make you particularly anxious. When dealing with social anxiety, it is easier to turn inward and focus on yourself and how others see you, always thinking it will definitely be negative. Just like that familiar thought of people looking at you when you get called upon to answer a question in class. But that isn't always the case. You need to stop focusing on yourself and what others think about you. Instead, focus on people, be mindful, and work to form true bonds.

It's easy to get caught up in anxious feelings and thoughts when in social situations that make you nervous. You are already convinced that all eyes are on you, and judging you, while you focus on your bodily sensations. You might think that when you pay more attention to how your body reacts, you will have better control of it.

On the downside, the extra focus you are giving yourself only increases your awareness of your nervous feeling, and this triggers more anxiety. It also stops you from giving full concentration to the conversations around you and how you perform.

When you switch to an external focus rather than an internal focus, it will make a difference in reducing your social anxiety. As I'm sure you'll agree, trying to pay full attention to two things at once can be very distracting. A better approach is to focus on the things happening around you, than trying to toggle between focusing on two things at once.

Adapt to the mentality that people are not thinking negative things about you, even if they notice you are a bit nervous. Humans are not perfect, so free yourself, be in the moment, and listen to what the other person is saying.

In a study, three candidates were assessed for the same job. In the end, the interviewee that spilled coffee on his shirt but scored high was chosen. The ideal candidate that made little to no mistake was not given the job. The reason the hiring manager gave was that the ideal candidate wasn't enviable as he was looking too perfect. (Barker, 2018).

The study suggested that being too perfect can have its repercussions. So, why not just be yourself and allow people to accept you for who you are?

Another research study showed that when people meet someone for the first time, they evaluate the meeting by looking at how well they perform instead of focusing on the topic of discussion. Try to be a good listener and be attentive to what the other person is saying; these are traits that are welcomed in conversations.

If this sounds like something that doesn't come naturally to you, just follow the tips below to learn how to focus on others more easily:

- Focus your attention on others, but not what they think of you. Try to engage them and make a true connection.
- Always remember anxiety isn't that visible. If someone notices that you are nervous, you shouldn't conclude that they think badly of you. There is a high chance that the other person is also nervous, just like you, or have also been nervous in the past before overcoming it.
- Listen more to what is actually being said, and less about your negative thoughts. The negative thoughts will only feed your anxiety.
- Be in the present. Try to focus on the present moment rather than worrying too much about what you will say next, or beating yourself up for a stumble that's already in the past.
- Don't be pressured to be perfect. Rather, try to be your true self, and be observant of the qualities people value.

Be More Social

Another way of challenging your fears and overcoming anxiety is to seek out supportive social environments. Instead of staying cooped up indoors, try to get out of your house (and your shell) and relate more with people. You can try out the suggestions below:

- Enroll in an assertiveness training class or social skills class. Classes like these are usually offered at community colleges or local adult education centers. So check around to know which is accessible to you.
- Volunteer. Being a volunteer can be enjoyable if you choose what you are comfortable with. You can choose to stuff envelopes for campaigns, or clean up around your community. Just do anything that you can focus on while also meeting new people.
- Develop your communication skills. Forming good relationships is influenced by the emotional intelligence skill of communication. If it is difficult for you to connect with people, then you should learn the basic skills of emotional intelligence.

Adapt to An Anti-Anxiety Lifestyle

Your body and mind are naturally linked. Research suggests that the way you treat your body has an effect on your anxiety level and how you manage your anxiety symptoms. Even though adopting lifestyle changes alone aren't enough to overcome your fears, it can support the other tips and treatment of anxiety disorder. Let's take a look at some lifestyle tips that will help you keep your anxiety symptoms at bay and support you in overcoming your anxiety.

- Be active. You need to prioritize taking part in physical activity. You can start by setting aside thirty minutes of your time daily to exercise. If you are not a fan of exercise, you can pair it with an activity you enjoy. For example, dancing to your favorite tunes, or consider running to the bus stop every day.
- Limit or avoid your caffeine intake. Tea, coffee, energy drinks, and soda all act as stimulants that can increase your

anxiety symptoms. You should consider limiting your caffeine intake to just mornings, or cut it off totally.

- Introduce more omega-3 fats to your diet. The roles of omega-3 fatty acids are to support your brain health, improve your outlook, mood, and strengthen your ability to handle anxiety symptoms. To get omega-3 fatty acids, you should consider consuming fatty fish like herring, salmon, sardines, anchovies, and mackerel. Other foods are walnuts, flaxseed, and seaweed.
- Quit smoking. Cigarettes contain nicotine, which is a powerful stimulant. Some people smoke to make them feel better, however, smoking will only increase your anxiety level, not decrease it. If you are addicted, you need to curb the habit to feel better.
- Drink alcohol moderately. When in a social situation, you may be tempted to drink alcohol, hoping it will calm down your nerves. Too much alcohol will only increase your risk of having an anxiety attack.
- Get quality sleep. Being sleep deprived will only make you defenseless to anxiety. Try to get enough quality sleep to help you remain calm when in stressful situations.

Create Objective Goals

When you feel anxious, you usually don't care to see the positives. Who knows? You might actually do great in the situation, but the anxiety wouldn't let you know, you choose to see your performance as awful. For this reason, therapists urge patients to create objective behavioral goals. These behavioral goals are what people around you will see and observe. How you feel (fear) or what you do (sweating, trembling, or blushing) doesn't matter, especially since you don't have control of them when in a social situation.

So, when you are working in a team, your objective behavior should be to voice your opinion. This will help you measure your progress. Also, you won't be focusing on yourself and whether you are nervous. Instead, you will be focusing on whether you achieved your goal.

You should also avoid focusing on people's reactions. How your teammates received your idea at the meeting shouldn't bother you because what matters most is that you took that first bold step to speak up. It doesn't matter if someone turned down your request; at least you asked. It doesn't matter if you can't always agree with someone else's opinion; your opinion matters, too. After all, you did what was needed, and you can't control people's actions.

Be Mindful

Practicing mindfulness meditation and being present in your environment and thoughts will make you be aware of your feelings and thoughts in a more positive and non-judgmental way.

According to a study published in the journal Social Cognitive and Affective Neuroscience, researchers revealed the impact meditation has on activities, specifically in the areas of the brain. The participants with a normal level of anxiety had taken part in four twenty-minute mindfulness meditation classes. It was discovered that there was a 39% decrease in anxiety levels of participants after partaking in mindfulness training.

Several other studies have revealed the benefits of mindfulness meditation to the body – it doesn't just reduce anxiety level but that of depression too. Research from the University of Amsterdam suggested that mindfulness training is a more accessible, cost-effective, and effective way to treat a social anxiety disorder (Bögels, 2014).

During mindfulness training, patients will be taught how to be in more control of their attention and reinforce their ability to be present by using meditation techniques.

Create An Exposure Hierarchy Social Anxiety

The exposure hierarchy is a list (similar to a ladder), where you chronologically write down the situations that trigger your anxiety, according to how serious it is. After writing them down, you perform the easiest of the behaviors, and keep going until you have completed all those you have listed.

You can start by identifying and rating how anxious each social situation makes you feel. For instance, the number "0" stands for no anxiety, while "10" would be the highest anxiety you have ever felt. Now, make a list of how you would feel in any situation, no matter how big or small it is — ranging from asking a stranger for help or presenting in front of a class. Also, write down your predictions, so that it won't be new to you when it's time to experience it.

Start testing your predictions, record your social situations, and how you felt. After a series of records, you may find out that talking to a stranger is now a "4" instead of the "9" you first predicted. This tracking helps you keep a record and track your progress, which is usually encouraging.

Learn to Talk

Hopefully, when trying to overcome shyness and social anxiety, you will learn how to be more confident when talking to people. I know how challenging talking to other people can be, even thinking of what to say can trigger anxiety. An awkward silence can feel like a lifetime, and it can be embarrassing, not knowing what to say next. However, you can start small by gradually talking to people, and this will help you feel less anxious each time you try.

You can apply some conversational techniques to help you get started. Ask open-ended questions and let the other person do most of the talking. Ask questions that don't require just a yes or no answer, ask personal questions with the hope of taking the conversation to a deeper level. Doing this will help you get to know the other person more. Once you start feeling comfortable and confident, you can now share some of your personal information. This is like an invitation for the person to ask you deeper questions, too.

Be Kind to Yourself

As humans, we are not perfect, and everyone is bound to make a mistake and feel humiliated at some point. What I want you to know is that overcoming anxiety is not that easy and not something you can do in one day; so cut yourself some slack!

There are times you will start thinking negatively, start losing your grip, and maybe even slip back into your bad habits. If you are feeling tired or stressed, you may start feeling more anxious, but never think that you have simply failed. All you need to do is take a minute and be kind to yourself. You will need patience and self-compassion to succeed, and they are your keys to freedom. If you are having a bad day, don't give up. Just be kind to yourself and get back up.

The Anxiety and Depression Association of America (ADAA), estimated that one-third of people suffering from social anxiety disorder procrastinated and waited for about ten years before speaking to a professional. This anxiety disorder has negative effects on many different aspects of life – ranging from your personal relationships to your workplace relationships.

I have given you some great ways to help you overcome your social anxiety. Even if it looks like a daunting task, it's worth trying so that you can live your best life. No matter how nervous you feel when in social situations, learn to silence your self-critical thoughts and be more confident in interacting with others. By learning and going over what I have given you above, you will learn to overcome your fears and build great and rewarding relationships.

Overcoming social anxiety is a gradual process that requires time for the new neural route for social interactions to be created. If your social anxiety doesn't get better and keeps interfering with your daily life after following all the tips I have given, then don't hesitate to seek professional help.

After having an idea of how to overcome anxiety, what's next? In the next chapter, I will be explaining some relaxation techniques you can use, how they work, and how to practice them.

CHAPTER FIVE:

Relaxation Techniques

In an everyday context, what do we mean when we say we are relaxed? Most of the time, when we say we are relaxed, we are simply saying that we are free from tension. Bringing it back to social anxiety, we see why it is important. If social anxiety makes you tense, then relaxation techniques should be able to help rid you of that tension.

Relaxation is closely related to mindfulness and meditation, but it is different. Consider relaxation as the end, while mindfulness and meditation are the means of getting there. For instance, when you do yoga or other mental exercises, you control your breath and your thoughts until you bring your whole body into a relaxed mode. What you just did is using mindfulness to achieve relaxation. So it stands to reason that certain conditions, like anxiety, that can destabilize the calmness of the body can be managed through certain relaxation techniques.

Several relaxation techniques have proven to be very effective against anxiety disorders, including social anxiety. These relaxation techniques are combined with other treatments for better results, especially in very severe cases. But it can also be used alone to counter many of the symptoms of social anxiety. For instance, relaxation techniques such as deep breathing and muscle relaxation can calm the nerves during a speech.

Is There Proof That It Works?

Several studies have been conducted to know if relaxation techniques are effective against social anxiety. One such study is a meta-analysis of fifty studies covering 2,801 patients. This study compared the results obtained from treating patients using relaxation techniques and those obtained with cognitive and behavioral treatments (CBT). The researchers found that there was no marked difference between the results. Don't forget that CBT is supposed to be the main psychological treatment for social anxiety. So if relaxation techniques perform just as well, then they too are effective against social anxiety.

Another meta-analysis study that was conducted in 2018 showed that relaxation techniques, when used for people with social anxiety, helped them reduce negative emotions such as depression, worry, and phobia.

Now that we have proof that it works, let us now look at some of the relaxation techniques you can use.

Relaxation Techniques for Social Anxiety

Diaphragmatic Breathing

Diaphragmatic breathing, also known as deep breathing, is a breathing pattern in which you expand your diaphragm so that your chest doesn't rise and fall, rather it is your stomach that does that. By doing this, you are taking deeper breaths and helping to alleviate your symptoms. Breathing is very important to life as it helps in supplying your body and organs with oxygen that is vital for survival. So, when you don't breathe well, it will upset the exchange of oxygen and carbon dioxide, which can contribute to anxiety.

Ideally, you don't have to wait until you have an anxiety attack before trying to pull up diaphragmatic breathing. Rather, you are expected to keep practicing it even when you are relaxed so that when it is time to use it, it will come to you easily. Otherwise, you might find it difficult to perform when the anxiety is already upon you. Another reason why you must practice deep breathing is that other relaxation techniques are based on it, making it an important technique to master.

How Important is Diaphragmatic Breathing?

When you are tense, your body enters what we call "fight-or-flight" mode. In this mode, your body is at alert, pretty much like when you are in a fight. If you are fighting, for instance, your body goes into this mode because it wants you to see and avoid as many physical attacks as possible. Most of your body processes are racing at such a time. To balance this increase, your heart beats faster to circulate enough blood. This can be normal if you are a normal person, and you are in an emergency. But if you are a person with social anxiety and you are in what you erroneously believe to be an emergency, this situation can quickly degenerate into an anxiety attack.

What deep breathing does for you, in this case, is that it helps you become aware of the changes in your body and helps you slow down the heart rate by dictating the pace and depth. This way, your body begins to realize there was no emergency, after all, just a harmless social situation. With this, your likelihood of escalating into an anxiety attack is greatly reduced.

How Can I Practice Diaphragmatic Breathing?

I mentioned before that it is good to get your body used to this pattern of breathing so that you can easily do it when the need arises. Now let me show you how you can practice diaphragmatic breathing, even when you are alone and already relaxed.

See the steps you can take to practice deep breathing:

1. Find a place that is free of distraction. When you are initially starting, you don't want any form of distraction, so that you can focus on your breath. That is why a quiet place, free of distractions, is vital. You also need to find a position that

allows you enough relaxation, such as lying face up or reclining in a chair. Relax all your muscles. You also need to feel free, so items such as glasses, a watch, or tight clothing may not be ideal.

2. To ensure that you are breathing correctly, make sure it is your stomach that rises and drops when you breathe in and breathe out, you need to place one hand on your chest, the other on your stomach, and ensure that the one your chest doesn't move during the exercise. With your hands in place, take a deep breath from your abdomen and count a slow one, two, three, to ensure the breath was really deep enough.
3. Pause the breath for a short while and exhale slowly while repeating your one, two, three count. Ensure it is your stomach that is falling back and not your chest.
4. Repeat the exercise for five to ten minutes, until your body is relaxed.

Continue doing this for several days until you master it. If you are having issues mastering the technique, you can join a yoga class or mindfulness meditation class. These classes will teach you some other techniques that also use deep breathing so that you can go past the task of mastering deep breathing.

Autogenic Training

Ever heard the saying "there is power in the word"? You must have, and it seems to be true that it is the very foundation of autogenic training. In this training, you are repeatedly telling yourself things that can get you relaxed. In autogenic training, you are telling yourself things like, "I am relaxed now." It is thought that when you repeat these statements to yourself, you can influence the way your autonomic nervous system functions. And it is the autonomic nervous system that controls heart rate.

A 2008 meta-analysis study by Stretter F. and Kupper S. showed that the autogenic technique is indeed effective for treating anxiety. If it can treat anxiety, then you can also use it to calm yourself down whenever you find yourself in a social situation.

So How Can You Practice It?

When preparing for autogenic exercise, the steps are similar to those for diaphragmatic breathing. Ensure you get to a place that is free of distractions, and ensure that you also feel free by avoiding tight or distracting clothing. Ensure you are lying flat on the floor, or you are reclining in a chair.

For the actual exercise, do the following:

- Start by practicing diaphragmatic breathing for a couple of minutes. Then gently tell yourself the words, "I am calm."
- Next, focus your attention on your arms. Then tell yourself, "My arms are heavy." Repeat it six more times. Then calmly tell yourself, "I am calm."
- Focus your attention on your arms again. This time quietly tell yourself, "My arms are warm." Repeat six more times. Then calmly tell yourself, "I am calm."
- Shift your attention to your legs and quietly tell yourself, "My legs are heavy." Repeat six more times. Then calmly tell yourself, "I am calm."
- Pay attention to your legs again. Do the same thing by calmly telling yourself, "My legs are very warm." Do this six more times. Then calmly tell yourself, "I am calm."
- Move on to your heartbeat. Focus your attention on it and calmly repeat to yourself, "My heart is beating calmly and regularly." Then calmly tell yourself, "I am calm."
- Next, you focus on your breath. Tell yourself calmly, "My breathing is calm and regular." Then calmly tell yourself, "I am calm."
- Focus your attention on your abdomen and quietly tell yourself, "My abdomen is warm." Do this six more times, then calmly tell yourself, "I am calm."
- Next is your forehead, quietly repeat to yourself, "My forehead is pleasantly cool." Do this six more times, then calmly tell yourself, "I am calm."

- Notice your body relaxing and enjoy the feeling that comes with it. Then calmly and quietly tell yourself, "My arms are firm, I breathe deeply, and my eyes are open."

Progressive muscle relaxation

People who suffer from social anxiety disorder experience tensed muscles a lot. This muscle tension is coming from the fact that they are on edge. That is why progressive muscle relaxation (PMR) is very effective for people with social and anxiety. PMR is an anxiety-reduction technique that seeks to eliminate tension from the major muscle groups and to replace them with relaxation. It was first introduced in 1930 by the American physician Edmund Jacobson.

This technique is so effective against anxiety and tension that if done properly, it can even make you fall asleep. If you master it, you will be amazed by the difference between a tensed muscle and a relaxed muscle. The latter is priceless. You should look forward to achieving it.

Just as other relaxation techniques, it can be used by itself or combined with others for a stronger effect. Also, it requires practice to acclimatize you with it. So practice it even when you are relaxed, so that when you are not, you can easily get your mind to do it.

Below are the steps for practicing Progressive Muscle Relaxation (PMR)

Like others before it, start by finding a quiet place, free of distractions. Begin in a very relaxed posture, such as lying flat or reclining on a chair. Try to stay away from tight or distracting clothing, and remove items that might bother you, such as earphones, glasses, watches, or bracelets. When you are ready, use the first six to seven minutes to practice your deep breathing.

After that, do the following, while keeping your body relaxed.

- Start with your forehead. Squeeze the muscles in your forehead gently and hold for about fifteen seconds. You will feel the muscles becoming tense. Then gently release while counting down for thirty seconds. You should notice the sensation of relaxation that overtakes the muscles. For best results, do this while breathing slowly and evenly.

- Next, move to your jaw. As with the forehead, tense the muscles in your jaw for about fifteen seconds and start to release the tension while counting down from thirty. While doing this, try to pay attention to the relaxation that comes to that region. Also, make sure that you are breathing slowly and deeply.
- Move on to your neck and shoulders. Apply tension to the muscles in this region by raising your shoulders and holding in place for about fifteen seconds. Then gently release the tension while counting down from thirty.
- Gently draw your hands into fists. Pull your formed fists towards your chest and hold in place for fifteen seconds. Squeeze the fists tightly and hold them very close to your chest. As with the previous exercises, release while counting down from thirty, and notice the relaxation that follows.
- Then move on to your buttocks. Simply increase the tension in your buttocks and hold for fifteen seconds. After the fifteen seconds, gradually release the tension while counting down from thirty. Breathe slowly and notice relaxation replacing the tension.
- For the legs, target your calves and quadriceps. Calmly squeeze and hold them for fifteen seconds, then release gradually for a time interval of thirty seconds.
- Lastly, slowly and calmly increase the tension in both your feet and toes, as much as you can. Release while counting down from thirty. Breathe slowly and notice the tension disappearing.

With this last one, relaxation should return to your body. Enjoy the feeling that follows and continue breathing evenly and slowly.

Guided imagery

Do you wish you had a technique that could help you ease both your mind and body within seconds and still be easy to perform? Then this will be a great strategy for you! Guided imagery is very effective for de-stressing, and also for developing a thick skin. It is also one of the relaxation techniques that have proven effective in treating social anxiety disorder.

I'm sure you're eager to try this out, so let me explain how it works so you can start practicing!

However, before we jump in, there are a few different ways you can do this. First, you can do this in a class with an instructor guiding you. You can also use a recording that guides you through the exercise. You can even choose to record your own audio and use it. Lastly, you can rely on your inner subconscious voice to tell you what to do. In all of the options, you must be guided by something - that is where it gets its name from. This guide tells you what to do and how to do it.

Now that you are familiar with the concept, let's walk through how you can start practicing it.

Get Comfortable

You need a quiet place and a relaxed position. You may choose to recline in a chair or stay in a cross-legged position.

Execute Diaphragmatic Breathing

While closing your eyes and focusing on your breath, breathe diaphragmatically as described earlier in this chapter. While doing this, imagine that you are breathing out stress and breathing in peace. Check that your chest and shoulders are not moving as you are breathing, but rather only your abdomen should be moving.

Pick a Scene that Suits You and Vividly Imagine It

A relaxed scene may be different things for different people. For some, it might be winning a lottery ticket and filling the garage with fast cars, or it might be spending quality time with loved ones. Whatever brings to mind a relaxed state for you, begin to imagine it vividly.

Perhaps you can recall the details of a very pleasing memory from years past, or you can choose to envision a scene from a movie or book you love. The bottom line here is that the memory you pull up is pleasing to you.

Immerse Yourself in the Sensory Details

Now that you are envisioning your perfect scene, you need to get into the moment. Try to get all of your senses involved in imagining the place. Imagine how it smells, what it feels like, and any other details, like the sound of rain on the roof or a crackling fire in the fireplace.

Relax

Now that you have a detailed image in your mind, using all of your senses, it is time to settle in and relax. While you are here, ensure that you are enjoying the scene and everything in it. Stay there for as long as it pleases you. While relaxing here, detach yourself from every stress and anxiety. When you've had your fill, and you decide it is time to return to reality, just count down from twenty and maintain that feeling of serenity when you finish your countdown.

Mindfulness Techniques for Staying Present in Social Situations

We've seen how social anxiety can interrupt your life. But we've also seen that it doesn't have to be. You can stand up to it and reclaim your life. And one of the relaxation weapons in your arsenal is mindfulness. Mindfulness has immense power that you can use to ease social anxiety. Little wonder traditional Buddhists believe in it so much. Health professionals are actively using the power of relaxation, mindfulness, and meditation to help treat several health conditions like anxiety, depression, pain, insomnia, and even post-traumatic stress disorder.

How about athletes who use the principles of relaxation to better their performances? Or CEOs of big firms who use its principles to keep their cool in the chaotic world of business? Relaxation techniques such as mindfulness and meditation are even finding their way into the school curriculum these days, as students and teachers are shown how to use it to control their emotions and improve their concentration.

What is mindfulness? Think of it like this: have you ever been in a really noisy environment, and you somehow manage to tune out all of the noise and focus on what was important to you, perhaps a book you were in the middle of? If yes, that was the power of mindfulness. You simply streamlined your mind to pay attention to that which was most important to you.

However, to use mindfulness for managing social anxiety, it is slightly different. If you have ever tried to avoid a negative thought before, then you know how difficult that can be. It is difficult because as you are trying to block off such thoughts, the brain assumes that thought is very important and actually holds on to it. So when we are using mindfulness for social anxiety, we are not trying to block off those unpleasant thoughts such as "I'm not good enough" or "they don't like me" or "I will embarrass myself." Instead, what we are trying to do is to recognize the existence of these thoughts, and still convince ourselves that they are not helpful to us - because they truly are not! So, rather than focusing on those negative thoughts, we treat them like the noise in the aforementioned example, and we focus on the conversation or the task at hand.

Let’s talk about the definition of mindfulness. Mindfulness is the ability to gather your thoughts into the present, even in a social situation. It is the ability to notice and focus on one’s thoughts and feelings, without being judgmental about them. What does that mean for you? It means you are letting go of the thoughts of whether you are good enough or not, and you are focusing on the present, without any form of distraction.

Below are a few mindfulness techniques you can use to ease symptoms of social anxiety.

Become aware that you are anxious

Let me ask you, how are you going to take action to kick out your anxiety if you are not aware that you are anxious? The key is recognizing this feeling. Thankfully, we have gone through the symptoms of social anxiety in the second chapter of this book. You can go over them and identify the symptoms that apply for you so that you have a better understanding of when you're feeling anxious. When you recognize it, you can then begin applying these hacks to ease it.

Blame the anxiety, not yourself

If you realize that you are suffering from social anxiety, don't blame yourself. Instead of that, shift the blame to the actual cause of your condition… the social anxiety disorder. Then try to take back control. Try to see the disorder as a foreign element that has come to bother you, and put up your defenses. Remind yourself that you, and you alone, get to decide how you feel. Then fall back on any of the techniques we've discussed so far.

Focus on your senses by using the "Remember the Five" technique

This technique is a mindfulness strategy that can help you deal with anxiety, distractions, and overwhelming thoughts. Whenever you find yourself becoming overwhelmed, use the "remember the five" technique to bring your mind to the present.

What is it all about? This exercise is aimed at attaching your senses to your current situation or environment.

To do it, stop whatever you are doing, close your eyes, and take a deep breath. Then, with your eyes closed, try to remember five items in your immediate surroundings. Not just the items, try to remember their shapes, their sizes, what they are made of, the color, and other things any other details you can recall. You have attended to your sense of sight.

Next, move on to your sense of sound. Try to differentiate five different sounds you are currently hearing. Are there cars on the street, maybe kids playing outside, or music? Get detailed - what type of music is it? What do the cars sound like as they pass?

Engage your sense of touch by trying to feel five things, like your clothing, your hands on your lap, or your feet on the floor.

With your senses engaged, linger in the moment. With the conclusion of this exercise, hopefully, you have freed your mind and released some tension.

Focus your attention outward

Remember how you typically focus all your attention on yourself when you are in a social setting? That is not good for your anxiety. Rather than bothering yourself over what other people may think about you or how you are going to embarrass yourself, shift your attention outward. You could decide to listen to the music playing down the hall, or to pay attention to the beautiful decorations around you, or better yet, the people you are meeting. By doing this, you are becoming more mindful of your environment, and less about the pressure you're putting on yourself. At first it may not be easy, but with practice, you will see improvement.

Don't get me wrong, I am not saying your anxiety will magically grow wings and fly away. Those feelings will be there, but they will be less powerful because you will be able to classify them as background noises. Even though you will acknowledge that they are there, you will not pay attention to them.

If you are finding it hard to be present and active in your environment, come up with a cliché that you can say to snap you out of your thoughts. For example, if you are meeting a new person and the anxiety starts to bubble up, snap out of it by telling yourself "focus," or any other word of your choosing that will remind you to stay present.

In this chapter, I discussed the different relaxation techniques you can use to prevent anxiety in social situations and how to use them. In the next chapter, I will be discussing people-pleasing, how it affects you, and ways to stop.

CHAPTER SIX:

Stop People-Pleasing

People-pleasing is so common that you might even mistake it for politeness. You might think, "I'm just being nice." But that way of thinking is how you will always find yourself saying "yes" when all you want to do is shout "no!"

I know that feeling because I have been there before, and, trust me, it is not a nice place to be. If you are like me, then you know that people-pleasing can rob you of your peace of mind, and it can also contribute to depression and anxiety.

If you are a people pleaser, then I am sure you will relate to the description above. However, there are many other signs of people-pleasing. Let's look at some of them.

Am I a People Pleaser?

I know that's the question you're asking yourself right now. The next few sentences of this book will answer that for you. Funnily enough, you can be a people pleaser and not know it. As I mentioned earlier, you may mistake it for kindness or politeness.

Here are some common habits that suggest you are a people pleaser:

- You find it difficult to say “no.”
- You find it difficult to voice your opinions and stand your ground.
- You’re very sensitive to perceived rejection from others, even when it is not there.
- You’re afraid of negative emotions.
- You’re altruistic or philanthropic to a fault.
- You allow yourself to suffer at the expense of others.
- You lack personal boundaries.
- Relationships make you emotionally dependent.
- You live on other people’s approval, always wanting it.
- You badly want to be liked by everyone.
- You hate criticism, and when it comes, you feel shattered for days.
- You have low self-esteem and self-worth.
- You are always conscious of what other people think of you, and you allow it to influence your actions.
- You can easily relate to other people's predicaments, often at your own expense.
- You always want to believe that other people are fair, even when it is clear they are abusive to you.
- You fear you might lose control over yourself.
- You help everyone you come across, even if you don’t like them
- You hardly ever ask for or receive help.
- You are constantly apologizing even when you haven’t done anything wrong.
- You easily attract people who need consolation.
- You have a constant fear of hurting people’s feelings.
- You don’t give yourself credit for anything.
- You believe that you are less than other people.
- You agree with people even when what they are saying is against your personal beliefs.

- You avoid telling others that they've hurt your feelings.

Where Does It Come from?

There is not a single, definite cause for people-pleasing. The condition stems from a combination of several factors, such as:

Past trauma

If you have suffered trauma before, you can have certain fears associated with the trauma. People-pleasing behaviors can surface as a response. People who have been victims of abuse may lose self-esteem or boundaries due to the experience.

Having a Low Self-esteem

The messages you got from people around you when you were growing up can greatly impact your self-esteem. If your self-esteem is low, you will be seeking approval, and you will become a people pleaser in the process.

Fear of rejection

If you have been rejected before by people, you may start to feel that you are no good, and other people will be likely to reject you, too. You may develop people-pleasing behaviors to avoid rejection again.

How Does it Affect You?

You may be saying, "Oh come on, I'm just being nice… maybe a little too much, but how does that negatively affect me?" Many ways. Let me show you some of them.

1. You suppress your emotions

When you are seeking the approval of people around you, you won't say anything that might ruin your chances of approval, so you may find yourself bottling up your emotions. These bottled up emotions can degenerate to damaging emotions such as rage, bitterness, grief, and anxiety. When you continue to suppress emotions, you are headed for either a physical, or psychological breakdown, or even both.

2. You put extreme pressure on yourself

Once you have started it, you must continue it. It's called "keeping up appearances." At first, when you couldn't say "no" to that request (even when it was too much for you), you thought you were being nice. But now that you have started it, you still can't say "no," and this just ends up piling up pressure on you because you want to maintain the selfless image you have created for yourself.

What do you get when you are struggling to keep up appearances? Nothing but stress. You might be thinking that it will make you feel good because you are putting yourself in people's good graces by doing them favors, but it is coming at the expense of your well-being. It's like wearing a mask for too long just to get other people's approval even when this mask is suffocating you.

3. People will use you

You may not know it yet, but there are a lot of bad people out there hiding in the name of friends, families, and acquaintances. We know them as narcissists, bullies, naysayers, energy vampires, and a host of other words. If you are a people pleaser, you will become an easy target for these people. You are an easy target because your nature makes it difficult for you to have personal boundaries, and you have an unquenchable desire to please people. This makes you a perfect item for use and abuse, and these people don't have boundaries, either. It is very difficult for you to get out because your life is dependent on approval. So the toxic cycle just continues.

4. No one knows your true nature

On the surface, this might seem appealing… "Oh, that's great, I will be unpredictable and invincible...." Before you start rejoicing about how you can be invincible and enigmatic by being unknown, hear me out. If no one truly knows who you are, you are lonely and disconnected. Trust me; this is not good for you, especially if you have social anxiety.

This is exactly what people-pleasing does to you. As a people pleaser, you will always put on the façade, and it is this façade that people around will know, and not the real you. Your original intention for putting up the façade is to get people's acceptance, but what you will get is disconnection. Where is the wisdom in that?

5. You won't enjoy relationships

Relationships are all about give and take. But as a people pleaser, some of your relationships are better captioned as "give and give." The people you are in a relationship with are only with you because of what you offer them. How on earth are you going to enjoy such a relationship? But being a people pleaser, you will just be suffering and smiling, because you want their approval.

6. Your friends and partners will find you frustrating

People who are close to you, such as a spouse, might notice how you do inexplicable things like apologize incessantly, and since they truly love you, it might start getting to them. Then, you can also fall into the common trap of sacrificing the time that should go into your relationships for pleasing others. Also, in some cases, you might lie to the people you love just because you want to spare their feelings, and they find out, it usually doesn't end well.

Ways to Stop People-Pleasing

I can hear you saying, "I've read enough already; show me how I can put a stop to people-pleasing!"

1. Seek internal validation

A people pleaser seeks outward approval and validation. If you can turn that around by validating yourself internally, then half the battle is won. But how can you validate yourself internally? Simple, by building up what makes you happy about yourself. If you are happy all by yourself, you don't need to rely on people anymore for that. So, to fight people-pleasing, invest your time in building up whatever makes you feel good. If you are already feeling good with yourself, do you still need people to make you feel good? Engage in those activities that make you feel great. If you love partying, by all means, attend parties often. If it is gardening that you love, set up and run a garden. Just do those things that make you feel good about yourself. Whenever you catch yourself craving external validation, knock it off by reminding yourself that you have a lot going for you.

2. Start small

When you were a toddler, you didn't just stand up one day and run across the sitting room, did you? You started with one or two baby steps. The same applies to stopping people-pleasing. Don't try to slam on the brakes and jolt yourself to a full stop on day one. If you do so, you will make a lot of enemies. So instead of suddenly refusing all new requests (where you previously would always say "yes"), try out saying yes, but doing a little of the request, not all. For instance, if a friend has just invited you to a party at a very inconvenient time of your life, you can go, stay a few minutes and return home.

3. Allow yourself time

Before now, your usual response to requests was an impulsive "yes" that you didn't give much thought. Try changing that by giving yourself time. Instead of just accepting requests, say something that can give you a little time to consider it, and decide if it is something you can do. You can prepare a default answer such as "Let me get back to you." or "let me check my schedule." or "let me check with my spouse." After some time, look for a way to politely say "no" to those requests that are out of order. If it is going to be difficult for you to say "no" to the person's face, you can choose to do that via email or text.

Two realizations that can help you learn how to say no without guilt are:

- You are not responsible for the happiness and comfort of people around you, they are responsible for theirs, and you are responsible for yours.
- You are expected to cater to yourself first before catering to others. So if anything is going to please someone at your expense, then it is a no-no.

4. Know your principles, priorities, and boundaries and stand by them

A person without these things is a pushover. You'll go along with anything you are told if you have no principles of your own. And if you lack boundaries, people can infringe upon you any time they want. Make sure you know your principles, priorities, and boundaries, and most importantly, ensure that the people around you know of your principles and boundaries.

5. Remove toxic people

Also, surround yourself with people that make you feel good about yourself, even without wanting anything from you. I know how difficult it is to remove toxic people from your life. Most of them are tightly woven into your family, circle of friends, or career. In such cases, it becomes more difficult, but you can manage them using the steps below:

- First of all, don't expect them to change. Toxic people have complex problems and desires of their own. Toxic people often believe that they are right, and you are wrong. So, realize that you can wish that they will change, but your wish cannot do it. Your efforts too cannot do it lest you lose yourself while trying to save them from themselves.
- Now that you have realized that they will not change, it is time to set some boundaries that you must maintain. If you don't set boundaries, toxic people will push you to extreme lengths. To do this, take time out to think about what you want from your friends, coworkers, families, and acquaintances. Keep them top of mind or write them down if need be. If, at any

point in your interaction with toxic people, you feel that something is off, cross-check it with your boundaries and be prepared to enforce them if they are being infringed on.

- Don't allow yourself to be pulled into crises that they deliberately create. Toxic people have a way of inducing crises so that they will get your sympathy and attention. You may feel that you are being a good Samaritan, however, you are allowing yourself to pick up negative energy. When they create drama and expect to get you entangled in it, remember that it is not a genuine distress call in order to maintain perspective.
- Understand your weaknesses and difficulties so that toxic people will not use it against you. They look for weaknesses in you and exploit them. For instance, they might notice that you are somebody who cannot just watch people suffer. Because of that, they will paint a nasty picture of them almost dying whenever they need a favor from you. But if you have realized that this is your area of weakness, you will easily notice when people are trying to exploit it.
- Realize that toxic people might resist your efforts to thwart their tactics. If you've had a toxic person in your life before, then you know they can easily throw tantrums whenever they feel ignored. When they sense that you are developing a resilience to their tactics, they may increase their efforts, and you may be tempted to give in. Instead, realize that it is normal for them to act that way. Continue with your defensive tactics, and when they see that they can no longer control you, they will leave your life and seek a place where they can satisfy their selfish intentions. At this stage, you can congratulate yourself knowing that you are free from toxicity.

6. Stop apologizing

Apologizing when you are in the wrong isn't bad. It's when you were not in the wrong and apologizing becomes second nature.

If you are to blame for something and you give a heartwarming apology, there is nothing wrong with that. But if you are always on the apologizing end, even when it is very clear that you are not to blame - that is what is wrong, and you need to stop it as soon as you finish reading this book.

Let me give you a scenario, as a people pleaser. I've done my fair share of apologizing when it was not my fault. Some time ago, my boss had asked me to place an order for lunch for the workers in the firm. I promptly did, sticking to his instruction of "gluten-free." But then when the order came, it turned out that the restaurant had messed up. It was not my fault, because I was sure of what I ordered, and it was even clearly written on the receipt, but I still felt bad because some workers could not eat it. I ended up apologizing to whoever would listen, as if it were my own doing.

You might be tempted to say, "You apologized, what's the big deal?" The truth is that whenever you apologize for something, you are indirectly accepting blame and heaping pressure on yourself. Somewhere deep down, your mood is affected by something you are innocent of.

Scenarios like this portray how fragile we (people pleasers) can be. But I've long gone past that, and I know you will be ready to make the transition when you finish this chapter.

Here are some tips that can help you apologize only when it is necessary:

Assessment: don't be quick to rush into an apology, take a short time to assess and appraise the situation. Ask yourself, "Am I responsible for this?" or "Is there something I could have done differently to avoid this?" If your answers to these two questions is an emphatic "No," please don't take the blame and apologize.

Conclusively, it is also important that I say this. Even though you are trying to put a stop to people-pleasing, it doesn't mean that you should transform into a cold-hearted monster. We still need touches of humanity here and there. Know where the difference lies between being nice and being a people pleaser.

Being a people pleaser just to feel approval or avoid getting your opinion out there will only hurt your self-esteem and make you more anxious in social situations. In this chapter, I explained what it means to be a people pleaser, how it affects your life, and how to stop being a people pleaser. In the next chapter, I will be discussing shyness; what causes it, how it can affect you, and ways you can cure your shyness.

CHAPTER SEVEN:

Cure Your Shyness

All of us have been shy at one point or another. When moderate, you can still say or do what you want, even though you are slightly shy. If you can still be yourself, it is normal. But with certain people, that is not the case. These people with extreme shyness issues are always incapacitated due to the extreme apprehension they feel whenever they are around people. They cannot be in the midst of people without feeling very awkward. It is strongly believed to be a result of low self-esteem. It is fueled by your fear of what other people think of you. Since you are overly concerned about what people think about you, you will become scared that you might be humiliated, rejected, or criticized. So to avoid the possibility of any of these happening, shy people will avoid every social situation.

It can be even stronger in people with a social anxiety disorder. This extreme shyness will trigger all the symptoms we've discussed earlier in this book. Humans are social animals, meaning that we thrive among other people. So if you allow a thing like shyness to make you avoid people, you need to do something about it.

Some Facts on Shyness

- **Shyness is dependent on age**, meaning that you can be shy as a child, and when you grow into an adult and experience new things, you also outgrow it.

- **Shyness can come and go**. You can go in and out of periods of shyness, depending on what is going on in your life at those times. If you are in a phase of your life where you are seriously battling with self-confidence, the chances are that you will be more shy. When you bounce back and reclaim your confidence, the shyness is reduced.
- **Shyness is closely related to self-consciousness**. People who are very conscious of themselves are more likely to be shy. Shyness is also closely linked to fear. So people who were fearful in childhood are more likely to end up as shy adults.

What Causes Shyness?

Just like people-pleasing, there is not a single particular cause for shyness. Rather, it is caused by a combination of different factors cutting across nature and nurture.

One thing that we know for sure is there is not a gene for shyness. It is not hereditary, you didn't get it from either of your parents or somebody in your family line. So it is natural occurrences that influence you to be shy or not. Some of the most common occurrences are when you are treated too harshly as a child, when you have a faulty perception of yourself, or when you undergo some life transitions that are difficult for you to handle, like getting a new job, going to a new school, or getting a divorce.

Let us look at some of the factors that can contribute to shyness:

Before you can cure shyness effectively, you need to understand where it comes from. For instance, it might be something in your past that injured your self-image and left you shy. It could be a very damaging personal belief you hold about yourself. If you succeed in identifying the cause, half the battle is won.

Therefore, let us take a little time to look at the possible cause of your shyness. They include:

- **Lack of self-confidence:** When your self-esteem is low, you are overly critical of yourself, and so you will believe that people see you the way you see yourself. To try and shield yourself from their negative review, you become shy.
- **Inferiority complex:** When you feel like you are the lowest person in the room, you will be very reluctant to speak up or express yourself because you've convinced yourself that you don't have anything to offer.
- **Perfectionism:** If you are an extreme perfectionist, you will always want to say and do impeccable things. And because you don't want to make any mistakes at all, you will just choose to keep to yourself and shyness kicks in.
- **Lack of social skills:** We've seen the clamor surrounding the inclusion of social skills in schools. This is because several people go through school without picking these up. When you lack social skills, you will become self-inhibited. And since you don't know how to socialize with people, you will end up keeping to yourself and being shy.
- **Faulty self-image:** If you have any degrading thoughts about yourself, you will end up being shy because a bad self-image will lead you to self-inhibition.
- **Undue fear of people:** If you've been a subject of abuse or you come from a dysfunctional family, you might be scared of people, and that can make you shy.

Effects of Shyness

It can slow your learning in an academic environment

If you are or have been a student before, then you know that one key ingredient for success in schools is your ability to interact with others and participate in group tasks. If you are shy, it can hamper that and reduce your performance and grades. This can even affect your self-confidence and make you perform below your actual abilities.

It slows down your career growth

The job market these days is very competitive, and only the strong survive. If you are shy, you may not be able to get a good job because you falter in the interview stages, and no company is looking to add liability to their workforce. Let's say you somehow get in; you won't be able to give good presentations that can earn you your boss' approval. You won't be able to speak up in meetings, and you will lose that opportunity to show how thoughtful and promotion-deserving you are.

Difficulties forming relationships

Extreme shyness can make you a loner. Since you are mostly shy when you are around others, you may prefer to just keep to yourself, and that is how you will not have good friends you can share things with.

Ways to Overcome Shyness

I think you have seen enough reason why you should cure yourself of that shyness today. If you haven't, let me summarize it for you. In a nutshell, shyness can hold you back from doing things that can be beneficial to you. It can also pile stress and anxiety on you, especially when you are in the midst of people.

But, I have good news for you. The first one is that you are not alone. Out of every ten people, four of them will agree that they are shy.

The second piece of good news I have for you is that no matter how shy you might consider yourself, you can overcome it. All it will take is time and effort, and you will see yourself breaking free from the grip of shyness.

I have compiled some techniques for you that you can use in your fight against shyness. These are techniques that have proven effective to countless people before you. If you can discipline yourself to follow them judiciously, you will see results in no time.

Plan ahead

You can plan by first identifying your triggers. Know those situations that make you shy and make accurate plans for them when you anticipate them. Decide on what to do when the situation presents itself, if possible, write your steps down. Most people are triggered by public speaking, while others have some more specific triggers such as a person, a song, or a venue. Be sure you know your triggers and plan for them.

Be curious and get informed

If you have an upcoming event where you are likely going to meet new people, you might want to arm yourself with some conversation starters. Get to know the new trends in technology, politics, business, or entertainment… whatever suits you. Check for the trending topics on social media and arm yourself with pieces of it. That way you will have something to say. And when you say something, and it passes off as smart, and people are digging it, you will feel comfortable saying more. Remember to keep your cool. These people don't even know that you are shy and you don't have to let them know. While doing this, remember that your intention is not to impress them with how much you know, you are just blending in and having good conversation.

Be kind to yourself

Most of the mental challenges, including shyness, are not cured by a snap of the fingers. They require a considerable amount of time and effort to go away. While you are working on your shyness, if you do not see drastic improvements, go easy on yourself. What is important is that you are making the effort, and you are making progress, even though you may not have noticed it. Don't concentrate too much on your pace, just concentrate on making the effort, no matter how small.

Be confident and act confident

Whenever we start learning a new task, our confidence will be low at first, but as we continue to practice, our confidence begins to rise. It was like that when you learned to drive a car, or ride a bicycle. The same applies to relating to people. You are shy because you lack confidence. But what if you can learn to be confident... by being confident? If you can start speaking confidently and acting confidently, you will notice that it feels good, and you will become more confident with the process. When you are feeling shy and anxious, the anxiety is not the problem; the real problem is that you are avoiding social interactions. If you can be confident enough to eliminate the avoidance, the anxiety will melt away.

Engage more

Remember that your shyness and anxiety increase as the number of people around you increases. You can handle a one-on-one conversation, but you wouldn't talk to a group. So why not start from smaller conversations and grow? To do this, initiate small talks, strike up random conversations with strangers at the gym, the grocery, the subway, or worship centers. Just get talking. As you do this more often, your confidence will grow. For even more improvement, talk to people you find attractive, ask them for a date, or a dance. Hearing someone say "yes" to you will begin to reorient the image you have about yourself. If you do get a "no" - shake it off and move on. Of the seven billion people on earth, not everyone will like you. But more than half will. So don't waste energy. Just go out more and meet new people.

Try new things, even if you are not comfortable with it

Clubs, sports teams, and classes are good places you can consider. This will allow you to meet new people and socialize more. You can also consider embarking on those projects you have always been wanting to do, but your shyness has held you back. You can decide to learn a new skill or undertake a difficult project. By all means, get out of your comfort zone and meet people.

You might be wondering how taking on difficult tasks can alleviate shyness. When you undertake a difficult task and come through with it, you feel better about yourself and your self-confidence surges. To eliminate shyness, you will have to develop confidence in various aspects of your life.

Also, when you try new activities, you are confronting the unknown, and you are eliminating anxiety by doing so because we feel anxious about the unknown.

Start talking

In my experience, I think that the anxiety we experience as shy people is usually at its peak when we have to stand before a group of people and make a speech. We call it "stage fright," but it is still shyness dressed in a different outfit. So to start confronting your shyness, I recommend joining a speech club. While there, take on speeches and presentations. Do it even when your mind and body are against it. Also, whenever you have an opportunity to address a crowd, embrace it! Don't be scared of doing badly. At first, you might, but as time goes on, your confidence will grow, and you will begin to unravel the seemingly herculean task. Even when you are with your friends and coworkers, make your opinion known often, speak up and try to be more talkative. As a shy person, what you consider as talkative may be another person's normal.

One attribute of confident people is that they don't care whether people will like what they have to say. They say it nonetheless because they are more concerned with connecting and sharing. And oftentimes they are confident of what they have to say. You can emulate that.

Additional note on shyness:

Some of you reading this book may be parents. You can help your children overcome shyness at an early stage. There are indications that shyness can be corrected early in one's life using social development. Unfortunately, this has never been a top priority in homes and schools. In homes, many parents can be overprotective, as they try to keep their children away from social settings. Schools, on the other hand, focus more on reading and writing, and they forget to help children develop the necessary social skills that can help them be better people when they grow up. Certain children show signs of withdrawal at an early age. If teachers and parents can pay attention to such children and model social skills and help encourage them to express themselves more and interact with other kids, they can eliminate the impending shyness.

To prevent shyness in your kids, you can help them develop the vital skills that will help them be more comfortable with their peers. These skills include:

- Showing them how to cope with change.
- Teaching them how to manage their anger.
- Treating them to a healthy dose of compassion and humor.
- Teaching them how to be assertive and have a voice of their own.
- Teaching them how to show kindness and help others.
- Teaching them how to keep secrets, when appropriate.

In this chapter, I explained how you can overcome your shyness and learn how to speak up around others. In the next chapter, I will be discussing social confidence, the benefits of having good social confidence, and how you can build your social confidence.

CHAPTER EIGHT:

How to Build Social Confidence

We have covered so much through the course of this book. And now, everything is beginning to come together. We've talked about social anxiety, and how you can rid yourself of it. We also looked at shyness, and how to stop it. We looked at people-pleasing, and how to overcome it. All of these topics are aimed at doing one critical thing, and that is to help you overcome the shyness and anxiety you experience whenever you are in a social setting. In a nutshell, all we've been doing is building your social confidence so that you do not become anxious, shy, or tense.

The topics we've discussed so far will improve your social life by improving your social confidence, but in this chapter, I want to give you practical tips that you can use to further improve your social confidence.

Before I show you the ways you can build your social confidence, let me motivate you by showing you what you stand to gain.

Benefits of Good Social Confidence

More friends, more fun

For us socially challenged people, sometimes we like to believe that nothing is better than the comfort of our bed, our computer and our favorite couch in the house. Nothing could be further from the truth. Life begins where social anxiety ends. If you are not socializing, you are not meeting people, and that is sad because people make life more fun and worth living. Our families, friends, and coworkers make life more fun. So much fun awaits you when you finally reclaim your social confidence.

Excellence in career and school

Schools and work environments are also social situations. And if you can't function very well in other social situations, how then will you be able to perform well in these? The obvious answer is that you can't. To truly make any headway in school or your career, you need good social confidence.

Freedom from shyness

Think about the last party you attended. The one where you sat alone in the corner, hoping that someone will come by and say hello… Why did that happen? Is it that you just found that particular spot cozy, or did you have a more cogent reason for keeping all to yourself? I think I might know why you opted for the option you chose; you simply didn't feel confident enough to socialize. If you had good social confidence, maybe you would have been the life of that party. A lack of social confidence is equal to shyness, and you've seen the negative impacts shyness can have on you.

Freedom from people-pleasing

We've discussed people-pleasing in this book, and I believe that you saw the debilitating effects it can have on you. I explained that it comes from your inner desire to be validated by others, and that you are often seeking that validation because you are not confident about yourself. But when you finally achieve social confidence, all of that changes. You no longer need to go out of your way for validation.

The points above are just a few examples of what social confidence can do for you. Now, let's see how you can build this all-important attribute from the ground up. No matter how low you've previously been with your social confidence, the steps below can help you get started.

Ways to Begin Building Social Confidence

To build good social confidence, you'll need to make changes to several aspects of your life. You'll have to create a confident outlook; improve your confidence, social skills, and practice confidence.

So we'll group our discourse into the three parts.

Creating a Confident Outlook

1. Accept yourself the way you are

You need to first accept your introverted nature and be in love with it. Accepting yourself the way you are is good for your self-image. Regardless of the buzz surrounding socializing, quiet and personal time is still priceless. Rather than suddenly hating who you are and trying to make an abrupt switch, learn to love the person you are. If you try to make that abrupt switch, it could lead to more stress and anxiety. A better way to make the transition is to focus on the social situations you are already comfortable with. Focus on improving the quality of the social interactions you have going for you. If you enjoy meeting and playing board games with a group of close friends, focus on improving the quality of the conversation and interaction that goes on there. Stay there and unwind before moving on to bigger things.

2. Do away with negative beliefs and thoughts

The second best thing for you is to avoid those thought patterns that can render your efforts null and void. Avoid thoughts like, "I am boring," or "I don't fit in," or even "I just can't socialize." These thought patterns buried deep in your subconscious will create your reality. For instance, imagine you are on a date and you are so busy telling yourself that you are boring, and they won't like you. What do you think will happen? You will end up being boring. Once everything in you has accepted that you are truly boring, you are definitely going to bore your date to death.

Once you have accepted that you are boring, you will start looking for evidence that confirms your belief. Even when these pieces of evidence are meaningless coincidences, you will just take them as clear confirmation of your suspicion. The result? Further pressure on yourself. So always try to reframe your mind from having such negative thoughts.

3. Let your expectations be realistic

You might know this already, but let me say it again. Not everyone will like you, and it is not everybody that you will like… you won't vibe with everyone. So don't fall apart because you tried to relate with just one or two people and it didn't happen. Tell yourself that you both don't click, and that's normal. So if you try to initiate a conversation with a stranger and they ignore you, it is not you, it's them too… shrug it off. Who knows what they might be battling with!

Creating a confident outlook also entails cutting yourself some slack. Let me show you a few steps to do that.

- Don't take yourself too seriously

One of the primary reasons for low social confidence is too much awareness. When you care too much about how you look, how you dress, how you walk, it is an indication that you are taking yourself too seriously, and it doesn't always end well. If you are the type of person that also cares too much about other people's opinions of you, just chill and realize that people have the liberty to their opinions, and you have no control over it.

Stop being judgmental on yourself. We've seen how judging yourself can lead to social anxiety and shyness. It can also negatively impact your social confidence. Cut yourself some slack and take a breath. For instance, if you find out that you are always judging what you say, try this: Quit filtering your words and just speak, because often, you have a thousand and one reasonable things to say, you are just being too careful.

- Don't give a crap

Try not to care so much. Apply the principles we talked about in the people-pleasing chapter of this book. Set your priorities and honor them.

Improving Yourself and Your Social Skills

We have two segments to this section. The first is improving every area of your life, and the other is improving your social skills.

For improving every area of your life, it is quite simple. Just be the best version of yourself. If you've always wanted to do away with that belly fat and get yourself a ripped body, hit the gym and get it done. If you've always wanted to be in a ballet class dancing to a beautiful symphony, by all means, sign up and get dancing. Whatever it is that will make your life more desirable, get it done. The idea is that when you have achieved the best version of yourself, your confidence level will naturally improve.

Now let's look at the other aspect, improving your social skills.

I cannot overemphasize the need for you to improve your social skills. Don't just look forward to socializing, spend time to prepare yourself for it. Some social skills you can look to develop are:

1. Knowing how to show interest in people

If you can master the skills of making people feel loved, valued, and wanted, they will naturally gravitate towards you. It is known as social competency, and it passes for social confidence, too. There are subtle non-verbal signals you can use to make people feel wanted. Some of these nonverbal signals are:

- Maintaining eye contact and having the right facial expressions.

- Sitting up tall and widening your chest.
- Smile always, as a way of letting them know you welcome them.
- When taking a posture, choose a still one. Ensure you are neither swaying nor fidgeting.
- Let your handshakes be firm.

2. Speak clearly and at a reasonable pace

Don't just mumble your words, and don't rush through it like it is a difficult task. Calm down and try to speak at a rate that people can easily understand. Apart from having more effective communication, this also portrays confidence. If at any point in your conversation, you notice that you are mumbling or speeding up, pause your statement, take a deep breath and try again. While doing this, don't let any of it show.

3. Be an effective listener

People are naturally drawn to those who can listen to and understand them. You can strategically position yourself to make lots of friends if you master the art of listening effectively. Don’t just listen, listen with intent. You intend to come up with the most suitable and thoughtful response possible. To do this, you will need to remove your attention from yourself and focus it on others. Focusing your attention on them does two things for you. First, it removes the tension from you, and secondly, it endears you to others because it tells them that you care about them.

4. Practicing confidence

It is not just enough for you to know the theories on improving social confidence, discipline yourself to apply them in your everyday life.

Let’s look at some steps you can take to practice social confidence:

- Expose yourself to the actual social situations

No matter the number of steps I give you on how to improve your social confidence, your confidence can only improve as you flex your confidence muscles. You can do that by exposing yourself to real social situations. As you try it, you become more confident. With this increasing confidence, your anxiety will begin to wane.

- Role play

If it is difficult for you to just get into social situations, you can start with role play. Have a trusted friend be the stranger and practice social skills with them. Focus on learning how to introduce yourself, start a conversation, and sustain it for a while.

- Socialize with the help of a friend

When starting your social freedom journey, consider going out with a friend or relative you are very comfortable around. Their presence can help you because you will realize you are not just among strangers. You came along with your good buddy, who will have your back any time.

There we have them; steps you can take to push your social confidence to heights you never thought possible.

In this chapter, I gave different tips you can use in building your social confidence and how to use them. In the next chapter, we will be taking it to the next level by learning how to improve your self-esteem.

CHAPTER NINE:

Improving Your Self Esteem

There is nothing more important than how we think and feel about ourselves. One of the things most people miss in our society is having a high opinion of one's self, who we are, what we do, and the love we have for ourselves.

In a few words, self-esteem is an opinion of oneself and their abilities. This opinion can be low, high, or somewhere in between. Despite having occasional doubts about oneself, having low self-esteem can be damaging, leaving you to feel unmotivated and insecure. Your reason for having low self-esteem may vary. You might be able to point out some of the specific things that affect how you see yourself (like bullying), or it could remain a mystery to you.

Having low self-esteem can be an unfortunate self-fulfilling prophecy because feeling worse about what you do and who you are makes it less motivating to do what it takes to boost your self-esteem. It now becomes easy to spiral down into a cycle of circular and negative thinking. This creates damaging, mired, and wrong beliefs, which aren't ideal, especially if you have a social anxiety disorder.

Either way, there are still things you can do to improve your self-esteem. Improving your self-esteem is a process that doesn't happen overnight. However, there are some things you can do to get started and speed up the process.

Tips for Improving Your Self Esteem

Below are some helpful tips you can use to improve your self-esteem. Everyone has it, and having access to the right tip will go a long way.

Master A New Skill

As humans, we are always learning on a near-constant basis, and considering how the world is evolving, we are left with little or no choice but to adapt to what the world brings. Mastering a new skill can help you a lot, especially within the work and school environments.

Due to the learning process involved in acquiring a new skill, you will not only have a new skill to your name but have the privilege to take on new tasks when necessary, increasing your sense of competency. You become more proactive and have the ability to talk on subjects that you didn't have any ideas about before. Overall, this will change how you see yourself and make you place more value on yourself over time.

Be Nice To Yourself

It is so typical of us to damage our self-esteem further by being self-critical. That shouldn't be the case; we must learn how to be nice to ourselves. That voice in your head that keeps reminding you that you are failing is more powerful than you realize, instead of allowing it to take control of your life, be kind to yourself, and challenge any negative thoughts.

A good way to keep this in check is always to treat yourself how you treat others. If you are very respectful and listen to what others have to say, learn to also do the same for yourself. Speak to yourself the same way you would speak to your mates. At first, this may prove difficult, but after much practice, you will get better at it and eventually master being nice to yourself.

Be Yourself (Do You)

Do you know who you are? Are you being your true self? Since our childhood days, we have been conditioned to act in a certain way. Once you figure out who you are and learn how to be yourself, you will definitely be in a happier place.

Never aim to please others. It can be nice initially, but you need to know your boundaries. When you start comparing yourself with others, you will start feeling inferior and find it hard to be yourself. Instead, try to focus more on your achievements and goals and not measure them with that of someone else. That kind of pressure isn't healthy for anyone, and you don't need it in your life. Just be yourself!

Move More (Get Exercising)

According to a 2016 study, there is a correlation between exercise and having higher self-esteem, including improved mental health. (Sani, Fathirezaie, & Talepasand, 2016).

Debbie Mandel, the author of *Addicted to Stress* suggested that when you engage in physical activity, you are creating both mental and physical empowerment, especially weight lifting.

Exercising will help you organize your day around taking care of yourself. Find a way to squeeze in some time just to relax and do something fun – you will see how relaxing it feels. Other ways you can take care of yourself is by getting enough sleep, eating proper nutrition, and giving yourself a treat once in a while.

Know That Nobody is Perfect

No one has it all, no one is perfect in all they do, and everyone should know this. We all have our areas of strengths and weaknesses. Some of us are creative, others are not. Others are detail-oriented; some of us are not. No matter how hard you try, you can't be perfect.

Believing that there are perfect people can be destructive to your daily life, so refrain from such thoughts. It can hinder you from taking necessary actions because you will become too afraid that you are not living up to a particular standard. You will prefer to procrastinate and not get the results you want. This can really make your self-esteem go low.

Sometimes, there are certain actions you take that never satisfy you. You are never satisfied with your performance or accomplishments. By doing this, your feelings and opinions about yourself will keep being negative, and you will keep lacking the motivation to take action.

A few things that helped me realize my true self and know no one is perfect:

- Going for good enough. When you are trying to make yourself perfect because you are of the notion that there are perfect people, you begin to get yourself wound up and find it difficult to complete a task. Instead, go for just a simple good enough mentality. Although it shouldn't be an excuse for you to slack off, just realize that there is something called "good enough," and when you get there, you have completed your task.
- Keep in mind that subscribing to the myth of perfect people will only hurt you and the people in your life. This reminder should be able to make you see life as what it is and what it is not. Life isn't always what is portrayed in songs, books, movies, or social media. Have a reality check in place just in case you are developing the idea that you need to be perfect. Having the wrong perception can harm you and possibly make you lose potential projects, contracts, jobs, and even relationships.
- Everyone makes mistakes. To err is human, and we get to make mistakes to learn things and grow. So, whenever you make a mistake, never beat yourself up, instead, learn from it, and try again. You have definitely learned one or two things through the mistakes you made, and you get better with the next try.

Focus On the Things You Can Change

In the words of best-selling author and life-changing speaker, Steve Maraboli,

"Incredible change happens in your life when you decide to take control of what you so have power over instead of craving over what you don't"

You need to know the difference between the things you can control and those you can't. It is easy to get caught up with things that are totally out of your control, and this will prevent you from achieving much. Instead, focus your energy on the things you know are within your control and see what you can do about them.

When you focus on the things you can change, you don't worry too much because you know you are doing as much as you can for your happy and healthy space. It doesn't just free you from your anxiety; it also gives you a sense of deeper self-trust, which will boost your self-esteem.

Do What Makes You Happy

If you choose to do the things that make you happy, you are instantly improving your self-esteem. There won't be any room to sink into your insecurities as happiness trumps them all. People have low self-esteem because they believe all others say about them, not knowing that muting those words is a pathway to happiness.

When you spend more time doing the things you love and enjoy, you likely start thinking positively, and this can be contagious too. I have never heard of someone that regretted choosing to do the things that make them happy. Even if it doesn't go as they pictured it, the decision to do the things that make them happy leaves room for little regret.

You can try scheduling in a little time for yourself every day. Even if it is for cooking, being in the bath, lying on the couch, watching movies, or reading a book, just do something fun that you like. If it makes you happy, then it is worth it.

Celebrate Small Victories

Our society today has conditioned us to only care about celebrating big wins and breeze by the small ones. Even if it appears insignificant to celebrate small victories like cooking your favorite meal, waking up in the morning, starting a new project, being debt-free, or going for a long walk, they still need to be celebrated.

Celebrating your small wins is a great way of boosting your self-esteem. Realize that life isn't made up of just big moments, but the small ones. So start celebrating!

Be Helpful And Considerate To Other People

Being helpful to people has proven to be beneficial on so many levels. You not only get the satisfaction that you helped someone in need, but you also get an increased sense of purpose, which improves your self-esteem. Being helpful and considerate can increase your level of accessibility in your workplace and shape you into an asset the company wouldn't want to lose. So, try to focus on being considerate to people in your daily life. You can try doing any of the things below:

- Allow someone into your lane while driving, instead of blocking them off.
- When someone is trying to vent, just be there and listen to what he or she has to say.
- Be helpful to someone in a practical way, even if it's just for a few minutes.
- Hold the door for someone.
- You can be a motivator to a friend or family member that is feeling down and unmotivated.

Define What Success Means To You

We all want to be successful. We go after fame, money, power, relationships, and education all in the pursuit of success. Have you ever paused to ask yourself what success means to you? Only a few people will pause to find out what it means for them. If you don't define your life plan, there is a high chance of you falling into another person's plan, even when what they plan for you isn't much.

If you don't define success for yourself, you might end up climbing the wrong ladder, pursuing someone else's success, and you will only get to realize this after you have gotten to the top of the wrong mountain.

To define your success, you need to set your objectives, goals, and paths based on what you want, desire, and not what other people want for you. For some people, helping others brings them joy, so success for them is through giving to others. Try to tease out what success means to you. To do anything successfully, you need to find the self-esteem within yourself to get you there.

Surround Yourself With Supportive And Positive Squad

Positive people are real and not self-centered. They don't just care about themselves, but about others, too. With positivity follows authenticity, and you get to have people looking out for your well-being.

Always aim to surround yourself with positive people that will help bring out your full potential and help the world see the best version of you. Let go of any toxic and unsupportive friends you have and focus more on having a healthy squad.

You should know who treats you badly or tears you down instead of building you up. Despite this, you may find it difficult to avoid the toxic people around you because you feel you can't do without them or that you've known them for so long. What if keeping them close does greater harm than good?

It will be difficult to improve your self-esteem if what influences your life the most keeps dragging you down.

In order to make the necessary changes and get the desired results:

- Spend less of your time with people that are not kind, unsupportive, or perfectionists. They will never contribute anything good to your dreams or goals.
- Spend more of that time with people who are uplifting, supportive, and positive. These people have more humane, kinder, and better ways of thinking about the world.
- Think about the things you watch, read, and listen to. Use the time you spend on an internet forum to do other things if you feel it makes you doubt who you are, and have some negative feelings about yourself.
- Spend time listening to podcasts, reading books, websites, and blogs that will help you feel better about yourself.
- Avoid people that trigger you to become anxious or cause you to fall into negative thought patterns, and find people who will make you feel good about yourself.

Finally, as humans, we are all born with equal worth and countless potential. Having the belief that you are anything less is false, and I want you to drop it right now. By putting in hard work and practicing self-compassion, the self-destructive thoughts that often hinder your self-esteem from growing can be unlearned. All you need to do is to follow all I have outlined above and start increasing your self-worth. Everyone has it in them; you only need the right push to recognize it.

In this chapter, you learned what having self-esteem means and the different ways you can improve your self-esteem. Next, we will be going into the healing process (therapy). Once your anxiety is getting out of control, then therapy is the next thing to seek.

CHAPTER TEN:

Therapy for Social Anxiety

Social anxiety disorder (SAD) is a common psychiatric disorder. Though often labeled as shyness, it can create crippling fear that affects your work performance, school performance, social attendance, and relationships. Up to 12% of Americans will be affected by it in their lifetime.

Diagnosing social anxiety disorder can be hard, especially since it is confused with normal fear and shyness. This has caused a lot of people to not seek help. To make things easy, the *Diagnostic and Statistical Manual of Mental Disorders, Fourth Edition* has listed the criteria that can be used to diagnose a social anxiety disorder. It also describes how the disorder shows up in children and adults.

Almost half of the people with social anxiety disorder experience anxiety in certain situations, especially those situations that require public appearance and public speaking, while others have a generalized form of anxiety, which makes them experience fear in almost all kinds of social situations.

Though most people get nervous when speaking in front of a group or at parties, what differentiates it from a social anxiety disorder is the level of distress and damage it causes. For instance, research has suggested that adults with a social anxiety disorder are more likely to miss work, while a youth with the disorder are also more likely to drop out of high school. In fact, intimate relationships can be affected –

which is a major reason people with a social anxiety disorder are less likely to marry early.

Still, because the symptoms of the disorder are often seen as minor, only half of the people with social anxiety disorder seek help or receive treatment. As I mentioned earlier, they typically experience the symptoms of SAD for at least ten years before seeking help. That is unfortunate because there are many treatments available that can help in reducing the symptoms of anxiety.

When To Seek Therapy For Social Anxiety

Have you been avoiding certain social situations for a few months? Have you been really stressed out because of this? If you are, then now is the time for you to seek help. If you always keep skipping events that you are interested in, but you are too scared to try it out, then it's time to seek help.

Similarly, you always assume you are not interested in things just because of that awkward feeling that comes with it. You know very well that you might find an activity fun, but you keep shoving it off and hiding behind cynicism.

If you have been finding it difficult to make new friends because going into a new environment sounds scary, or you see yourself being left alone while everyone is trying to mingle, or when someone tries to ask you out on a date, you have more than a million excuses for not going, you may have SAD. You keep pushing down the feeling of loneliness, telling yourself that it is what you are meant to live with.

Research has suggested that environmental and genetic factors interact to cause social anxiety. Though, to treat social anxiety, instead of focusing on why you have a problem, it will be beneficial to look at what is maintaining the anxiety and address the factors using cognitive behavioral therapy. Multiple research studies suggest that cognitive behavioral therapy (CBT) is an effective way of treating anxiety disorders, especially social anxiety disorders. All in all, the best way social anxiety disorder can be treated is through Cognitive

Behavioral Therapy or medication. First, let's see what CBT is all about.

Cognitive Behavioral Therapy (CBT)

Cognitive Behavioral Therapy (CBT) is a common form of therapy that came into the limelight in the 1980s and 1990s for the treatment of anxiety disorders. According to research, CBT is a form of therapy that has consistently helped patients overcome their clinical anxiety disorders.

Cognitive Behavioral Therapy is not just a one-set method, but a combination of different techniques that depend on the particular anxiety disorder being treated. For instance, the CBT used for the treatment of social anxiety disorder is different from the one used in treating depression and other types of anxiety disorder.

Since there are so many different techniques of CBT, you must find a therapist who is experienced and knows the particular and most effective techniques for treating social anxiety disorder.

CBT aims to avail patients with techniques and practices so that the patients with social anxiety disorder can have new ways in which they think and behave in situations that seem terrifying to them. The therapy can be offered to an individual or to a group.

In exposure therapy, patients are exposed to the feared situation, and ways are suggested to help them manage the fear. For instance, if the school's upcoming prom night or the upcoming office party is already feeling overwhelming, a way to cope with this is to set an achievable goal, like starting a conversation with one or two people at the party. In the other variation of CBT, patients will practice and learn relaxation techniques and social skills to help them cope with anxiety. Though this isn't as well-studied as the exposure therapy.

Cognitive Behavioral Therapy usually consists of about twelve to sixteen weekly sessions that last for sixty to ninety minutes. Studies have suggested that patients with anxiety disorder go through six to twelve weeks of CBT before any visible improvement can be seen.

What CBT for Social Anxiety Entails

- Facing social situations that give you anxiety, gradually and efficiently, instead of avoiding the situation.
- Learning to control the physical symptoms associated with anxiety with the use of breathing exercises and relaxation techniques.
- Challenging unhelpful and negative thoughts that trigger and fuel your anxiety. Switch them with a more balanced view.
- Even though you can learn breathing exercises, relaxation, and relaxation techniques, you can also benefit from the guidance and extra support a therapist offers.

Goals of CBT for Social Anxiety Disorder

The major goal of CBT is to identify your irrational thoughts and beliefs and replace them with more realistic views. In the CBT process, you need to work on some areas, and they are:

- How to be more assertive
- Anger, guilt, and embarrassment over the past
- Your misconceptions over your self-worth and abilities
- Overcoming procrastination that is related to social anxiety
- Being more realistic and confronting perfectionism

During your CBT process, it may feel like a student-teacher relationship, with the therapist playing the role of a teacher. The concepts will be outlined, and the therapist will help you on your path to change and self-discovery. Also, you will be assigned homework that is crucial to your progress.

Keys to Success in CBT

According to research, there are different keys to success in CBT for social anxiety disorder. The possibility of CBT helping you depends greatly on your expectation of success, your ability to face discomforting thoughts, and your willingness to complete your homework assignments.

Patients who have the zeal to work hard and are positive that CBT offers help, have a higher chance to succeed. Though, the CBT is an intensive therapy that needs active participation from the patient. In the end, the improvement will be long-lasting and worth the hard work.

CBT Methods

Cognitive Behavioral Therapy consists of different techniques, of which many focus on problematic thinking. The cognitive methods help patients lessen the anxiety they feel in interpersonal relationships and in social situations. CBT promises to give patients of social anxiety disorder a feeling of control over how they feel in social situations.

The fundamental goal of CBT is to change your core beliefs, which influence the way you interpret your environment. Changing those core beliefs will lead to a long-lasting recovery from your social anxiety symptoms.

A crucial problem CBT focuses on is the presence of automatic negative thoughts patients of social anxiety disorder have, and the automatic negative ways of thinking that are often twisted with their reality, likely increase their anxiety and reduce their coping ability. These thoughts automatically take place when they think of any anxiety-provoking situation.

For instance, people with the fear of making new friends will elicit thoughts of failure and embarrassment anytime they think of the situation. The aim of CBT is to replace such cognitive distortions with a more realistic view.

At one point in your life, someone has probably told you always to think positively when in situations that trigger anxiety. Sadly, it isn't that easy to do; if it were, a lot of people would've resolved their anxiety issue long ago! Since your brain has been hardwired over time to have anxious and negative thoughts, it will need time to start thinking in a new way. Simply telling yourself, "I will handle the situation better and be less anxious" won't work, based on how you are thinking.

To change your automatic negative thinking for the long-term, you will need to practice every day for several months. Initially, you will be asked to catch your negative thoughts and make them logically neutral. This will later become easier as you work your way up to realistic thoughts. Then it becomes automatic and habitual.

After a while, your memory processes will be affected, and the neural pathways inside your brain will get altered. You start thinking, acting, and feeling different, but with patience, practice, and persistence, progress will be made. Initially, it is a conscious process, but with constant practice and repetition, it becomes an automatic process.

Behavioral Methods

Systematic desensitization is one of the commonly used behavioral techniques to treat social anxiety disorder. It is a type of exposure training that requires your exposure to anxiety-provoking situations to elicit less fear over time.

The exposure training for SAD is always a gradual process. Any exposure training without a gradual step-by-step process will only do more damage than good. Your anxiety will get worse, as you remain in a vicious cycle, which will eventually lead to depression.

With the help of a CBT therapist, you are gradually exposing yourself to social situations that make you anxious so that they will no longer elicit fear. For a start, you can practice imagined exposure by using role playing to practice for a job interview, giving a speech, or introducing yourself to a stranger. Once your imagined and practiced situation gets easier, you can move to the situation in real life. Exposure training moving too fast, or if the situations are too demanding, can go wrong.

Internet CBT for SAD

Providing Cognitive behavioral therapy over the Internet (i-CBT) is gaining popularity and becoming more and more common. Some research supports its use, especially when supported by a professional in mental health.

Since CBT follows a strictly structured format, it is suitable for online applications, consisting of therapy supported interventions or self-help. For patients with severe anxiety who find it difficult to leave the comfort of their home and attend therapy appointments in person, this form of CBT is helpful, too.

We need to use all the cognitive strategies at our disposal, strengthen our resolve to be persistent and consistent in therapies, and make use of all forms of experimental or behavioral activity that will help us manage our social anxiety disorders.

Just like with cognitive therapy, experiments or behavioral activities need to be detailed and comprehensive. The therapist needs to have a list of several behavioral activities that give the patient confidence and peace as they work on the activities.

Finally, for effective and successful treatment of anxiety, behavioral and cognitive therapy needs to be thorough and comprehensive. Reinforcement needs to be a continuous process, and the person needs to be motivated enough to stick to the thirty-minute a day practice routine.

CBT is not the path of lesser resistance for either the patient or the therapist. However, it is the most effective way to surmount social anxiety disorder. The majority of people with a social anxiety disorder will agree to work hard and diligently undertake their therapy, they will tell you they are highly motivated, ready and willing because the work they have to do is nothing when compared to the daily nightmares they had to endure while living with social anxiety.

Having SAD is never easy; it is an everyday struggle and many people hide in denial. Seeking help for it shows you are willing to make progress and remove the shackles of fear. It is this hope of making progress and eventually attaining success that keeps you focused with a positive mind while you proceed forward, aiming for your ultimate goal – freedom!

FINAL WORDS

Social anxiety and all of the other issues that come with it can be difficult to manage. But I strongly believe that with all we've discussed, you have come to understand where your anxiety comes from and how you can nip it in the bud. The fact that you have read this book shows how hungry you are to eliminate social anxiety and achieve social confidence. That is a good thing, but it doesn't stop at just reading.

Don't just read this book and hide away in your comfort zone. The best way to eliminate social anxiety is to be in a social setting. No matter the number of books you read or courses you take, it still boils down to your effort and your discipline to put what you have read into practice. In every section of this book, I have given you well-researched solutions that have worked wonders for myself and countless others. It is my sincere desire that you obtain the same result.

As a way of refreshing the key concepts in this book, let's go over the chapters we've discussed. We opened our discussion with the subject matter "social anxiety." I explained what it means, the types, the likely causes, how you can know if you have it and so on. The purpose was to help you know everything about your problem because there is no way you can combat it without fully knowing it.

From there, we became more specific with our discourse on social anxiety. We looked at when it happens, what it feels like, the core cues that trigger it. We also looked at the physical, behavioral, and emotional symptoms you can experience whenever it happens. I included that chapter to further reiterate that countless people, including myself, know everything you are going through. It is not unique to you and you alone. However, most of those people, including myself, have weathered the storm and eliminated those symptoms so we can live the lives we deserve.

From there, we attacked social anxiety. I gave you several tips that you can adapt in your fight against social anxiety. In that chapter, I made it clear that avoiding social situations is not the solution. The solution is confronting your fears and working your way through it. I gave you tips you can use, including changing your perspective on the issue, avoiding negative coping strategies, and being compassionate with people around you. Let me emphasize that none of the tips in that section were included thoughtlessly. All of them are tips that have been studied by psychologists, and they all proved to be effective against social anxiety. Be kind to yourself and use them.

Then we moved our discussion deeper into how you can go beyond managing social anxiety to overcoming it, like countless others before you. We said that the first thing you should do is to identify the fears and thoughts that fuel your social anxiety. I identified some fears, such as, “they won’t like me,” “I’m probably going to embarrass myself,” and so on. I went on to show you how you can begin to analyze and challenge those fears. Because, trust me, oftentimes, these fears are unfounded, and through logical evaluation, you can start to see this for yourself. In that chapter, we identified some thought patterns that escalate your social anxiety. For example, mind-reading, fortune-telling, catastrophizing and personalizing. Then we said instead of spending your time and energy on those destabilizing thought patterns, you should shift your focus to others instead. I showed you how you could start adopting the social anxiety ladder and a pro-socializing lifestyle as a way of helping your condition.

Sometimes, social anxiety can pile so much pressure on you, that if not managed, you can degenerate into an anxiety attack. I listed some relaxation techniques that can help you calm your nerves whenever you feel your heart beating against your chest. We discussed techniques such as diaphragmatic breathing, autogenic training, progressive muscle relaxation, and guided imagery. I told you the importance of practicing these relaxation techniques, even when you are already relaxed, so that you can easily execute them whenever anxiety is upon you.

The next chapter dealt with yet another problem found with us socially-challenged people, and that is the issue of people-pleasing. I opened that chapter by showing you the signs that tell you are a people pleaser so you don't mistake it for being kind. Then I gave you steps to overcome it, like starting small, giving yourself time, validating and loving yourself.

Then we looked at shyness, its effects, and how to overcome it. We also looked at ways you can begin to build good social confidence and improve your self-esteem. I included that chapter because it is the lack of these attributes that cause social anxiety in the first place. We saw how we could eliminate social anxiety by boosting our social confidence and self-esteem.

We closed the book by discussing the use of therapy for treating social anxiety. We looked at the signs that therapy might be necessary, as well as key therapies like cognitive-behavioral therapy (CBT) and role-playing.

One thing I want you to take away from this book is that social anxiety, shyness, people-pleasing, and lack of social confidence are a bad place to be in your life, but fortunately for you, you can do something about it. You have already started doing so by buying and reading this book. I hope that you will make a conscious effort to see it to the end. Don't just read this book and add it to the collection of books on social anxiety. Read it, and take action.

See you on the social side of life, the part where everything is happening… Good luck!

RESOURCES

ADAA. (2019). *Social Anxiety Disorder.* Retrieved from Anxiety and Depression Association of America: https://adaa.org/understanding-anxiety/social-anxiety-disorder

Albono, A. M. (2014, August 12). *When young people suffer social anxiety disorder: what parents can do.* Retrieved from CareForYourMind: http://careforyourmind.org/when-young-people-suffer-social-anxiety-disorder-what-parents-can-do/

Bhandari, S. (2019, May 20). *What Is Social Anxiety Disorder?* Retrieved from WebMD: https://www.webmd.com/anxiety-panic/guide/mental-health-social-anxiety-disorder#2

Cohut, M. (2019, August 30). *4 top tips for coping with social anxiety.* Retrieved from https://www.medicalnewstoday.com/articles/326211.php#1

Cuncic, A. (2019, November 26). *How to Practice Progressive Muscle Relaxation.* Retrieved from Verywellmind: https://www.verywellmind.com/how-do-i-practice-progressive-muscle-relaxation-3024400

Daskal, L (2017) *9 Simple Ways to Boost Your Self-Esteem Quickly.* Retrieved from https://www.inc.com/lolly-daskal/19-simple-ways-to-boost-your-self-esteem-quickly.html

Felman, A. (2018, February 5). *What's to know about social anxiety disorder?* Retrieved from MedicalNewsToday: https://www.medicalnewstoday.com/articles/176891.php#what-is-social-anxiety-disorder

Griffin, T. (2019, October 6). *How to Be Socially Confident.* Retrieved from WikiHow: https://www.wikihow.com/Be-Socially-Confident

Lo, M. (2019). *5 Ways to Start Building Social Confidence Today.* Retrieved from Lifehack: https://www.lifehack.org/372358/5-ways-start-building-social-confidence-today

Luna, A. (2020, January). *People-Pleasing: The Hidden Dangers of Always Being "Too Nice".* Retrieved from Lonerwolf: https://lonerwolf.com/people-pleasing/

Project, G. (2019, October 20). *5 Necessary Tips to Building Social Confidence.* Retrieved from ThriveGlobal: https://thriveglobal.com/stories/5-necessary-tips-to-building-social-confidence-2/

Rube, T. (2020, January 20). *How to Tell if you are a people pleaser.* Retrieved from WikiHow: https://www.wikihow.com/Tell-if-You-Are-a-People-Pleaser

Sani, S. Fathirezaie, Z. & Talepasand S. (2016) *Physical activity and self-esteem: testing direct and indirect relationships associated with psychological and physical mechanisms.* Retrieved from https://www.ncbi.nlm.nih.gov/pmc/articles/PMC5068479/#!po=63.0435

Shanley, D. (2019). *7 Ways to Overcome Shyness and Social Anxiety.* Retrieved from PsychCentral: https://psychcentral.com/blog/7-ways-to-overcome-shyness-and-social-anxiety/

Smith, M. M. Segal, and Shubin, J. (2019) *Social Anxiety Disorder.* Retrieved from https://www.helpguide.org/articles/anxiety/social-anxiety-disorder.htm

Tartakovsky, M. (2018) *6 Ways to Overcome Social Anxiety.* Retrieved from https://psychcentral.com/lib/6-ways-to-overcome-social-anxiety/

ThisWayUp (n.d) *How do you feel shy.* Retrieved from https://thiswayup.org.au/how-do-you-feel/shy/

Reachout.com (n.d) *10 tips for improving your self-esteem.* Retrieved from https://au.reachout.com/articles/10-tips-for-improving-your-self-esteem

Master Stress Management

Reduce Stress, Worry Less, and Improve Your Mood. Discover How to Stay Calm Under Pressure Through Emotional Resilience, Mental Toughness, and Mindfulness Techniques

Derick Howell

TABLE OF CONTENTS

INTRODUCTION

Say you're at your favorite café, reading this book, and as you glance up from taking a sip of your delicious coffee, you notice the people standing in line. Your attention wanders to the woman in a black dress, three people from the counter. Now, take a really good look at her. And I don't mean a simple glance -- I mean, really take your time to look at her. She is probably not missing fingers, covered in scars, or even looking sickly at all. She appears perfectly healthy, yet this doesn't mean that she is not suffering from a disease that you cannot see, like high cholesterol, high blood pressure, or some other disease. The diseases we get nowadays differ from what used to affect our parents or grandparents. The kind of diseases we get now also have different causes and consequences.

If a caveman inadvertently ate meat that was contaminated, the consequences were clear -- they would die a few days later. Now, when it comes to having a bad diet, the consequences are not as clearly defined. You could end up with a variety of conditions as a result of a poor diet, such as cardiovascular problems, obesity, diabetes, and so forth, that could affect the quality of your life. But this outcome depends on a lot of factors, including your genetic makeup, the type of junk food you consistently ate, how much junk food you ate, your personality, and your stress level.

Stress is everywhere and there is no way to avoid it. Whether you're stuck in traffic, late for work, have an approaching deadline, relationship problems, trauma, and so on, we have all been in stressful situations.

Ever noticed how your breathing quickens, your pulse goes up, and your muscles tense whenever something stressful happens? You may even get an energy boost and you are ready to take on whatever comes your way. While this might be great when you are in danger, it doesn't work when what's causing your stress is your three-year-old son or your demanding boss. What do you do then? How do you handle this stress?

Life has a lot of demands and every day more keeps coming up. These demands can either cause good or bad stress. I bet you didn't know that not all stress is bad. For instance, getting married or moving to a bigger house can be stressful. But most people don't see it as bad stress because these are good things. You are about to marry the love of your life, but planning the wedding took its toll on you. Moving requires you to pack, unpack, and rearrange everything so your new house truly feels like home. However, do you have the time to get this all done?

Unfortunately, many of us are aware that we suffer from stress, but we often feel that we have no control over it and we usually don't have the tools or skills to lessen its effects and manage our overall stress levels. Like many, perhaps you are in search of some effective methods and skills you can use to reduce your stress levels.

Whether you are aware that you are stressed, or you suspect that you could be, this is the book for you. It contains a wide range of well-detailed techniques and tips aimed at helping you reign in your stress and improve your functioning and focus, while also helping improve your quality of life. These techniques aren't only for stress reduction -- they are meant to teach you how to handle stress and build your resilience to it and its effects. This book has actionable steps that you can jump into right now and apply for a quick stress fix and others that seek to permanently take away the physical and mental pressures that stress causes, helping you regain control and changing how you react to it.

You could be wondering, how can I be so sure of these techniques? What proof is there that these exercises relieve stress?

Well, I have been teaching people about stress and how to manage it for many years now. These tips and tricks are backed by research, extensive studies over many years, and personal experience.

People everywhere, myself included, have embraced these techniques and are experiencing their benefits. They worry less, have fewer mood swings and outbursts, and are calm under pressure because they have built mental toughness and emotional resilience. And the benefits don't stop there. Learning to reduce and manage your stress is good for you, both mentally and physically. It boosts your happiness and well-being and helps reverse some of the effects of stress, such as high cortisol and adrenaline levels.

I use mindfulness, breathing techniques, and meditation every day. I have to juggle a lot, so these skills help keep me sane and on track. Reading this book will not only change how you view stress, but also show you that managing stress is easy -- you just have to be mindful of it. These techniques will help you gain control of the emotions that seemed out of your control, such as anger, rage, or helplessness. They will change how you think, as well as your behaviors, habits, and actions, and teach you new ways of dealing with difficult situations.

As you read on, keep your mind open and allow me to help you as you equip yourself with the tools and skills necessary for stress management. Find a book and a pen and take note of the important concepts discussed in this book. Understand that you are no longer helpless in the face of stress -- you can take charge now! Nobody wants to live their life stressed and, while you cannot eliminate it from your life, you can master how to control it. The first step is by reading this book.

Happy reading!

CHAPTER ONE:

Stress 101: The Basics Of Stress

Think about it:

What's the first thing that comes to mind when someone says the word "stress"? Perhaps you think of your harsh boss and high-pressure job, your tattered finances, breaking marriage, or horrific event that happened to you years ago but still haunt you. Whatever your definition, the fact remains that most of us don't really know what stress is. We experience it from time to time, but when asked to define exactly what it is, we may be at a loss for words. In fact, most times, we only realize we are stressed when we are on the verge of breaking. So, what is stress exactly?

What is stress?

Defining what stress is can be hard since it is a highly subjective experience. However, the term stress, according to the American Institute of Stress, can be defined as the body's nonspecific reaction to any demands for change. Hans Selye conceived of this definition of stress in the year 1936. He was a Hungarian-Canadian endocrinologist who researched the hypothetical non-scientific response of organisms to stressors. He stated that stress was stressful, whether you received good or bad news or if the impulse was negative or positive. Hans Selye's research into stress began after he observed patients with chronic illnesses exhibiting similar symptoms, which he would later attribute to stress. He also observed this same phenomenon when lab rats were exposed to cold, drugs, or surgical procedures. They displayed a common set of responses, which he called General Adaptation Syndrome. This syndrome happened in three phases -- first, the initial "alarm phase", followed by a "resistance" or "adaptation phase", and eventually, exhaustion and death.

According to the Mayo Clinic, the alarm phase refers to the initial symptoms in the body when under stress. This fight or flight response prepares you to either flee or protect yourself in bad situations. In this stage, your heart rate increases, cortisol is released, which increases your energy, and your muscles tense, ready for what might happen. The second stage, or the resistance phase, comes after the fight or flight response when the body begins mending itself. Cortisol levels reduce and your pulse rate and blood pressure begin to go back to their normal levels. However, the alarm stage of stress states that even though your body has entered the recovery phase, it's still on high alert. If you dealt with your stressful situation and it is no longer an issue, your body will continue with its repairs, regulating your hormonal levels, blood pressure, and heart rate.

However, if your stress persists, your body will remain in this heightened state of alertness and it will eventually adapt to living with a higher stress level. Your body will then undergo changes you might not be aware of. Higuera notes that your body will continue secreting cortisol and other hormones and your heart rate and blood pressure will remain high. You may also exhibit irritability, frustration, and problems concentrating. If the resistance stage continues for too long without pause or cessation, it can lead to the exhaustion stage.

The exhaustion stage comes as a result of prolonged or chronic stress. It occurs when you have struggled with stress for too long that it has drained you physically, mentally, and emotionally and you no longer have the strength to combat your stress. According to Higuera, at this point, you might feel helpless, tired, or feel your circumstance is hopeless. In this stage, you might experience fatigue, burnout, depression, or anxiety, along with a decreased tolerance for existing or taking on new stress. Your immunity at this point is quite weakened, leaving you prone to opportunistic and stress-related illnesses.

This theory on stress and the GAS syndrome were derived from an experiment in which Higuera injected lab rats with various organ extracts. At first, he thought he had discovered a new hormone, but he quickly dispelled that theory after getting the same result, regardless of where he injected the substances. The adrenal cortex would swell and there would be a reduction in the functionality of the thymus, gastric, and duodenal ulcers. These results, combined with the prior observations he made about patients with different diseases displaying the same symptoms, led to his description of stress. He was also the first person to describe the body's stress coping system, the hypothalamic-pituitary-adrenal axis (HPA axis) system, which we will talk about later.

Felman, a writer for Medical News Today, says that whenever you feel threatened, your body releases chemicals that enable you to protect yourself from injury. These chemicals, cortisol, adrenaline, and noradrenaline can increase your heart rate, raise your blood pressure, and make you more alert. As I mentioned above, this reaction is known as your fight-or-flight response and is essential for survival. This heightened state fuels you to deal with the threat and improves your ability to handle the dangerous or challenging situation. Factors that can lead to stress are called stressors, the American Institute of Stress explains, and they can include noise, scary moments, your first day at work, fighting with your spouse, a speeding car, and so on. The more stressors we are under, the more stressed we tend to get.

This stress response, however, can sometimes be triggered too easily, for instance when we are subjected to too many stressors at once, as is the case with everyday life. Once the threat or change has passed, your body is supposed to revert to its normal, relaxed state. Unfortunately, the continuous, nonstop demands and complications of everyday, modern life mean that, for some people, their internal alarm systems never shut off.

Stress can mean various things to different people. What might be stressing you could be of little concern to another person. We get stressed when the demands of life become too much and we struggle to cope with them. These demands can be anything from family and finances to your career, relationships, or any other situation that might pose a real or perceived challenge or threat to your well-being.

People also handle stress differently. Some are able to handle pressure, while others buckle under it. When we are faced with challenging situations, it is how we react to them that determines how much stress we will be under and the effects it will have on our health. If you feel that you might be lacking the resources needed to resolve your stressful situation, you might have a stronger reaction to stress, which can eventually trigger health problems, says Felman. If, on the other hand, you feel that you have the right resources to handle the situation, your stress levels are more likely to be lower with fewer health problems because of it.

Stress doesn't necessarily have to come from bad experiences or circumstances. As I mentioned above, even positive experiences, such as giving birth to a baby, taking a trip with your family, moving to a bigger, nicer house, or even being promoted can cause some stress. This is because there is a major change involved, extra effort is needed, or new responsibilities have come up and there is a need for adaptation. Having to step into unchartered territory and wondering how we will deal with this unknown can be stressful.

Like I mentioned before, not all stress is bad -- some of it is even beneficial and it can help save your life or help you perform better. It is the persistently negative response to a stressor that can lead to health problems and affect your happiness. However, if you are aware of your stressors and how you react to them, it can help lessen the adverse effects of stress and any negative feelings that might come up. This is where stress management comes in. Stress management gives you the tools you need to reset your internal alarm system. It enables your mind and body to adapt to long-term stressors and become more resilient to their effects. Without these tools, your body will always be on high alert and, over time, you could develop long-term stress that can lead to serious health problems.

Causes of stress

Stress is caused in part by two things, stressors and your perceptions, and it helps to know your stressors so that you can easily manage your stress. Factors or situations that lead to stress are referred to as stressors and many of us tend to think of stressors as being negative, such as a hectic work schedule or a problematic relationship. However, a stressor can be anything that demands a lot from you, including positive events.

Not all stressors come from external events, though. Sometimes, stress can be self-generated, for instance, when you worry about something that has a 50/50 chance of happening or not happening, fearing the unknown, having your beliefs challenged, or having irrational, self-defeating thoughts about life. These can include worrying that you will never be good enough, pretty enough, or smart enough.

Your perception of a stressor can also lead to stress. As mentioned before, a stressor to you might not be a stressor to someone else. Take, for instance, how public speaking terrifies most of us, while others crave the spotlight. One person might thrive under pressure and another might crack. These different reactions are because of our different perceptions of the situations. Other external exacerbators include major changes in your life or environment, workplace, social standing, losing a loved one, illness, family problems, lack of money or time, problems at work, driving in heavy traffic, uncertainty, or waiting on results, etc.

How your body reacts to stress

So now we know that stress can be positive or negative. Positive stress helps keep us alert and avoid danger, but when one is exposed to prolonged stress, it can become negative and you can end up overworked with stress-related tensions begin to build in your body. The body has an automatic stress coping system that kicks in, causing physiological changes that enable the body to deal with stressful situations. It is called the hypothalamic-pituitary-adrenal axis (HPA axis) system. This HPA axis system is a set of complex direct influences and feedback loops between the hypothalamus, pituitary glands, and the adrenal glands.

According to DeMorrow, in his 2018 International Journal of Molecular Sciences, these three organs form a major neuroendocrine system that controls the body's reaction to stress by regulating many of the bodily functions. These include digestion, the immune system, your moods and emotions, your sexual drive, energy storage, and use. It is the mechanism for interactions between your glands, hormones, and part of your midbrain that control the GAS syndrome.

Our bodies are made to experience stress and react to it. During a stress response, your body undergoes several changes, all because of the chemicals released. Since your body is about to face or handle something challenging, some of your bodily functions, such as digestion or your immune systems, are slowed since they are not very useful at the moment. All the focus is on increasing your oxygen intake and blood flow to your muscles, brain, and necessary body parts and ensuring your muscles are engaged. So you breathe faster, your blood pressure and heart rate are higher, your muscles become tense, and you enter a state of hyper-awareness.

When you are under stress for a long while, you enter a state called distress, which is when you get a negative reaction to stress. Distress can affect the body's internal systems, leading to problems such as headaches, ulcers, upset stomach, high blood pressure, loss of sexual drive, chest pains, and even sleeping problems. It can also cause premature graying of hair. There are also emotional problems caused by stress, which can include outbursts of anger, anxiety, depression, irritability, panic attacks, restlessness, and sadness.

You can also experience burnout, a general sense of unease, problems concentrating on what you are doing, fatigue, forgetfulness, and bad habits -- some people bite their nails to try and ease the anxiety within. Stress can also lead to behavioral changes, such as having food cravings, eating too much or too little, and losing your appetite altogether. Those under stress also tend to abuse drugs and alcohol, as they try to find an escape. They tend to withdraw socially, keeping to themselves and not engaging with family or friends and their relationships can fail because of this.

Research has also shown that stress can bring on or worsen certain conditions, such as heart disease, liver cirrhosis, lung disease, and even suicide. These conditions can be brought on by the various unhealthy ways we try to combat stress, such as abusing alcohol and other drugs. Instead of relieving the body of stress and returning it into a relaxed state, these substances offer temporary relief -- still, the body remains in an alarmed state, causing more health problems. This condition leaves people caught in a vicious cycle that can lead to death if it is not stopped.

Types of stress

Our bodies react to stress depending on whether it is new or short-term, also called acute stress, or whether it has been around for a while or long-term, referred to as chronic stress. These are the two main types of stress many of us face. Let's take a look at each one.

Acute stress

The Mayo Clinic website defines acute stress as temporary stress that goes away quickly and it is the most common way everyone experiences stress. It is caused by thinking about the pressure of things and events that have recently happened or what will happen soon. It is also called the fight-or-flight response and it is your body's immediate response to stressors, be it a perceived or real threat, challenge, or scare. It is an immediate, intense response and sometimes it can be thrilling, due to the release of adrenaline. It helps you manage dangerous or exciting situations. It is what you feel when you hit the brakes to avoid hitting something, or when you have a fast-approaching deadline. This type of stress reduces or completely ends once the stressor is resolved.

A single instance of acute stress is not harmful to your health -- it can actually be beneficial and doesn't cause the same amount of damage as long-term stress. However, it can cause tension, headaches, stomach problems, high blood pressure, and other mildly severe health issues. Repeated instances of acute stress or severe acute stress can cause mental health problems, such as Acute Stress Disorder (ASD), and eventually lead to chronic stress. You can develop Acute Stress Disorder after being exposed to one or many traumatic events. An example of prolonged Acute Stress Disorder is Post-Traumatic Stress Disorder (PTSD). Symptoms of ASD can develop after witnessing traumatic or disturbing experiences, such as death or serious injury firsthand. These symptoms can start or get worse after the traumatic event and can last anywhere between three days to a month.

Examples of persons who might suffer from ASD include car accident victims, assault victims, or soldiers that have experienced war. Sometimes this can even develop into Post-Traumatic Stress Syndrome, which lasts longer than ASD. There is another form of acute stress known as Episodic Acute Stress that affects people whose stress triggers are frequent. For instance, if you have too many commitments and poor organizational skills, you can find yourself suffering from Episodic Acute Stress.

Dealing with acute stress

When your body's stress response is triggered by acute stress, you can reduce or reverse the effects by using quick relaxation techniques. These techniques are meant to help you relax quicker, feel less stressed, and recover faster from acute stress, so you can continue on with your daily activities.

To help manage your acute stress, you can try:

- Breathing exercises to help bring your heart rate down and slow your breathing.
- Cognitive reframing techniques, such as Cognitive Behavioral Therapy to help you change the way you view stressful situations.
- Progressive muscle relaxation methods, such as clenching and releasing different muscles to release tension.
- Mini-meditations to calm and center yourself and help you focus on the present moment.

Chronic stress

Chronic stress is stress that is experienced over long periods of time. It is regarded as the most harmful kind of stress because it eats away at us physically, mentally, and emotionally and we only realize that we have chronic stress once it is too late. It can cause burnout if it is not effectively managed because the stress response is triggered all the time and your body has no time to recover and repair itself before dealing with another wave of stress. This means that your stress response is triggered indefinitely, leaving you in an alarm state at all times, says Mayo Clinic staff.

This type of stress occurs daily, for instance, stressing over finances, an unhappy marriage, a dysfunctional family, or trouble at work. All these stressors can cause you distress daily because you don't see an end or an escape from these stressors. You eventually stop seeking solutions for these problems and resign yourself to fate.

Chronic stress can continue to go unnoticed, as we become used to the emotions generated and this heightened state, unlike acute stress, which is new and often has an immediate solution. This state of chronic stress can become part of your personality because you never deal with it, making you more prone to the effects of stress, regardless of the situations you might face. People with chronic stress are more likely to breakdown and even commit suicide or violent acts as ways of trying to cope with their stress.

Long-term stress can cause health issues, such as heart disease, gastrointestinal issues, panic attacks, anxiety, depression, and the other medical issues we mentioned before. This is why the management of chronic stress is crucial and it often takes a combination of short-term and long term techniques to relieve this kind of stress.

Dealing with chronic stress

With chronic stress, the body's stress response is prolonged, unlike with acute stress, and so the methods used to manage it must reduce the strain of stress on the body, giving it time to heal itself before it deals with more stress.

For chronic stress, you should:

- Exercise regularly to keep your body and mind healthy and also to release feel-good hormones to combat the stress hormones. You can try yoga, aerobics, Tai Chi, and other forms of exercise.
- Maintain a balanced and healthy diet that not only fuels your body but also helps boost your immunity and reduce your overall stress levels, so you can function better.
- Cultivate supportive relationships between family and friends, so you have a solid support system whenever you need it.
- Meditate deeply and often to help build your resilience to stress and also relieve acute stress.
- Other things you can do include listening to music because it calms the soul. Play with and stroke your pet -- this helps release feel-good hormones and it's a great mood booster.
- Practice mindfulness and positive self-talk to keep negative, self-defeating thoughts and emotions away.

Emotional stress is a type of chronic stress that can hit harder than other types of stress. Take, for instance, the stress caused when you fight with a loved one. It tends to cause a greater physical reaction and a more profound sense of distress than acute stress. It often leads to anxiety, anger, rumination, and other strong emotional responses that can take quite a toll on your body. Therefore, to manage it, you need to use a combination of techniques aimed at helping you process, diffuse, and gain emotional resilience toward these emotional stressors.

To deal with emotional stress, you can try journaling. A journal is a book where you can write down your thoughts and feelings surrounding occurrences in your life. As a stress management tool, it should be done consistently or even periodically, focusing on emotional processing and gratitude. You can write in detail about events happening in your life, your thoughts, feelings, and emotions and brainstorm solutions to what's bothering you. Whatever journaling method you choose depends on your personality, the time you have, and doing what feels right to you.

Managing chronic stress involves using these strategies, as well as some of the short-term stress-relieving techniques used for acute stress. Fortunately, it doesn't have to take stress ravaging and damaging your health, relationships, or quality of life for you to start practicing stress management techniques today.

CHAPTER TWO:

Reduce And Manage Stress

Now that you know what stress is, what causes it, the stages your body goes through while under stress, and the different types of stress, you can now move onto identifying different ways to reduce or manage the different types of stress you might be under. The first step is knowing what your triggers are. Once you have identified them, you can easily identify what you can control and start from there. For instance, if you have trouble sleeping because of stress, try reducing your caffeine intake and removing all electronics from your bedroom. This can help you wind down before bed. Other times, stress might be caused by work or the demands of an ill loved one. In these cases, what you can change is your reaction to the situation.

Stress-relieving methods

Stress can get you stuck in a bad cycle and the neural pathways in your brain can get stronger, making you sensitive to stressors and flooding your body with cortisol, adrenaline, and other stress hormones that it can't metabolize fast enough, notes Scott. What was intended to be an occasional stress response, quickly evolves into a daily occurrence, leaving your body stuck in any one of the three stages of the GAS syndrome. This prolonged period of stress can cause adverse effects to your physical and mental health and, without proper measures in place to reduce the effects, stress can lead to death.

Using quick stress relievers

Scott, in his article, An Overview of Stress Management, states that many different methods can be used to relieve different types of stress. Let's take a deeper look at some quick stress relievers. These methods or techniques are used to relieve stress fast and work in minutes to calm your stress response. When your stress response is not activated, you can deal with problems or situations more thoughtfully and proactively and you are less likely to lash out in frustration at others. This can be great for your relationships and interactions. Quickly dealing with stress can help reduce its effects and also prevent it from turning into long-term stress. These quick fixes may not build your resilience against future stress, but they can minimize the stress you are facing now and help calm your body after triggering the stress response.

1. Breathing exercises

An easy and fast way to bring your heart rate down and relax is by focusing on your breathing. Once the stress response kicks in, your breath can quicken due to the release of adrenaline and cortisol in your body. However, just focusing on your breathing can make a lot of difference and help bring down your stress levels. The intake of oxygen can help calm your body and mind in a very short time.

Take in deep breaths through your nose and fill your belly with air. As you inhale, slowly count to five, then hold your breath for about two seconds and slowly breathe out through your nose or mouth as you count to five again. As you breathe in, imagine that you are inhaling peaceful, energetic air, and it is spreading throughout your body, taking away the tension and stress. As you exhale, see yourself breathing out the stress and tension that has been washed away by the new peaceful air you took in.

2. Take a walk

Exercise is another great stress-relieving tool that can also work fast. When you take a walk, you get to enjoy the scenery and get out of your mind, on top of getting all the benefits of exercise itself. You don't have to take a long walk -- even short walks can help reduce stress. So, whenever you feel frustrated from work, take a short walk in the park during your break to rejuvenate your mind and body.

3. Progressive Muscle Relaxation (PMR)

PMR is an effective technique that helps reduce the body's tension, as well as psychological stress. This method involves tensing and relaxing the different muscles in your body, group by group. By doing this, you are releasing both physical and psychological tension. Research has shown that this method decreases your stress reactivity and your chances of experiencing chronic stress. It is also great for minimizing emotional stress and building resilience against stress.

How to do PMR

- Set aside some time and set the alarm so you can fully relax, not having to worry about losing track of time. Find somewhere private, so you can be more comfortable, whether you choose to sit, stand, or lie down. If you choose to lie down, stretch out and allow your body to have enough free space and to make circulation easier.
- Begin by taking deep breaths and tensing all the muscles in your face. Try and make a tight grimace, shut your eyes, and clench your teeth and hold this position for about five to ten seconds as you inhale deeply.
- Now exhale and relax your facial muscles. As you do this, you will feel all the tension flow out of your facial muscles. Take a few moments to enjoy the feeling before moving to the next step.
- Next, move to your neck and continue your way down to your toes, repeating whenever necessary until you feel all the tension is gone. You should experience a wave of relaxation sweep over your body once you are done. As you flex and relax your various muscles, you can change it up and do this for your whole body, causing it to relax rapidly. With practice, you can tell where there is tension or tightness in your muscles

and be able to focus on them and relax more. This can then become your go-to method for diffusing stressful situations, especially those that involve physical tension.

4. Try guided imagery

Guided imagery is a stress relief method wherein you picture yourself in your happy place, whether you are at the beach, at a spa getting pampered, or at your favorite restaurant. These images allow you to indulge in a vivid daydream, complete with all the emotions and thoughts. What makes guided imagery a great technique is that it can be done anywhere -- it is free, it takes very little to master the practice, and it provides immediate relief.

There are several ways you can practice guided imagery for stress relief. You can be guided by an instructor through audio or video recordings, or you can create your own visual recordings and use your inner voice as your guide. Guided imagery provides relaxation, insight into your subconscious, and leaves you stress-free with a positive mindset to boot. It can be a useful way to disrupt ruminating thought patterns and build your stress resilience.

5. Aromatherapy

Aromatherapy has been used over the years as a form of stress relief. Inhaling therapeutic aromas can help you energize, relax, and center. They have also been shown to alter brainwaves, allowing you to enter deeper states of relaxation while decreasing stress hormones in the body. Aromatherapy is favored in spas and other places of relaxation because it calms the body and helps release tension.

6. Get a hug

Physical touch from a loved one can help relieve stress fast. Getting a hug, for instance, is a simple way to cause the production of oxytocin, the cuddle hormone, which suppresses the production of norepinephrine, a stress hormone, reduces blood pressure, and causes you to feel good. Oxytocin is linked to higher levels of happiness and lowering stress.

7. Cut down on caffeine

Caffeine is a stimulant present in coffee, tea, chocolate, and energy drinks. In low doses, it can be used to stimulate the body and increase alertness, however, in higher doses, it can lead to sleeplessness and anxiety. Everyone has a different caffeine tolerance threshold. If you notice you get jittery whenever you drink caffeinated drinks, consider cutting back on them. If you have trouble sleeping, consider not drinking any caffeinated drinks in the afternoon, so the caffeine you had earlier has completely passed out of your system by the time you go to bed.

8. Laugh

"The doctor said I should exercise more to relieve my stress, so I decided to start running. I'm somewhere in Chile now and I need a ride back home." A good hearty laugh not only relieves stress but also helps release tension in the body and triggers other physical and emotional changes. It fortifies your immune system, reduces pain, boosts your mood, and protects you from the damaging effect of stress. Laughter brings your mind back into the present moment, distracting you from stressful thoughts. Humor can help you connect with others, stay focused, let go of anger and anxiety, and stay alert. Laughter makes you seem more approachable, thus enhancing your emotional relationships, which supports your emotional health.

These techniques are great, especially when you are in the middle of a stressful situation and you need fast relief.

Develop stress-relieving habits

While quick stress-relieving techniques come in handy sometimes, they can fail to aptly handle stress, especially with long-term stress. Since stress is a state of mind caused by external or internal factors, it is very important that you develop long-term healthy habits that combat stress and help you build resilience towards stress-inducing factors in everyday life. Since you cannot avoid all stressors in your life, you can learn to change how you react to them.

1. Meditation

Meditation is a great stress-relieving tool. It works for both short-term and long-term stress and there are many types of meditation techniques, each with their own appeal. You can develop a mantra or have a phrase you repeat in your mind or out loud, whenever you need to take in deep, relaxing breaths. Mindful meditation can also prove helpful when dealing with both acute and chronic stress. It involves taking time to be in the moment, recognizing your thoughts, and not being judgmental of them, as well as paying attention to what you see, hear, smell, taste, and touch. When you are focused on the present, you won't be able to keep thinking or worrying about things that have already happened or those that might happen.

Meditation and mindfulness take practice to master, but they can make a big difference in your overall stress levels. However, many people don't try meditation because they think it is hard to do or that you need lengthy sessions for it to be effective. This is not true. You can meditate for whatever duration you like and still reap the stress-reducing benefits of meditation.

For a quick meditation, you can set a time so that you can relax without worrying about meditating too long and missing appointments. Relax, shut your eyes, and take a few deep breaths, filling your belly with air and breathing out to release the tension. Clear your mind of all thoughts and feelings and focus on thinking about nothing or focus on just being. If random thoughts come into your mind, acknowledge them and let them go and return to your present state. This refocusing of the mind and bringing it back to the present moment is what meditation is all about and it will make meditation easier for you. Continue doing this for the duration you have set, whether it is five, ten, or even twenty minutes, and you will return to your day feeling refreshed and relaxed.

- While meditating, here are a few tips to keep in mind. Make sure that you are comfortable because small discomforts can distract you from your meditation.

- Don't get too hung up on getting it right, as this can make your meditation more stressful. Instead, let your thoughts enter your mind but focus on redirecting your attention to the present moment, rather than dwelling on these thoughts.
- You can play some calming music or use aromatherapy to enhance your meditation. This is optional, though, you do not need any tools and silence works just as well.
- Try and alternate between short and long meditation sessions. You can meditate for about ten to twenty minutes every day and work in longer sessions that last thirty minutes or more, a few times a week. This will help you improve your meditation techniques and increase your resilience to stress.

2. Practice mindfulness

Moore defines mindfulness as the practice of being more cognizant of your thoughts, feelings, and environment in the present moment. You become aware of everything, without judging your thoughts, feelings, or what's going on in your environment. You are present and not dwelling in the past or worrying about the future. It involves being aware of your senses, noticing your breathing, feeling the various sensations in your body, and being in the present moment.

You can gain mindfulness through meditation and practice it in your daily life. The benefits of developing mindfulness are similar to those of meditation and it has been found to be effective with conditions such as anxiety and depression. Mindfulness reduces stress by stopping rumination. It keeps people from dwelling on negative or self-defeating thoughts. When paired with cognitive therapy techniques, it has proven beneficial in reducing and managing stress, sleep disorders, panic attacks, and even stress disorders.

3. Regular exercise

The benefits of regular exercise have been well documented. However, its psychological benefits are often overlooked. It is a great mood and confidence booster that allows you to interact more socially while providing you with positive distractions to keep your mind occupied. Exercise can alleviate depression symptoms, fatigue, tension, anger, and low energy levels. It is also a great way to release pent up energy and lessen feelings of worry and fear. It reduces your body's reaction to anxiety, as well as the frequency and intensity of panic attacks. This is because it reduces your stress hormones levels and releases feel-good hormones instead. There are various types of exercise that you can engage in to help you cope with stress, such as yoga, aerobics, Tai Chi, boxing, and so on.

4. Keeping a healthy diet

Maintaining a healthy diet can do more than just fuel your body. Good nutrition can help you keep your immunity up, thus preventing diseases and giving you that energy boost when you require it, and it can even help boost your mood. When we are stressed, we tend to skip meals, compensating by eating unhealthy snacks and generally adopting poor eating habits since stress can also affect your appetite. You can use food as a coping mechanism for your stress and trigger weight gain, which can lead to other problems. By maintaining a healthy diet and eating schedule, you are giving your body the fuel it needs to combat stress. Ensure that you eat breakfast, have healthy snacks in case you feel hungry, reduce your caffeine intake since it can mess with your sleep patterns, and remove all the bad, unhealthy food from your home.

5. Have supportive relationships

A strong support system is an important stress-coping mechanism. Whenever you are feeling overwhelmed, talking to someone, either a family member or a trusted friend, can help you better handle your stress. These support systems offer different types of social support, such as emotional support, which is displayed through hugs, listening, and empathizing. Esteem or moral support is shown through expressions of encouragement and confidence. For instance, your support group can point out the qualities and strengths you forgot you had and let you know they believe in you. This boosts your self-confidence because you end up believing in yourself more.

Another type of social support you can get is informational support, where you get advice and share information that can help you understand what steps to take when dealing with a particular type of stress. You can also get tangible support, which involves someone else taking over your responsibilities so you can handle your problem. It can also be shown by someone taking a supportive stand with you and actively helping you deal with your issues. An example of tangible support would be someone bringing you lunch or dinner when you are ill.

6. Take time off

When you take time off, also disconnect from technology. While complete disconnection is perhaps not a feasible option, try taking some time off from your devices during the day and an hour before you go to bed. Looking at screens all day can throw your circadian rhythm off and make getting a good night's sleep hard. This disrupted sleep pattern can worsen stress symptoms and their effects.

7. Eliminating stressors

Stressors are everywhere, both internally and externally, and while completely eliminating them is impossible, you can remove the biggest stressors in your life. For instance, getting out of a bad marriage or relationship can lessen your overall stress and help you effectively deal with other areas in your life that might be stressing you, such as work. For areas where you can't eliminate the stressor, try to minimize it to a manageable level. For instance, if your job is very demanding and this is creating a stressful environment for you, try to delegate some of the workload or apply for a different, less demanding position. This way, you can reduce your stress because you are not as overwhelmed or overworked.

8. Try Cognitive Behavioral Therapy

According to *Psychcentral*, Cognitive Behavioral Therapy (CBT) is a type of psychotherapy treatment that aims to change how you react, your thought-patterns, emotions, behaviors, and habits towards stressors. It is a short-term form of therapy directed at current issues, such as stress, and is based on the opinion that how an individual thinks and feels influences how they behave. The goal of CBT is to solve problems, such as ASD, by changing how you think and feel in order to change how you react. It not only aims to help alleviate the symptoms of acute stress, it can also prevent you from developing PTSD.

During CBT sessions, you learn how to identify the painful or upsetting thoughts that trigger your stress response and you determine whether they are realistic or not. If they are deemed unrealistic, you are taught techniques to help you change your thought and emotion patterns so you can think and react more logically to a situation.

Other habits you can acquire include listening to music, learning to say no, journaling, getting quality sleep, making the most of your free time, and more.

Understand that it is impossible to remove stress from your life completely. However, by continuous stress management and paying attention to stressors in your life, you can counter some of the adverse effects of stress and increase your ability to cope with any challenges that might come up. There is no one-size-fits-all method of relieving stress. Whatever method works for you might not work for someone else, so take time to find the right combination of methods that are right for you.

CHAPTER THREE:

Identifying The Stressors In Your Life

Effectively managing your stress starts with first identifying what is stressing you and coming up with strategies to deal with them. The Mayo Clinic explains that knowing what creates your stress is the first step toward leading a healthier, less stressful life. Stressors or stress-inducing factors are the things that trigger your stress response. Identifying them sounds pretty straight forward, but sometimes getting to the bottom of your stress is harder than it sounds. With acute stress, it is easy to identify stressors, such as a job interview, a divorce, or any of the many reasons that cause short-term stress. However, with chronic stress, it can get a lot more complicated. To begin with, sometimes it is difficult to tell that you might have chronic stress until it is too late and you are already suffering its adverse effects. It is also easy to overlook our thoughts, emotions, behaviors, and habits as contributors to our overall stress levels.

Sure, sometimes you may be aware of the things you worry about, such as work deadlines, but maybe it could be your procrastination habit and not the demands of the job that are actually causing your stress. To truly identify your stressors, you have to thoroughly examine your thoughts, habits, attitudes, and behaviors.

- Do you find yourself rationalizing away stress as brief, even though you cannot remember the last time you relaxed? "I just have so much work to do right now."

- Do you describe stress as an integral part of your home or work life? “Things at work are always hectic.” Or do you use it to define your personality? “I have nervous energy. I am wired like that, that’s all.”
- Do you blame your stress on circumstances or other people? “My boss is overworking me.” Or do you view it as a normal occurrence? “It’s nothing new -- working here is quite demanding, but I am used to it.”
- Does any of this sound familiar? Until you accept the role you play in creating and maintaining your stress level, it will always be out of your control.

Olpin and Hesson, in their book “Stress Management for Life”, explain that stressors can be divided into two broad groups, external and internal stressors. External stressors are events or things that happen to you, such as traumatic events, workplace stress, environmental factors, and so on. Internal exasperations, on the other hand, are the stressors that are self-induced. These include thoughts and feelings that come to mind and cause you to worry. These internal stressors can include your fears, anxiety, and lack of control. We can also divide stressors into smaller groups, which can help narrow down the stress-inducing factors in your life.

1. Emotional stressors

These stress inducers can also be referred to as internal stressors because they are self-induced. They can include fears and anxieties over unknown situations, such as worrying what kind of impression you will make on your first day at work or on a blind date or certain personality traits that you may have, such as perfectionism, pessimism, hopelessness, being suspicious or paranoid of people, and so forth. These internal stress factors can shape your thinking, your self-perception, and the perceptions you have about others. These stressors are very individualistic and how they affect people also differs from person to person.

2. Family stressors

These stressors include changes that occur in your family life, such as a change in your relationship status, a fight with a family member or child, expecting a baby, getting married, experiencing empty-nest syndrome (which occurs when your kids grow up and move out of the house), financial problems, etc.

3. Social stressors

These stressors come whenever you interact with others. They can include getting anxious over dating, attending a party or a social gathering, or publicly addressing people. Similar to emotional stressors, social stressors are also individualized. For instance, you may love speaking in public, but the mere thought of addressing people may cause your classmate to freeze or break out in hives.

4. Change stressors

These are the stressful feelings you get when it comes to dealing with important changes in your life. The changes can either be positive, such as getting married, moving to a bigger house, or having a baby, or negative, such as the death of a family member, a breakup, divorce, or getting fired.

5. Work stressors

These triggers are caused by the demands of your workplace, whether at home or an office, or your career. They can include tight deadlines, an overbearing, unpredictable boss or, if you work from home, endless family demands that interrupt your work.

6. Chemical stressors

These include any drugs, such as alcohol, caffeine, nicotine, or pills that you might be abusing in an effort to deal with your chronic stress. More often than not, these chemical stressors end up worsening the stress response.

7. Physical stressors

These include any activities that might overwork or tax your body, such as going long hours without sleep, not eating enough food, not eating healthy food, standing or being in an uncomfortable position for a while, too much exercise, pregnancy, disease, and many other things.

8. Decision and phobia stressors

Decision stressors involve any decision making instances that might cause stress, such as choosing a life partner, deciding to have a baby, career choice, etc. Phobia stressors include any situations you might get yourself in that you might be very afraid of, for instance, flying, being in small confined spaces, getting dirty, and so forth.

Other stressor categories include disease stressors, pain stressors, and environmental stressors. As you can see, there are several kinds of stressors that can induce a stress reaction from you. Using this list of stressor categories, list down all the stressors in your life and note where your main stressors lie. You might discover that some of your stressors fall into multiple categories.

Closely examine this list and decide what stressors are in your control and which are not. If having to clean your whole apartment on your day off is cutting into your leisure time, consider sparing some money for a cleaning service. If pressing your clothes is causing you to go to bed too late, consider sending them to the cleaners or buying wrinkle-free clothing. If these solutions seem a bit pricey, try and rearrange your monthly budget and allocate money for these services, so you can get more time to rest because your time is valuable, too.

As I have said, you cannot completely eliminate stressors, only reduce their strength or potency. For instance, if your workplace is too noisy, try getting some earplugs to reduce the volume and help improve your concentration. If you have to drive two hours through heavy traffic to get to work, consider carpooling, mass transportation options, or carrying a book or some music for the journey to work.

Start Journaling

I've already talked a bit about journaling and what it is. Journaling is a simple way of having a relationship with your mind. Journaling requires the use of the left side of the brain, which is the analytical and rational side. While your left side is preoccupied with writing down what happened, your right side, which is also your creative side, is free to wander. By allowing your creative side to flourish, you can find ingenious ways to deal with your issues and it can make a big difference in your daily well-being.

Keeping a stress journal can help you identify the stressors in your life and eventually help manage your stress. By writing down your perceptions and emotions, you can tell when something causes you to feel overwhelmed or stressed. Journaling can also help you identify hidden or potential stressors that you may be overlooking and could contribute to your chronic stress. It is theorized that writing boosts mental health by guiding us towards dealing with inhibited emotions, thus reducing inhibition stress. It helps us process difficult situations and events and also helps us come up with a coherent story about what happened, such as with an accident or other traumatic events. We are able to work through traumatic memories through repeated exposure to them and, once we are aware of them, we can start working on eliminating them.

Journaling has tremendous benefits. For some, it is a way of tracking food intake, in an effort to lose weight. Others use it as a historical account or record of their lives that they can share with others, while others use it as a way to deal with their depressive moods. In addition to journaling for these and more reasons, what makes journaling a great stress reducer is that you can organize your thoughts once you write them down and deal with feelings you had not fully realized you had.

Journaling clears your mind from thoughts that may be weighing you down or overwhelming you. By writing down your thoughts, you are essentially clearing your mind of all the clutter you have stored in your brain. You can sift through what is important and what you can disregard and stop paying mind to. Journaling also helps get rid of the negative, self-defeating thoughts that you have. Studies in the Psychological Science Journal have shown that writing down your thoughts and throwing away the paper you wrote them on is an effective way of clearing your head. This theory was tested on some students who suffered from negative body image issues. It was found that the students who wrote down their thoughts and threw away the paper were affected less by these negative thoughts. The physical act of throwing away the paper containing the thoughts was a symbolic act of disregarding these bad thoughts and thus clearing their minds of them. This can work for you too and it can help you feel better and deal with your problems once your mind is clearer.

Journaling helps facilitate problem-solving. Since it helps clear your mind, you can approach whatever issue you are facing with a clear, level mind. By writing down your problems or whatever is stressing you, you can detach from your feelings and effectively reflect on them. This thought reflection can spark ideas on how you can better deal with what is stressing you and eventually come up with possible solutions.

It can improve your physical health, too. A study conducted in 2006 showed that patients suffering from chronic illnesses who journaled about stressful situations experienced fewer physical symptoms than those who didn't. Researchers followed 112 patients who suffered from asthma and arthritis and asked them to journal for about 20 minutes every day for three days in a row about any emotionally stressful occurrence in their day or about their daily plans. Those who journaled showed a 50 percent improvement in their condition after about four months.

Journaling also helps improve your working memory. As you write down the details of your day, traumatic experience, or stressful situation, you are essentially reliving it. By writing down what happened, you are able to capture a lot of detail of what happened. This is especially useful when dealing with traumatic stressors. By retracing your trauma or the events that lead to it, you can pinpoint what may be triggering your current stress response. You become more self-aware and you can easily detect unhealthy thought-patterns, emotions, and behaviors. Now you can regain control over your life and you can shift from a negative mindset to a more positive one by effectively dealing with the stress-inducing agents in your life.

When it comes to journaling, there are no definitive rules about how you should go about it. What is important is to find your rhythm by doing what works for you, whether this means journaling daily, weekly, or monthly. However, for this method to work, you need to be consistent. When you start off, you may need to journal more often to help you identify your stressor and also to help you deal with your emotions and effectively reduce your stress. As you go on, you can reduce the frequency to once a week since you already know what is causing you to stress and you have put in measures to mitigate this recurrent stress. You can carry around your journal to help you deal with instances of acute stress in combination with other quick stress fixes.

Whenever you feel the pressure coming on and you are getting stressed, write it down in your journal. Note down:

- What happened.
- What you think caused your stress (if you don't know, try and make a guess).
- How you felt about the event. What you experienced, both physically and emotionally.
- How you responded to what happened.
- What you did after to help you calm down and feel better.

This log will help you see patterns and recurrent themes in what causes your stress.

However, while writing down everything may feel good, to really reap the benefits of journaling and help reduce stress and keep other mental health problems at bay, you have to journal constructively. Here are some tips to assist you.

a. Whenever you can, find a private, personalized space to journal that is free of distractions.
b. Like I mentioned before, start journaling at least three to five times a week and try and be consistent and consecutive.
c. Give yourself enough time to think over and reflect on what you wrote. Take this time to balance yourself by reigning in your emotions.
d. If you are journaling about a traumatic event, don't feel pressured to recount the event in detail. You can just write about how it made you feel and how you feel now.
e. Structure your writing however you want. You can use past or present tense, notes, bullet points, or just write endlessly.
f. Keep your journal private. It is meant for your eyes only, not your spouse, parents, or friends. Not even your therapist should go through your journal, but you can talk about your experiences in your therapy sessions.

If you are baffled and don't know where to start, here are some topics to help you begin.

- An unforgettable time in your life, whether good or bad.
- If you could have three wishes, what would you wish for?
- What is your purpose in life?
- Write about a childhood memory and how it made you feel.
- Think about where you'd like to be in two or five years.
- What are your dreams, hopes, or fears?
- Where did you think you would be five years ago? What did you value at the time? Is it still important to you?
- What are you thankful for? You could start with just one thing, big or small, and go from there.
- What aspect(s) of your life require changing or elimination?
- How are you feeling mentally, physically, and emotionally?
- What challenges are you dealing with now?

- Think of the best and worst-case scenario that could happen to you right now. How would you react?

You can also use these simple guidelines to help jumpstart your thoughts. Think of the acronym W.R.I.T.E. whenever you want to start journaling.

i. W: What would you like to write about? Think about your thoughts, emotions, where you are in life at the moment, current events, or things you are striving toward or trying to avoid. You can use some of the topic ideas I mentioned before.
ii. R: Review what you wrote. Take time and go over what you wrote while calming yourself with a few deep breaths or some meditation. Try and keep your thoughts in the present by using statements such as "I feel…", "Today…" or "Here…"
iii. I: Investigate and explore your thoughts and feelings through your writing. Don't stop writing, even when you run out of things to write. If your mind seems to be wandering, take a few moments to refocus, go over what you wrote, and continue.
iv. T: Time yourself to ensure you journal for about ten minutes, or for however long your current goal is.
v. E: Exit with a strategy and introspection. Go over what you wrote and think over it and summarize it in a few words. For example, "As I read this, I notice that…" You can note any actions you might want to take below.

Once you identify and organize your stressors, it gets a lot easier to deal with them.

CHAPTER FOUR:

Four Pillars of Stress Management

Too much stress in your life is not good. When it becomes too much, you need to find a way to eliminate or cope with it. Coping mechanisms give you a way to hit reset and restore yourself to normal. When dealing with predictable stressors, you can react in two ways: either change the situation you are in or how you react to the situation. When working out how to react to these stressors, it helps to think of the four pillars of stress management. In his book, "The Mindful Way Through Stress", Shamash Alidina writes that the four pillars of stress are: Avoid, Alter, Accept, and Adapt. These are also referred to as the 4 A's of stress management and they are designed to help you decide which option to select in any given scenario. Let's take a more in-depth look at what each of them entails.

Avoid

Even though it is not possible to avoid every stressful situation in your life, you'd be surprised how much stress you can avoid simply by eliminating or avoiding unnecessary stressors in your life. You can significantly impact your mental health by applying this simple skill. There are several ways you can avoid stressors and improve the quality of your life in the process.

- Learn to say “no” – The first thing you must do is to know your limits and learn to stick to them. You must know how much you can take on before you start feeling overwhelmed, or the pressure becomes too much. This pertains to your professional and personal life. If you take on more than you can handle, you will end up stretched thin, tired, and overwhelmed, making this a great recipe for stress. You must distinguish between the ‘shoulds’ and the ‘musts’ in your life, so you can know when to say no and avoid taking on too much.

  For instance, if your boss often asks you to work overtime and you never get to spend any time with your family, this can cause strain on you and your family. You can avoid this potentially stressful situation by saying no to working overtime too often. If you cannot take on any extra work at a particular time because you are already occupied, saying no can help you have enough time to clear your plate. You can also drop, delegate, or postpone any extra work you might have and focus on a bit at a time.

- Avoid people who induce stress in your life -- by now, you already know the various ways in which you can identify potential stressors in your life. These stressors can sometimes be people and dealing with human stressors is the biggest challenge we face when eliminating stress. If you identify certain persons in your life as stressors, you should work to limit your time around or with them. Ending the relationship is another viable option you should also consider. For instance, if you are in a toxic relationship or marriage, consider leaving your significant other if you are suffering from stress and other stress-related illnesses.

- Take more control of your environment -- your surroundings are a big piece of your life and the things in it can be the culprits behind your long-term stress. These environmental factors include watching the news, heavy traffic, running late for work, leaving the office late, and so on. By staying away from these stressors, you are able to avoid triggering your stress response. If the news is too depressing, you can choose not to watch it, if traffic is always making you late, you can use other forms of transportation or carpooling and so forth.

- Go through your to-do-list and reduce your workload. Closely examine the list of things, tasks, and responsibilities you have. If you are trying to handle too much, you will be overwhelmed, so look at what you should prioritize and work on that first. You can get to the other tasks in due time. Much of the stress we feel doesn't come from having too much to do but instead from not finishing what we started out doing. Be careful not to procrastinate, as this will only worsen your situation and leave you with a huge list of things that still have to be done.

Alter

If you cannot avoid a stressor or a stressful situation, you can try to alter it. This means that you will have to change either the way you communicate or operate in your daily life. During stressful times, you should make changes that positively impact your stress levels. Here are a few ways Alidina states you can alter the stressful situation you are in.

- Convey your feelings rather than bottling them up -- Dealing with how things make you feel when they happen can go a long way in reducing your overall stress levels. If someone or something is troubling you, be more assertive and convey your issues in a calm, open, and respectful manner. Communicate using "I" statements when requesting others to change their behavior. For instance, "I feel infuriated by what you did." "Can you help me handle this situation?" If you have a nearing deadline or a heavy workload and your coworker is getting chatty, let them know that you only have a bit of time to talk, and then you have to get back to work. Try delegating tasks and other responsibilities whenever possible. If you fail to express your feeling and bottle them up, you will build resentment, and this will only worsen your stress.

- Respectfully ask others to change their behavior – You should also be willing to do the same. By doing this, you can avoid turning small problems into big ones if they aren't resolved. For instance, if you are tired of being the butt of your coworkers jokes at the office, ask them to leave you out of their comedy routine, and you may be inclined to enjoy their jokes more.

- Compromise – If you ask someone to change, you should also be willing to do the same. If you can meet each other halfway, then there is a good chance that you will work everything out and find a happy middle ground. For instance, if you are overwhelmed by work and chores at home, talk to your spouse about them helping out to help ease your workload. This can include getting the kids from school or getting dinner ready if you are running late. If something is not getting done how you would like it, rather than making a fuss and doing it yourself, try and talk to whoever is responsible and see how you can work things out. Let's say you are remodeling your bedroom, and you want to do it in a particular style; however, your spouse wants it in another style. Instead of arguing about whose style is better, find ways to incorporate aspects of both styles in the room. This will show that you respect their choices while still getting what you want and will also make everyone happy.

- Balance your schedule – If you focus too much on work and don't slot in time for family or to rest and relax, you will soon burn out. It is, therefore, essential that you find a balance between your work and family life, solo pursuits and social activities, daily responsibilities, and your free time, and so forth. Focusing on one area can cause you to neglect the rest, and this can cause tension, frustration, and, eventually, stress. For instance, if you work a lot and never have time for your family or spouse, it can lead to them feeling frustrated, resentful, and abandoned. This can cause fights and make your home a hostile environment rather than a place you can relax. Working too much can also overwhelm you since you never have time to rest and cause you to burnout. Always ensure that you slot in enough time for all aspects of your life, family, work, social life, hobbies, etc.

Adapt

If you cannot avoid or change the stressor, adapt to it. This often means you have to change yourself, how you react, your expectations, and attitudes. Doing this will help you regain some control over what is stressing you. You can adapt to a stressor in several ways:

- Change how you view problems – Reframe your problems by viewing them for a different or more positive perspective. You can even try looking at the situation from another person's eyes. This can help you find ways to handle or solve these problems. Take being stuck in traffic, for instance, rather than getting frustrated and angry that you are getting late, look at it as an opportunity for some much needed 'me' time. You can use this time to regroup your thoughts, listen to your favorite playlist or radio station, and really enjoy that alone time. If someone is constantly making fun of you and it is getting to you, rather than get pissed off and keep wondering why they keep picking on you, try talking to them to really understand the root cause of the problem. It could be their way of showing affection, trying to reach out in friendship, or they could be totally oblivious to how it is making you feel. By talking to them, you are essentially putting yourself in their shoes, and you can better understand their reasons for acting how they do, and thus you can react differently.

- Put it into perspective – What this means is that you need to look at the bigger picture. Ask yourself whether whatever you are stressing about now will still matter in a few months or years to come. Is it worth all the effort, hurt, or pain you are going through? If the answer is no, refocus your time and energy elsewhere on things that matter. Evaluate situations by looking at their long term effects. For instance, ask yourself whether your work is more important than your family?

- Change your standards – Redefine your need for perfection, so you can function with less frustration and stress. Set sensible standards for yourself and others and be happy with good, quality work. You are setting yourself up for failure and will only end up frustrated if you try to overdo things for the sake of perfection. What you should focus on is progress, not perfection. Rather than getting upset that a particular task has not been done how you wanted, look and see if they accomplished the goals for the task and if the results are acceptable.

- Stop gloomy, negative thoughts as they occur – whenever you find yourself having negative, self-defeating thoughts, stop and disregard them as they occur, instead of fussing over them. Through thought-stopping, you can overcome anxiety, depression, low self-esteem, and other negative feelings, which can cause stress even in non-stressful situations. Through mindfulness, you can learn how to be more aware of yourself and your surroundings in the present and you'll be able to easily tell whenever negative thoughts creep in. In such a case, focus on the positives and turn that negative, disempowering thought into a positive, empowering one. Instead of focusing on how someone else is better at something than you, look at the good things you can do and what you can learn from them to improve on your skills.

- Be grateful – Whenever stress is bringing you down, take some time to think and reflect on all the good things in your life -- this includes your talents and positive qualities. This point is tied to the previous one because being grateful is one way in which you can stop negative thoughts. By reflecting on everything you are grateful for, you become happier, and your body releases feel-good hormones that reduce the level of stress hormones in your body. It also helps you keep things in perspective.

Accept

Some stressors can't be prevented, avoided, or changed. They are unavoidable and inevitable, such as the death of a loved one, suffering from a serious illness, or suffering financially because of a national recession. In such cases, the best thing is to accept what is happening and find ways to cope with the ensuing stress. Acceptance can be difficult in some cases, but in the long run, it is easier than resisting, denying, or not dealing with the situation you are facing. The following are some tips you can use to help you accept the things you cannot change:

- Don't try to control everything – A lot of things in life are beyond your control, such as other people's behavior, time, death, etc., and stressing over it serves no purpose. Instead, focus on what you can control, which is the way you choose to react to these issues. In a case where you have lost a loved one, don't mourn their death but rather celebrate their life and focus on the good times and memories you shared.

- Talk to someone about what you are going through – It can be a family member, a friend, a counselor, or a therapist. The fact that you cannot change or avoid this problem does not mean that your feelings are invalid. Far from it, it is normal to feel down or helpless when you are facing such a stressor. However, talking to someone can help you work through your feelings and come to terms with everything. After talking to someone, you will feel better since you have lifted a weight off of you.

- Learn to forgive yourself and others – Being angry, hurt, or resentful takes a lot of energy. We live in a flawed world and errors are bound to happen. Learn to let go and understand that forgiving takes some practice, but by doing it, you free yourself of these energy-draining emotions. A lot of opportunities and memories could pass you by because you have closed yourself off, holding onto these emotions. Why hold onto these emotions when all they do is make you sad and feel bad when you could let them go and be free?

- Learn from your errors – There is a lot of value in identifying teachable moments. While you cannot change the events that lead to that specific moment, you can learn from them. For instance, if your habit of procrastinating caused you to miss a deadline and it hurt your performance, you might not be able to change the result, but you can learn from it. Register the feeling of regret and hurt you feel in this moment and use it to remind you to allocate enough time to get the ork done and in good time. If you made mistakes that led you into a stressful situation, don't be too hard on yourself. Reflect on the events that lead you here in a non-obsessive way and learn from them.

- Look at the bright side and exercise positive self-talk – Losing objectivity can happen quite easily, especially when you are stressed. Whenever you face major challenges in your life, view them as opportunities for personal growth, rather than the end. A single negative thought can trigger another and soon your head is full of self-defeating thoughts. This negative mental avalanche can make it hard to focus on things and get them done, which will only worsen your current stress levels. Be positive. Rather than saying, "I am bad with money and I won't be able to get my financial situation under control," try this: "I know I have made mistakes with my finances, but I know I am resilient and I will get through these tough times."

In the world we live in, truly eliminating stress is impossible, but by learning how to manage stress and lessen the frustration it causes, you can lead a better life. By mastering the 4 A's of stress management, you will expand your stress management toolkit. This toolkit can help balance the stressors affecting you, increase your ability to cope with stress, or do both. Choosing the right technique is another vital part of using this skill set. You have to know which stressors you can avoid, alter, accept, or adapt to. This way, you know how to handle them whenever they come up and you can continue living a relatively stress-free life.

CHAPTER FIVE:

How to Worry Less And Enjoy Life More

We all worry about work, school, money, family, relationships, and life in general. It is what keeps most of us awake at night and slowly eats at us whether we are at work, at home, or even when trying to relax. Worry can be defined as continuous anxiety and fear and it can be exhausting and energy-draining both physically and mentally. This constant worrying can cause stress, fear, and anxiety and stop you from truly enjoying your life and living it to the fullest. For most of us, it has become more of a habit, something we do automatically. We cling to it because it is familiar, even though it adds no value to our lives. Fortunately for us, just like other habits, it can be changed.

It is easy to say that we should stop worrying and just live our lives, but people are different, and we go through different issues. However, we all want to be able to focus more on our goals and lead pleasing, fulfilling lives. Here are some ways you can do just that:

Find out what is causing your worry

The first step is determining the source of your worry. Do thoughts of the future cause you to lose sleep? Or are you unable to tell what is causing you to feel uneasy? Maybe it's physical and once you know what it is, you can address it, or is it as a result of stress? Before you can get rid of your worry, you have to figure out what's causing it. In chapter three, we looked at the different ways you can identify a stressor. The same principles can be applied when trying to determine what you are worrying about. When you write down what's worrying you, you acknowledge its cause, which takes away the anxiety of knowing that something is bothering you but being unable to put your finger on it. It makes it less daunting.

Determine if worrying has become a habit

Not everyone suffers from habitual worrying, however, many people do. After determining the causes of your worry, ask yourself whether it has become a habit for you? Perhaps you developed it after experiencing something traumatic, dangerous, neglect, or overprotection when you were younger. If you can identify this, maybe you can view your worry as a character trait that you developed. Now that you know it is a habit, you can change or break it.

Change how you think about worry

Many times we can find solutions to problems by changing how we view or think about them. The same principle can be applied when dealing with worry. Jonathan Alpert, author of the article "6 Powerful Steps to Stop Worrying and Start Living", suggests that you ask yourself, "What's the purpose of worry? Does it cause, prevent, or worsen my problem?" By answering these few questions, you can understand your worry a bit better.

Give yourself some time to think about worry

I know this might seem counterproductive, but keep an open mind. Alpert notes that many chronic worriers feel as though they do not have any control over what's worrying them. You will often hear people saying, "Don't worry about it" or "Just don't think about it." However, this thought-stopping approach rarely works because it is phrased negatively and we never respond positively to negative stimuli. We tend not to process such negative statements well and doing so forces us to think about whatever it is we were told not to think about.

Take, for example, if someone tells you, "Don't think about a green cat with long ears." For you not to think about such a cat, you would first have to imagine what it looks like. You would think about how green the cat is. Are its whiskers also green? How long are its ears? And so on. As you can see, rather than not think about this cat, you are now going over details in your head, trying to figure out what this cat looks like. You are thinking about a green cat with long ears, despite being told not to.

So, if someone told you not to worry about something, let's say money or a particular situation, the same thing would happen. You would need to think about whatever it is in order not to think of it. This is why you need to designate some time to worry. You can take about twenty minutes a day and really think about whatever is worrying you. Pick a time during the day when you are relaxed and really ponder on these thoughts. If you can, worry more intensely than you would any other time. But remember, you should never slot this worry-session near bedtime, as it can interfere with your sleep.

This exercise will have a paradoxical effect on you because now that you have really thought about what's worrying you, you have defined and acknowledged it. Thus, you have regained control from this unknown entity. Just remember not to keep thinking about it all day.

Determine whether it is fact or fiction

After pondering over your worries, you'll have a pretty good idea of what they are and you can determine whether they are real or not. This is important because there is no point in thinking about things that might never happen. Doing so only clouds your mind, makes it hard to focus on things, and drains your energy.

Take a piece of paper and make four columns. In the first one, write down a worry you have. Next, determine whether it is fact or fiction and if you have any proof to support your theory. In the third column, note down a different way you could look at what's worrying you, and in the last one, write down whether you think what you were worried about was helpful or not.

To illustrate this exercise, let's use an example of someone who has a date on Saturday but is worried that she may miss it if she gets sick.

Column 1 – "I am worried about missing my date on Saturday if I get sick."

Column 2 – "I am not sick now. In fact, I feel great." So this thought is not real, its fiction.

Column 3 – "I'll eat right, get enough rest, and ensure I take care of myself so that I am healthy for my date on Saturday."

Column 4 – "I didn't get sick and I got to go on a fabulous date. My worries were unfounded and needless and did not affect my health."

Ask yourself whether you have control over it

We rarely have control over the many things we worry about and dwelling over them only causes us anguish. It's therefore important to take a step back and ask yourself whether you have control over what you are worrying about. For instance, death -- it is inevitable and there is little we can do about it, apart from making preparations to ease the grief of losing someone.

Challenge worrisome thoughts

Chronic worriers tend to look at the world in ways that make it seem more threatening. For instance, you think things will go wrong all the time and jump to the worst-case scenario, every time. According to Robinson and Smith, these type of thoughts, referred to as cognitive distortions, can also include:

- All-or-nothing type of thinking – things are either black or white. There is no middle ground. This type of thinking is prevalent in perfectionists who view things not going their way or not being up to their standards as fails, making them failures.
- Overgeneralization – this refers to expecting that one negative experience you had to hold true every other time. For instance, "My last date went badly. I will never have a relationship."
- Seeing only the bad – this is when you seem only to notice what went wrong, rather than what went right. For example, "I got the last question wrong. I'm such an idiot."
- Finding ways to put down your positive moments like they don't count – you often downplay your wins, saying it was luck or you failed less than others.
- Believing that your feelings reflect reality – "I made a mistake during my presentation. Everyone must think I am a fool."
- Making negative leaps without any evidence – "I know something is going to go wrong." You act like you know what will happen, or like you can read minds, "I know they will hate me."
- Defining yourself based on your mistakes or perceived lack of skills.
- Taking responsibility for things you have no control over. "It is my fault that my husband had an accident. I should have done something to warn him."

To challenge them, you can follow the steps listed below.

- Give yourself time to worry.
- Determine whether your worry is fact or fiction.
- Can you view it more positively?
- Is the thought helpful? How will worrying help me find a solution?
- Ask whether you have control over it.
- If someone close to you had this worry, what would you say to them?

Talk to someone about what's worrying you

Talking about your feelings or what's on your mind with a trusted friend or family member can relieve some of the worry and anxiety you might be feeling. As the saying goes, a problem shared is half solved. So find someone to confide in and tell them about your worries. You can talk to a counselor or a therapist if you don't want to talk to someone close to you.

There are a few reasons that might make you a bit hesitant about opening up, such as not wanting to worry those close to you, or you may wish to keep your worries confidential, as sharing them might make you seem weak. You could also be lacking time to meet up with anyone because you are too busy. Whatever the reason may be, opening up can be beneficial to both your physical and mental health.

An experiment was conducted at the University of Southern California to measure the benefits of talking about your worries with someone else. They split participants into two groups and had one share their worries about making a speech while being recorded and the other participants weren't given this opportunity. Those who talked about their worries were found to have significantly lower levels of cortisol in their bodies than those who didn't. The researchers also found that those who shared their worries with other participants had the lowest cortisol levels.

According to Andrews, what this indicates is that sharing your worries with someone will greatly lower stress hormone levels in your body and sharing them with someone who was or is in a similar situation will give the best results. So if you have relationship worries, you can ease them by talking to someone who has been through them or something similar.

Practice accepting uncertainty

Self-help author Susan Jeffers notes in her book "Embracing Uncertainty" that life is random and you can never know how things will play out, but worrying about them is not the answer. Many of us think of uncertainty as something dangerous and that doing nothing about it is irresponsible. So we worry, trying to find ways how we can eliminate this uncertainty. However, worrying about the unknown is only helpful if it helps you think of ways you can cope. This is rarely the case because, as you think about the unknown, you only come up with more bad thoughts. You'll end up stuck in a loop because you keep coming up with more problems as you try to find solutions to others. These thoughts end up making you feel worse about what you are worrying about.

If a new supervisor is brought in at your workplace, you might be uncertain of your future at the company and worry about losing your job. However, worrying only makes you more anxious and less productive at work, which might eventually get you fired or not.

You have a mole on your back and you think it could be cancerous, so you examine it and even see a doctor who reassures you that it is not cancerous. However, you keep worrying about it and convince yourself that you need a second opinion because doctors are not infallible. What ends up happening is you waste your time and money trying to treat a disease you don't have. Your inability to handle uncertainty has led you to worry more as you search for answers.

To help you handle accepting uncertainty, you need to identify the advantages of accepting uncertainty. The first one is that you will worry a lot less, you seek out less reassurance, you are more confident in facing your fears, and thus you can enjoy your life more. And while you might think that a downside to accepting uncertainty is that you might be surprised by a bad outcome because you overlooked something and thus disaster might ensue, there is a big chance that it might never happen.

Secondly, what uncertainties are you willing to accept? Recognize that there is uncertainty in everything. For instance, when you are driving, going somewhere new, meeting someone for the first time, starting a new project, and so on, there is always uncertainty. We already accept several uncertainties in life because we cannot control or know what will happen, so why not add a bit more to the list.

Thirdly, have you ever met anyone who has absolute certainty about everything in life? The answer to this will probably be no since we can never be certain of the future. You have to remind yourself that since uncertainty is inevitable, your life will be easier if you accept it.

By answering these questions, you can take back control because you have demystified your uncertainties.

Learn acceptance-based mindfulness meditation

Conventionally, mindfulness meditation involves becoming aware of yourself and everything around you. It is about paying attention in a certain way on purpose, presently and without passing judgment. The most common way of practicing mindfulness meditation entails sitting quietly and focusing on your breath. It is a simple way of training your attention. There is, however, another way that is centered around calmly accepting what is going on inside you, thus helping to reduce its effects. This type of meditation is known as acceptance-based mindful meditation.

A study conducted in 2017 compared the effects of acceptance-based versus attention-based mindful meditation in reducing short-term worry. The participants all used progressive muscle relaxation techniques. The attention-based group worked on watching their breath and bringing back their attention to it whenever they noticed their thoughts wandering. In contrast, the acceptance-based group focused on just noticing, letting, and perhaps labeling the inner experiences that come up, such as thoughts, feelings, or any physical sensations.

It was found that directing your attention inward, taking notice of your worrisome thoughts and feelings, and acknowledging them, helped reduce their frequency. Simply observing them and not judging or reacting to them helps reduce the effect they have on you, states Robinson and Smith in their article, "How to Stop Worrying".

Let go of perfectionism

Wanting everything to be done your way and perfectly can lead to excessive worrying. Research has shown that people who worry more are more likely to be perfectionists and this loop worsens both conditions. Become more aware of your perfectionistic nature, or your overly responsible beliefs, and how they impact your life and those around you. Once you acknowledge them, it becomes easier to overcome them. Learn to accept things when they are good enough and don't sweat the small stuff. Also, set lower standards to reduce pressure on yourself and those around you since you don't have to worry about attaining perfection.

Get out of your head and move

Getting physically active can help interrupt worrisome thoughts and the stress and anxiety they cause. Exercise is a natural and effective way of dealing with anxiety. The hormone released when you work out helps relieve stress and tension, boost your sense of wellbeing, and boost your energy. By paying attention to the many sensations your body is experiencing during exercise, you will stop focusing on worrisome thoughts, says Robinson and Smith. You can also:

- Take a yoga class – Yoga and Tai Chi are great for helping refocus your mind by keeping your attention on your movement and helping you relax.
- Meditate – You can try other forms of meditation and combine it with your acceptance-based mindful meditation techniques.
- You can also try using other stress-relieving techniques to help you calm down whenever you feel like the worry is becoming too much.

To recap, below are a few of the things we looked at:

- Most of what you are worried about will never happen.
- Keep yourself from getting lost in vague fears. What this means is you can easily get lost in your mind as it exaggerates your worries and anxieties. Determine whether they are real or not.
- You are not a mind reader, so stop trying to guess what someone else is thinking. Instead, find a way to ask them.
- Avoid doing things when you are mentally vulnerable. Whenever you feel like you are reaching your limit or worn out, avoid taking on new tasks. Rather complete what you are working on and take a break.
- Talk about what's worrying you.
- Get moving.
- Be more aware of the present moment by practicing mindfulness.

When you try to ignore it or stuff it down, worry only gets louder and causes more stress. But by applying these tips, you can tame those worrisome thoughts and reduce your fear, anxiety, and stress. However, since worry is a habit, changing it will take some work and it won't happen overnight. But with these tips, you can break your worry habit and replace it with a new, positive one.

CHAPTER SIX:

How To Develop Emotional Resilience

Have you ever wondered how you can pick yourself up after a stressful event? Or how you can deal with difficult events in your life, such as the death of a loved one, a serious illness, a terror attack, and other traumatizing events? These are examples of extremely challenging situations that could occur and, as a result, we are flooded with emotions, worry, stress, and uncertainty about these potential events. Yet over time, people have adapted to these life-altering situations and the emotions that accompany them. How were they able to do so? By developing emotional resilience.

What is emotional resilience?

According to the American Psychological Association, emotional resilience can be defined as the process of adapting to adversity, traumatic experiences, tragedy, or other stressors. The steps we take in looking after our well-being help us deal with the pressure and lessen the effects stress has on our lives. This is known as developing emotional resilience. It's developing your ability to bounce back from challenging situations and to adapt in the face of these situations. Since it is impossible to guard against the ups and downs of life, we must develop emotional resilience. It is not a personality trait, but rather a habit you can develop. By taking the necessary steps, you can achieve it.

Being resilient doesn't mean you do not experience difficulty or distress because sadness and emotional pain is a common trait in everyone who has been through adversity or trauma. However, you are able to roll with the punches better and have an easier time dealing with stress, whether acute or chronic. Developing emotional resilience is not about winning a battle, rather it's about strengthening yourself so you can weather the situation and handle it better in the future. Don't think of it as a bend-but-don't-break kind of trait, rather accepting that you may be broken, but you are growing and can put back together the broken pieces.

Life today requires that we adapt to changes that did not exist before and it's only natural to feel emotionally beat down from time to time. When we become emotionally resilient, we are able to empower ourselves to see what we are going through as temporary and push through the pain and suffering. We also gain insight into how to avoid actions that might lead us to stressful situations.

Take John, for example -- he is a teacher, a loving, faithful husband, and a dependable worker. He gets to work on time and is always focused, keen to learn from his errors, and always gets things done because he tries not to put things off like many of his friends. He is happy with his life and what he has been able to achieve.

Research has shown that people who can deal with minor stressors more easily can handle major ones. This is one of the benefits of resilience. It benefits your daily life, as well as during a stressful event.

Components of emotional resilience

In her article "What is Emotional Resilience and How to Build It?", Chowdhury explains that developing emotional resilience is based on three pillars. They are what resilience is founded on and can also be used to improve it. These include:

- Physical elements – This includes improving your physical strength and well-being, energy levels, and vitality.
- Mental elements – This includes working on aspects such as your focus, attention, self-esteem, self-expression, adjustability, emotional awareness, thinking, reasoning, self-confidence, and more.
- Social elements – This includes working on your interpersonal relationships with either your family, coworkers, children, community and others, including your communication, likeability, group conformity skills, and cooperation. Developing your social skills can be defined as the successful interaction between yourself and the environment you are in. Through communication, contact, and cooperating, we can coexist with other people in our community. By improving how we interact with others, adjusting to their ways, or perceiving their problems, we can develop resilience and face negative emotions and outcomes more positively. You can do this by developing your ability to empathize with others, read social cues, whether verbal or non-verbal, get a handle on your social anxiety and other phobias, and employ the power of self-expression.

Emotional resilience traits you can develop

Scott, an author at *verywellmind.com*, states that developing emotional resilience works at improving your:

1. Self-awareness

This is the ability to be in tune with your feelings, perceptions, and internal conflicts. You understand what you are feeling and why you feel this way. Self-awareness helps you gain a more in-depth understanding of the role your feelings play in your actions. Instead of searching for help externally or blaming the world for your woes, self-awareness gives you the courage to look inwards for the answers you seek. It helps you become more conscious and capable. With this ability, you also gain a better understanding of how others feel because you are in touch with your own feelings.

2. Persistence

This means working on improving your consistency and commitment to keep trying to be better. It keeps your motivation alive when dealing with either internal or external stressors. You become more action-oriented and, in the face of stress, you can trust in the process and believe that everything will be alright.

3. Control over your emotions

This entails reigning in your emotions and not letting them control or overwhelm you. Having a handle on your emotions gives you more self-control and you can refocus and recollect yourself more easily. You are less likely to be overcome by stress or let these emotions affect your life by making assumptions or drawing conclusions without any evidence.

4. Flexible thinking and perspective

This is a powerful aspect of mental health that involves incorporating positive thinking, logic, and rationality, remaining optimistic and adjustable. You can improve this kind of thinking by:

- Allowing yourself to feel strong emotions, instead of avoiding them or bottling them up inside and also recognizing the importance of knowing when to avoid them.
- Being proactive in dealing with your problems and also taking a break to rest and rejuvenate yourself.
- Learning when to spend time with loved ones and when to have some 'me' time.
- Learning when to rely on yourself and when to accept help.

If you have these skills, you are more likely to lead a well-balanced life. Resilient people accept and learn from their mistakes and failures instead of denying them. Rather than wallow in difficulty, allow it to make you stronger by finding meaning in these challenges and not seeing yourself as the victim.

5. Your relationships and support systems

For you to be emotionally resilient, you need to have good personal relationships. It is both a requisite and a by-product of resilience. The ability to create stronger interpersonal bonds shows that you have already taken a step toward being resilient. These relationships help widen our perspectives on how we view our problems, ourselves, and the world. Humans are social creatures and being around supportive people gives us the courage and strength to deal with our issues, endure them and learn from them. To develop your resilience in the long run, you must gain the ability to improve your relationships and be willing to create and build new ones. Also, recognize the value of surrounding yourself with supportive friends and loved ones.

6. Your internal control point

This focuses on helping you understand that you are in control of your life, not outside forces. It aims at helping you get a more realistic world view by getting you out of your head and helping you deal with the vague fears and worries you may have. By proactively dealing with stressors in your life, you become more solution-oriented and are less likely to wallow in these negative thoughts. You also feel a greater sense of control because you can do something about your stressful situations rather than feel helpless. This feeling of empowerment can help reduce your overall stress levels.

7. Your optimism

This works by assisting you to see the bright side in every situation. When faced with adversity, instead of accepting defeat or letting these situations bring you down, you see the upside to them, believe in yourself, and that you have the strength to push through. This changes how you deal with your issues because you have shifted from a victim state of mind to become a problem-solver. Because you are more open-minded, you see more options that would be closed to you if you didn't believe that everything will work out in the end.

8. Your sense of humor

This involves developing the ability to laugh at your woes. This is a very helpful skill because it works on changing how you view stressors and thus mitigates their effects. Laughter is a great way of releasing feel-good hormones that can help calm you and enable you to review your stressful situation from a different perspective. It changes how the body reacts to a stressful situation. Instead of triggering the stress response and flooding the body with cortisol and adrenaline, the body releases endorphins to counter the stress.

How to develop emotional resilience

Gaining the capacity to deal with adversity can be developed by using the right knowledge, training, and motivation. Whether you are dealing with problems at work or at home with resilience, you can deal with the situation effectively and guard against emotional trauma. The reason some people are better at managing stress is their resilience. Being exposed to toxic situations, such as burnout, can elicit intense feelings and we often deploy our coping mechanisms to deal with them. Emotionally resilient people are quick to make use of these skills, while less resilient people find coping harder. And even though some people are born more resilient and emotionally balanced than others, with the right training, we all can improve ourselves and develop our emotional resilience.

A big part of building emotional resilience is accepting that it is linked to other parts of your life. For instance, building resilience at home can also help you at work and vice versa. By changing how you think (cognition), how you examine and evaluate things (perception), and how you react to things (action), you can significantly improve how you feel, think, and behave. No matter what aspect the training is aimed at, its effects will be seen in other aspects of your life.

There's plenty of research on the theory of resilience. Here are some of those findings:

Professor Michael Rutter theorized that resilience is an interactive process involving exposure to toxic stressors that has a positive outcome for the person facing it. He also found that being briefly submitted to major stressors, such as getting fired, a disaster, or being separated from a loved one can trigger and influence one's resilience. His findings supported the possibility of the part genetics play in the amount of resilience one is born with.

Norman Garmezy found that our differences as individuals play a major role in determining one's resilience level. Family, community and social surroundings can affect your temperamental abilities and mold how you view and react to stress. Lastly, he theorized that interventions to develop or strengthen resilience must encompass all individual and environmental factors since addressing one doesn't help in building overall resilience.

Dr. Emmy Werner was the first person to discover that resilience is a variable that changes over time and differs depending on age and sex. She determined that depending on our age or sex, we are likely to react with different levels of resilience to varying stressors.

Dr. Michael Ungar came up with the concept of the "7 Tensions" that test our emotional resilience. He stated that they are present in all cultures, but how we react to them is affected by our cultural beliefs. These 7 Tensions are Material Resources, your Identity, Cultural Conformity, your Relationships, Social Justice, Cohesion, and lastly, Autonomy and Control.

These theories have affected how we view emotional resilience and also play a part in how we work to develop it.

Buddha once said that the secret of being mentally and physically healthy is not to mourn the past, worry over what is to come or anticipate problems, but to live earnestly and wisely in the present moment. To do so, we need to:

- Foster self-acceptance
- Improve our stress management skills
- Build our self-esteem
- Be mindful, focused, and aware of the present
- Be wise when expressing emotions
- React to stress in a way that doesn't affect us or those around us.

Here are some exercises you can use to develop your emotional resilience:

a) The power of positive thinking

Take some time and write down a few thoughts that are worrying you. Next to this column, Chowdhury suggests to write down a positive thought to replace it. For instance, "I am having trouble with my finances" can be replaced with "I should get financial guidance from friends, family, or an expert." Or, "I won't be able to do this" can be replaced with "Let me try, what's the worst that can happen." This is a simple way of showing how easily you can change your perspective on things.

b) Fostering gratitude

Gratitude is a pretty powerful emotion that comes when we learn to appreciate what we have, instead of complaining and fussing over what we don't have or lost. A lack of gratitude keeps us from advancing and decreases our ability to bounce back. Try keeping a gratitude journal, where you list everything you are grateful for, even during stressful times. Filling in the journal will help remind you that there are good things in life that are worth living for. For instance, you can start by writing down goals you have accomplished this week, what you might have that others lack, reasons why you are grateful to your family, ten good things that happened to you, and so on.

c) Gaining self-awareness and assessing yourself

Self-awareness entails knowing how our minds work by getting a deeper understanding of what led to a particular situation, how we choose to react to it, and the consequences of our reactions and the emotions they elicit. Make a list with four columns with the first showing the stressor, its cause, your reaction, and the consequences. Identifying and getting familiar with this process can help you gain the power to handle problems more effectively. Look for opportunities to discover something about yourself. You might be surprised to find that you have grown in some way as a result of undergoing certain challenges. This can include having better relationships, an increased sense of your worth, a greater appreciation for life, being strong even in the face of adversity, and so forth.

d) Using stress management techniques

Be now, we are quite familiar with the different ways we can cope with and manage our stress, but we rarely use them. In doing so, we leave ourselves open to succumbing to stress and its effects. Your journey to developing your emotional resilience involves utilizing these various coping mechanisms. They include meditation, mindfulness, deep breathing, laughter, talking to someone, and so on.

e) Connecting with others and building a support system

As I stated before, it is important to have good relationships with family members, friends, and anyone who is important to you. Accepting help and support from them can help strengthen your emotional resilience. Some people have found that helping others also has benefits to the helper, such as feeling happy because you can help someone else. You can join groups such as faith-based groups, civic groups, or any local support group that can help you feel like you are a part of something.

f) Giving yourself a break

Master being kinder to yourself, as it can help you reduce the amount of pressure you feel while in stressful circumstances. You can achieve this by doing several things, such as rewarding yourself for your achievements no matter how small, taking a break and maybe going on holiday or pampering yourself, resolving conflicts rather than leaving them to plague you, getting a change of scenery to help you refocus, and learning to pardon yourself for your flaws and shortcomings.

You should also recognize that:

- Your thoughts influence your actions.
- It is important to acknowledge stress and be willing to cope with it effectively.
- You should be open-minded about change and flexible when adapting to unfamiliar situations.
- You should learn to accept the truth of the matter by altering how you react to stress.
- Foster self-compassion and empathy to help embrace the inner you.
- You should accept and learn from your mistakes.

Developing resilience helps improve your self-esteem, mindfulness, relationships, flexibility, spiritual freedom, and perspective. Resilience can also help you gain a non-judgmental mind, get a better handle on your emotions, and acquire some positive stress coping techniques.

CHAPTER SEVEN:

Powerful Ways To Build Mental Toughness

Mental strength plays a vital role in helping you develop resilience. It is crucial to strengthen your mental willpower to enable you to live your best life. But what is mental toughness and how can you develop it? Let's take a more in-depth look at mental toughness and the ways you can build it.

What is mental toughness?

"How to Become Mentally Strong: 14 Strategies for Building Resilience" by Ribeiro defines mental toughness or strength as an individual's ability to deal with stress-inducing factors, pressure, and challenges effectively. It is also the ability to persevere and perform to the best of your ability, regardless of the situation you are in. It is, however, difficult to definitively describe mental toughness because mentally tough habits are more directly observed when compared to cognition, attitude, and the results that are linked to being mentally tough.

Gaining mental strength is detrimental to living your best life. Similar to how we develop physical strength by working out, we can build our mental strength by using mental tools and methods aimed at sharpening our mental capacity. Having optimal mental health allows us to live life to the fullest, forge meaningful relationships and connections while gaining positive self-esteem. It helps us tame the fear and anxiety that might hinder us from trying new things, taking risks, and coping with uncertainty and difficult situations. Here is an example of how mental toughness helped someone weather a difficult situation.

When Danelle Ballengee headed out on her usual trail run near Moab, it was supposed to be just another run. However, this Tuesday morning, the two-time world champion in extreme adventure racing would face one of the toughest moments in her life. She was running with her dog, Taz, who loved tagging along and as they were halfway along the trail, Danelle slipped on an ice patch and fell down a steep rock face, hitting ledges on the way. She finally landed about 80 feet below the trail. The impact of the fall shattered her pelvis, caused internal bleeding, and she was covered in cuts and scrapes.

She tried crawling to safety, but she was in so much pain she could only manage to crawl a quarter of a mile in five hours. Her dog Taz kept her company while occasionally going out to seek help. She was found nearly three days later after leaving for her run, thanks to her dog. She was quickly rushed to get treatment. She underwent surgery to repair her pelvis since it had shattered in four places. After that, she endured months of painful rehabilitation, along with dealing with difficult emotions, such as wondering if she would ever be able to run again.

However, after months of grueling therapy, she was able to walk and run again and she placed fifth in a 60-mile adventure race that included cycling in the mountains, kayaking, running a rope course, and more. Because she was resilient and mentally tough, Danelle was able to rationally handle her trauma and the difficult emotions she had while going through physiotherapy by focusing on her goals of recovering and competing again. Before she was rescued, her dog provided her with the emotional support she needed to not give up.

Mental toughness involves developing daily habits and behaviors that help build your resilience and also giving up the negative habits and behaviors that hold you back. To build your mental muscle, you must choose to make your personal development a priority. The steps you take in bettering yourself, such as practicing mindfulness and gratitude, can also help in developing your mental toughness. You must also give up bad habits, such as feeling sorry for yourself, being too hard on yourself, perfectionism, and so on. Once you apply these mental strengthening tools, the key to really strengthening your mental muscle is to exercise it.

While stressors can cause some people to crash, mentally tough individuals view it as an opportunity rather than a threat and confidently take them on because they are optimistic. When developing mental strength, it's imperative that you understand what being mentally tough means. Toughness is developed by going through something subjectively distressing and being able to lean in, pay more attention, and create room for you to take thoughtful action in line with your core values. It is similar to developing psychological flexibility, which is an individual's ability to make conscious decisions based on what the circumstances afford, changing, or persisting in behavior as per the chosen values.

What this simply means is to take your thoughts and feeling less seriously and act on long-term values and goals, instead of short-term thoughts, impulses, and feelings. Think of psychological flexibility as learning to react to distress more thoughtfully, rather than impulsively. It is an integral part of mental health and performance.

According to Dr. Archer and Collins, in their article "What is Psychological Flexibility?", psychological flexibility is a measure of how we adapt to the demands of changing situations, how we reconfigure our mental resources, change our perspective, be open and aware of behaviors that are in line with our core values, and strike a balance between desires, needs, and other parts of our lives. Understanding what psychological flexibility is vital because our thoughts and feelings tend to be unpredictable indicators of long-term value. If we act based on them, we tend to overlook more important sustained patterns that add meaning, vitality, and richness to our lives.

Before, positive emotions, thoughts, and fulfilling psychological needs, such as autonomy, belonging, competence, and so forth, were viewed as the foundations of building psychological health. However, studies have shown that even though these factors are important to psychological health, they fail to cover many of the changing, conflicting forces that arise as people navigate their environments and social worlds. So by building your psychological flexibility, you can improve your mental health and toughness.

How to develop mental strength

I've already mentioned the benefits of building mental toughness, including reducing anxiety and stress and boosting self-confidence and esteem while equipping you with the skills you need to handle tough situations. According to Jeffrey in his "7 Steps to Discover Your Personal Core Values", while resilience helps you survive, mental fortitude helps you prosper in the face of this adversity. This begins by taking notice of what is going through your mind without labeling these thoughts or feelings and then finding the drive needed to evolve positive thoughts about the situation you are in. To help you develop your mental strength, follow the tips listed below.

i. Identify your core values

We experience greater fulfillment when we live by our values. They are a part of us and show what we stand for -- basically, they represent our individual essence. They control how we behave by providing a personal code of conduct. When we don't honor them, we go through emotional, mental, and sometimes physical turmoil. For some, this turmoil is around health, for others, it's about financial stability, career growth, family, and so on.

Unfortunately, not many people know what their values are and we rarely understand what is truly important to us. Instead, we focus on our social, media, and cultural values. Can you think of five things you value most, whether they are principles you live by or aspects of your ideal self? Without this self-discovery process, it can be hard to know what your true values are and you might end up theorizing on what you should value. You should understand that this a challenging task that will require you to apply self-honesty, determination, and patience.

You can follow these steps to help you identify your core values:

a) Clear your mind and adopt a beginner's mindset -- someone who has no preconceived ideas about what core values should be. This will allow you to access your innermost thoughts and get you into the right mental and emotional state.
b) List your personal values. While creating this list can be a daunting task, doing so will help you discover them or reveal them to you. If you are having trouble determining your values, you can review your peak moments. Think of your most memorable moments and ponder over why you value them. Now, do the complete opposite and think of a time you were upset or angry and ask yourself what happened, how you felt, and what value was not honored and caused you to react that way. Lastly, think of your own code of conduct. What do you hold dear other than your basic needs? Is it your creativity? Or health? Solving these questions will help you identify your values.
c) Group your personal values into similar categories. Take the list you made in the previous step and cluster values that might be related. Values, such as timeliness and responsibility, are related, so are belonging and intimacy and so forth.
d) Identify the recurring theme in each group. For instance, if a value group includes honesty, integrity, straightforwardness, and truth, select a word that summarizes all of them. In this case, it would be integrity because it is a recurring theme in these values. Do this for all your groups until you have a shorter list of your primary views.
e) Determine your main core values because your value list might still be quite long, even after the previous step. Ask

yourself what values are vital to your life? Which represents your way of being? And lastly, which are vital in supporting your inner self? Answering these questions will help you filter the list further and come up with your core values. Rank them according to importance, but don't do this step in one sitting. After completing one round, sleep on it and come back to it the next day to be completely sure that how you ranked your values is correct. You now have a list of your core values.

ii. Apply the 4 C's of mental toughness. Mental toughness techniques revolve around these themes:

- Controlling anxiety
- Visualization
- Thinking positively
- Setting goals
- Controlling your attention

An article in *Positive Psychology* by Ribeiro states that the 4C's of mental toughness describes four mental traits that one can possess to increase their mental strength. Gaining one or more of these traits is the key to succeeding. They are:

- Commitment – This centers around the extent of your personal focus and reliability. Having a high level of commitment means you can set goals effectively and consistently achieve them without losing focus. It shows that you are good at creating routines and habits and sticking to them. Being on the opposite end indicates that you have difficulty establishing routines, prioritizing goals, or adapting to new habits. You also get easily distracted by your emotions, other people, or competing tasks.
- Control – This involves analyzing the extent of your control in your life, including over your thoughts, emotions, and life's purpose. This component is linked to self-esteem and confidence. When you have a high level of control, you are comfortable, regardless of the circumstances, and you are

confident in yourself. You are also able to control your emotions and less likely to act on impulse or emotional response. It shows that you have more mental strength compared to someone with less control, who is easily affected by their thoughts, emotions, and circumstances.

These two represent the resilience part of building mental toughness because the ability to bounce back from adversity means you know that you are in control and that you can change your situation. It also requires you to focus, establish new habits, and stick with them.

- Confidence – This centers around your belief in your capabilities of being productive and able. This is referred to as your self-belief and your ability to influence others. Being on the high end of this scale means you are confident that you will accomplish tasks, handle setbacks well while maintaining your normal routine, and grow from it all. To be on the low end means you lack self-confidence.
- Challenge – This centers around your drive and adaptability. Being able to accept a high level of challenge means you are driven to achieve your goals and you view challenges, setbacks, and failures as lessons and opportunities for improvement. You are mentally flexible and agile. Being on the reverse end means you are threatened by challenges and avoid taking risks because you fear failure.

iii. Utilize your mental energy carefully and learn to develop mental stamina

You can quickly drain your mental energy by obsessing over what you can't control. For instance, worrying about the weather will not change it and you can't prevent it, but you can prepare for it. Preserve your mental energy for more productive tasks, which can include setting goals or problem-solving. Learn to identify mental energy drainers and avoid them whenever you can. By regularly practicing ways to develop your mental stamina and how to use your mental energy more carefully, you can turn it into a habit.

iv. Practice positivity by replacing negative thoughts with productive ones

Through mindfulness, you can gain awareness of your thoughts and it can improve your mental strength and resilience. Self-defeating thoughts, such as saying you cannot do something or thinking that you are not good enough, can keep you from fully enjoying your life. These thoughts can get out of hand and affect your behavior, too. Develop your mental muscle by recognizing and replacing negative thoughts with positive, productive ones. The thoughts don't need to be overly positive, but they should be realistic. For instance, you can acknowledge your weaknesses but also see that you have strengths, too.

v. Reflect on your progress

Find time to reflect and monitor the progress you are making in developing your mental muscle. Find out what you have learned about yourself, your thoughts, feelings, and behaviors. As you do so, remember that developing mental toughness is a process, so take time to appreciate what you have accomplished and how far you have come.

vi. Learn to embrace pain

Pain demands to be felt. It is only when we choose to fight it, avoid it, or suppress it that it turns into suffering. Rather than hiding or avoiding dealing with pain, choose to experience it. One way you can do this is through mindfulness and meditation. These two practices teach you to be more aware and in gaining this awareness, you can embrace your pain. This helps reduce the effects it has on you. It has been shown that through meditation, individuals can mitigate the effects of a painful experience and develop the ability to respond to pain differently. Instead of reacting to the pain and triggering the body's stress response, they acknowledge the pain, let themselves feel it and let it go.

vii. Develop a mantra

The *Brain and Behavior* journal published the results of a 2015 study that showed that reciting a mantra, whether it is a phrase or a single word, helped keep the brain occupied and thus prevented it from obsessing. This is referred to as the mantra effect. A mantra is a prolonged, repeated utterance and is among the many mental practices used to reduce anxiety and stress. According to Stulberg, the author of "How to Develop Mental Toughness Mantras", repetitive, meditative practices have been found to have a calming effect, especially on intrinsic, self-related mental, and emotional processes. Repetitive speech practices were shown to cause a significant reduction in obsessive thought processes and created a long-lasting calming psychological effect in individuals who practiced mantra related meditation.

Benefits of building mental strength

1. You gain emotional stability, which allows you to make better decisions when under pressure. It helps you maintain your ability to remain objective and perform as you normally would, despite how you feel.
2. It helps you gain perspective and be able to push through tough situations. It helps you keep your eyes on the prize through adversity.
3. With mental strength, you readily embrace change because you understand that it is inevitable. As you build your mental strength, you also develop adaptability and flexibility in how you think.
4. Mental toughness allows you to detach from a situation and understand that it is not about you. Rather than wasting time thinking why all this is happening to you, you can use that time to focus on what you can control, such as how you react.

5. It helps you develop resilience, which strengthens you and helps you better handle stress, anxiety, and fear. It also prepares you for challenges and adversity by helping you accept emotions and retain control over them. You are able to retain your focus and develop the right attitudes toward obstacles and uncertainty.
6. You can focus on doing what is best for you because you are not worried about pleasing others or what they think of you. This sense of self-confidence and self-reassurance is because you are mentally strong.
7. You exercise more patience in your actions and you don't act on impulse. Whenever our emotions are high, we tend to make rash decisions. As you build your mental capacity, you begin to understand that anything worthwhile takes time and you need to work at it. This refers to accepting that you are a work in progress and that is okay.

Daskal notes in her article "18 Powerful Ways to Build Your Mental Toughness" that by applying these tips, you can build your mental strength and get a step closer to gaining control over your stress.

CHAPTER EIGHT:

Relaxation Techniques

Relaxation, for most people, means kicking back, lying on the couch and zoning out as you watch some TV after a long day. This type of relaxation, however, does very little to reduce the effects of the stress you have been under all day. Instead of activating your body's relaxation response, it merely distracts you from dealing with the stress. Stress can cause a lot of damage to your body if left unchecked, which is why you must find ways to cope with your stressors and manage your stress. There are several ways to cope with stress and one of them is through relaxation techniques. These techniques aim to trigger your body's relaxation response.

Remember that no single relaxation technique works for everyone because we are all different. Therefore, you must find the right method for you. It should be something that resonates with you, fits your style, and lets your mind trigger the relaxation response. Finding it may require some trial and error, but you will find the best method or combination of methods for you. Once you do, you can employ it or them to help manage your stress and anxiety, boost your mood and energy levels, and improve your health, in general. Practicing these relaxation methods, even for a few minutes a day, can calm you and help mitigate your stress.

The relaxation response

The relaxation response is a term that was coined by Dr. Herbert Benson, a cardiologist, author, professor, and founder of the Harvard Mind/Body Medical Institute. He defined this response as a person's ability to elicit their body to trigger brain signals and release chemicals that slow down their organs and muscles while increasing blood flow to the brain. It is the opposite of the fight-or-flight response, our survival mechanism, which is triggered when we are feeling overwhelmed, anxious, fearful, or stressed.

In chapter one, we talked about what happens when our bodies go into fight-or-flight mode. Our heart rate goes up, our blood pressure rises, and cortisol, adrenaline, and other stress chemicals are released. These chemicals increase our energy and cause our muscles to tense in readiness for what might happen. However, if this heightened state persists, it can have damaging effects on the body. This is why we must mitigate it by triggering the relaxation response.

In the article "Using the Relaxation Response to Reduce Stress", MacDonald notes that the relaxation response occurs when our bodies are no longer in danger, whether real or perceived, and body functions return to normal -- that is, our pulse and blood pressure go down, our breathing slows down, and our muscles relax. During the relaxation response, your body moves from being physiologically aroused or alert to a calmer state. This calm is achieved by reversing what the stress response triggered.

- Your heart rate and blood pressure are lowered.
- Your digestive and immune functions are brought back to normal.
- There is increased blood flow back to your extremities.
- Cortisol, adrenaline, and other stress hormones stop being released.

Inducing the relaxation response

During ancient times, our stress response helped us survive. It was triggered somewhat rarely, whenever we were in danger from threats, such as predators. However, nowadays, it is triggered a lot more often, even multiple times a day and we never have a chance to calm down and let our bodies recover from it. It is during such times that inducing the relaxation response can help calm the body and mind. According to Scott, the author of “Relaxation Response for Reversing Stress”, this can be especially helpful when dealing with chronic stress. The body is in a continuous state of physiological arousal and the body doesn’t have time to relax before the next stressor hits. This can lead to lower immunity and negative emotional consequences, such as developing anxiety, angry outbursts, and burnout.

Relaxation techniques are a great way to trigger this relaxation response and help you manage your stress. These strategies help your body experience relaxation automatically whenever and wherever you are and they help reduce the time spent in stress mode and any damaging effects it may have had.

Tips for starting your relaxation practice

1. Before starting your relaxation practice, it is recommended that you first talk to a doctor, especially if you have any severe or chronic symptoms. Your symptoms could be a sign that you have an underlying condition you are unaware of. So it is best to get a full diagnosis of your health before commencing. For instance, if your anxiety persists, seeking medical help will help determine whether it is acute/chronic or if it is a symptom of another condition, such as chronic stress or anxiety disorder. Knowing this, you can use your relaxation technique to target the underlying condition, rather than just fix the symptoms.

2. Using these techniques requires practice and patience. With methods like meditation or mindfulness, it is hard to get it right the first time. Also, to truly benefit from these relaxation methods, your practice has to be consistent.
3. Whenever possible, find a cool, quiet place to practice your relaxation techniques. It should also be free of anything that might distract you or divert your attention. There are exceptions, such as when dealing with acute stress. For instance, you may not need to find a quiet room to do some deep breathing exercises while in a stressful situation.
4. Try and practice your relaxation technique at the same time and place every day. This repetition will help get your mind used to it and make it a habit.
5. Find a comfortable position. You can sit with your legs crossed or stretched out, stand, or lie down. Whatever position you choose, make sure you are comfortable because a relaxation session can last anywhere from five minutes to over an hour or even more. Discomfort can easily distract you and affect your relaxation, so make sure you prevent this. Also, wear comfortable clothes, take off your shoes, jewelry, and anything else that you might feel may cause you discomfort. To trigger your relaxation response, you have to get into a relaxed state, and comfort is key.
6. You can choose to close your eyes or focus on a single spot to keep your eyes from wandering in the room.
7. Empty your mind and focus on the focal point of whatever relaxation method you are using. If you are doing breathing exercises, you may focus on your breath, or if you are using progressive muscle relaxation, you will focus on your breath and the sensations in your body, looking for tense areas and working on releasing that tension.
8. Remember, relaxation doesn't have to mean being or sitting still -- it includes anything that helps you relax, even exercise.
9. Keep a practice journal to record your thoughts, feelings, and observations about your practice. It can provide invaluable insight into helping you create the ideal relaxation practice.

10. Be consistent even though you might not practice every day, try and practice often.

Let's take a look at some of these relaxation techniques.

Relaxation techniques

Relaxation methods or techniques are practices whose goal is to relax the body by inducing the relaxation response. Some of these methods include guided imagery or visualization techniques, deep-breathing exercises, biofeedback, and many more. Some of their effects include slower breathing, lower pulse, and blood pressure and an improved sense of well-being.

A lot of research has been done on the different types of relaxation methods and it was found that they can be very helpful in managing several health conditions, including stress. They have also been verified as safe to use for all healthy people, although you should always consult a health care professional before using these methods. They can provide more insight on how you should go about them and also give you other tips and tricks you can use to improve your relaxation practice.

i. Breathing exercises

Scott at *verywellmind.com* writes that deep breathing is a highly effective stress relieving and relaxation method. Breathing exercises are highly recommended because they can work anywhere and at any time, even in the middle of stressful situations. Becoming aware of your breath can help you be more in tune with your body and its stress response and notice when you need to relax your breathing. They are extremely simple, convenient, and effective. In chapter two, we looked at how to do breathing exercises in general, but there are several different types of breathing exercises you can try. Let's take a look at a few of them:

- **Pursed lip breathing** – This method makes you slow your breathing down by making a deliberate effort every time you breathe. To do it, relax your shoulders and keep your mouth closed as you slowly inhale through your nose for two seconds. Pucker your lips like you are trying to whistle then exhale slowly through your mouth for four seconds. Repeat this method four to five times a day.

- **Mindful diaphragmic breathing** – This method helps you use your diaphragm properly and, hence, breathe more deeply. When starting, you may tire easily, but it will get easier as you advance. Lie flat on your back and slightly bend your knees. You can place a pillow under your knees if you need some support. Place your right hand on your upper chest and the other under your ribcage. This will allow you to feel how your diaphragm moves when you breathe. Inhale slowly and feel how your stomach presses into your hand. While keeping your other hand as still as possible, exhale slowly through pursed lips as you clench your stomach muscles to expel as much air as you can.

  You can place a book or have someone place their hand on your abdomen to make this exercise harder. Once you learn how to do it while lying down, you can try belly breathing while sitting on a chair and even advance to doing it while performing other duties.

- **Visualization breathing** – This method uses imagery or focus phrases or words to guide your breathing. For instance, get into a comfortable position just like in diaphragmic breathing and, as you inhale, imagine your abdomen is a balloon filling with air. As you exhale, visualize the air escaping from the balloon slowly. You don't even have to force it out -- it escapes on its own. Alternatively, as you inhale, you can also imagine all of the stress and tension you are feeling moving from your body into your chest. As you exhale, see the stress leave your body through your breath and dissipate the tension. You can also use phrases such as, "I am inhaling calm," or "I am letting go of my stress", as you breathe in and out. You can start practicing with a 10-minute session every day and gradually increase the duration of your sessions.

Other breathing techniques include the counted breathing method, also known as the 4-7-8 method, alternate nostril breathing, lion's breath, equal breathing, coherent breathing, and more. Most of these breathing exercises can be done immediately, so enjoy yourself as you experiment with these different techniques.

Tips on deep breathing

- Let your abdomen expand and contract, instead of moving your shoulders. Breathing this way is deeper and similar to how babies breathe, thus more natural. It allows for increased lung capacity, unlike the shallow breathing we normally do.
- Don't quicken or slow your breathing down too much -- breathe as you normally would, just more deeply.
- Start by doing it for about 5 to 10 minutes a day and increase it as you get more used to the technique. You can start with 2 minutes if five feel like too long.
- If your thoughts drift, don't get alarmed or worried that you are doing it wrong. Rather, notice that you have drifted and refocus on your breath.

ii. Meditation

When it comes to relieving stress, meditation is a powerful skill to have because it works on calming the mind and body while helping you build resilience. Ideal for both acute and chronic stress management, meditation is a helpful skill to have. This ancient practice can take many forms, such as spiritual meditation, mindfulness meditation, focused meditation, movement meditation, mantra meditation, and transcendental meditation.

1. **Mindfulness meditation**

Mindfulness meditation is a type of meditation that aims at making you more aware of the present moment. By switching your focus to what is happening right now, you can engage fully in what you are doing. You are attentive to your thoughts as they pass through your mind, but you don't engage them or become judgmental of them. You are just an observer taking note of any patterns that might come up. Mindfulness combines concentration with awareness and, as you practice, you might find that focusing on an object or your breath helps you focus on your thoughts, sensations, or emotions. Mindfulness meditation uses meditation techniques to cultivate mindfulness and relieve stress, anxiety, and other conditions and it also helps build resilience, as noted in the *HelpGuide.org* article, "Relaxation Techniques for Stress Relief." You can combine it with other activities, such as walking or exercising.

How to practice mindfulness meditation

When you are beginning your meditation session, find a quiet place, free of disturbances, and make sure you are sitting comfortably with your back straight. Close your eyes and pick a focal point -- this can be your breath or a mantra that you can repeat as you meditate. Don't get worried about any distracting thoughts that might be going through your mind or about how you are doing. Doing this will beat the purpose of this relaxation technique. Instead of fighting them, let them be and return your attention to your focal point.

2. **Body scan meditation**

This meditation technique directs your attention to various parts of your body. Much like progressive muscle relaxation, you start at your feet and work your way to the top of your body. However, rather than tensing and relaxing your various muscles, you focus on how each part of your body feels, without defining the feeling as good or bad.

How to practice body scan meditation

a. Lie on your back with your legs outstretched and keep your hands at your sides. You can choose to close your eyes or leave them open and find a focal point to concentrate on. Using your preferred breathing technique, focus on your breathing for about three minutes or until you feel yourself starting to relax.

b. Now, turn your attention to the toes on your right foot. Take notice of any sensations you feel as you also pay attention to your breathing. Imagine that each deep breath flows to your toes and remain focused on them for about 5 to 10 seconds.
c. Direct your attention to another part of your foot, such as the sole, and repeat the step above. After about two minutes, move on to your ankle, calf, knee, thigh, hip, and do the same for your left leg. Afterward, you can move to other parts of your body and take note of any pain or discomfort.
d. Once you are done with the whole body, lie still and relax for a bit in silence, while taking note of how your body feels now. After about five minutes, open your eyes, and stretch your body if necessary.

Getting the hang of any meditation technique takes time and a lot of trial and error and not all styles are right for everyone since they require different abilities and mindsets. So maintaining realistic expectations as you start your meditation practice can really help you find the right technique for you.

iii. Visualization

This method is also referred to as guided imagery. It is a form of meditation that involves picturing a scene in your mind where you are safe, free, and at peace -- a place where you can let go of all your tension, stress, fear, and anxiety. As stated before, you can practice visualization either by yourself, use an app, or an audio or visual recording to guide you through the imagery. You can also add soothing music or sounds to help you make the image more realistic.

Practicing visualization, as explained in the article "Visualization and Guided Imagery Techniques for Stress Reduction", requires that you close your eyes and imagine yourself in your restful place. Try to imagine it as vividly as you can. Think of everything you see, hear, taste, smell, or even feel. Incorporating as many of your senses as possible into your visualization helps make it more effective. For instance, if you are thinking about a tropical beach, see the sun rising over the water, hear the birds sing, smell and taste the salty ocean air, and feel the warm waves splash on your feet.

Let this sensation overwhelm you and wash away your worries as you explore your tropical island. When you feel totally relaxed, open your eyes and come back to the present moment. Don't worry if you zone out or forget where you are during your session -- this is absolutely normal. You might also feel some heaviness in your limbs, twitching in your muscles, or even find yourself yawning. Again it is normal to have these responses when you are deeply relaxed.

Other relaxation methods you can try include exercise or rhythmic movements, such as dancing, walking, swimming, or running. You can also give yourself a massage to ease tensions in your body. It is important to make these relaxation methods part of your regular life. As you practice them more regularly, your body becomes more skilled at handling and even reversing its stress response when necessary, so you do not remain stressed for long periods.

CHAPTER NINE:

Mindfulness Techniques - Relieving Stress In The Moment

By now, you have probably noticed that I mention mindfulness a lot throughout this book. Mindfulness is defined as the capacity to be present and fully cognizant of our actions and where we are and not reacting or getting overwhelmed by what's going on in our environment. While it is an ability we all naturally possess, our capacity to readily utilize it comes from practicing it every day. Mindfulness aims to awaken the inner workings of our physical, mental, and emotional processes. Therefore, it can be used to help relieve stress, which can disrupt these processes. These methods are referred to as mindfulness techniques. Let's take a deeper look at them.

What is Mindfulness-Based Stress Reduction (MBSR)?

MBSR can be described as a program that aims to help participants gain mindfulness and thus change how they handle stress and reduce its effects. This program was created by Jon Kabat-Zinn in 1979 to help in the treatment of people suffering from stress, depression, anxiety, and other mental conditions. He theorized that getting patients to work on the mindfulness exercises in a group format would help develop their ability to view their pain more objectively and also learn how to relate to it differently, thus suffer from it less.

This quote, from psychiatrist Viktor Frankl, can help explain how it works: "There is a space between stimulus and response. That space contains our power to choose how we respond and our growth and freedom lies in our response." Simply put, there is a moment where we can choose how to react to stressors or pain before we actually react to them. However, many of us are unaware of this space because we get caught up in our habitual patterns and reactions to life.

If someone cuts you off on the highway, you might think, "What is wrong with that person", but your heart is already beating faster and your grip on the wheel has gotten tighter. You get angry and this anger feeds your thoughts and now you think that this person deserves to be taught a lesson. So you speed up next to him and get into a staredown and even exchange heated words, letting him know that you know what he did.

This is an example of a stressful situation fueled by a continuous, unconscious interaction between our habits, emotions, and thoughts. You might argue that you didn't have much of an option in the situation because you might have been unaware of your stress reaction, however, the space we mentioned earlier was there between the moment you were cut off and how you reacted. In his article "Mindfulness-Based Stress Reduction: What It Is, How It Helps", Baum notes that MBSR helps us become more aware of our habitual reactions and assists us in relating to ourselves in a different way to disrupt this cycle and give us more choices. After this reflection, you may realize that reacting to the guy who cut off on the highway only worsened your stress and may not have affected him as it did you, or maybe you made him angrier, which could escalate the situation.

In the future, if something happens while you are driving and you notice your grip tighten, your pulse quicken, or you start breathing faster, try to take the moment to realize that your body is alerting you that a stress reaction is happening. Now, you are in the space between stimulus and response, where you can choose to take a few breaths and pacify yourself and to relax your shoulders and hands. You could even consider the bad state the other driver must be in for him to drive that way. You could wish him well because if he were in a good state, he wouldn't be driving like that. By adopting the techniques taught in MBSR, you begin to see that you can change the long-held fears that may have been holding you back.

MBSR is a customizable and adaptable approach to relieving stress and it is comprised of three main components, namely mindfulness meditation, body scanning, and yoga. Rather than follow the steps stipulated for the practice, you practice it in the manner that best suits you. This means that MBSR is different for everyone, even though it is based on the same principles.

The Center for Mindfulness gives the following necessities for practicing MBSR:

- Turning the experience into a challenge instead of a chore. This changes the observation of your life from something else you have to do to be healthy to something you look forward to -- an adventure.
- The emphasis of consistency in your practice and the importance of individual effort and motivation. What this means is practicing even on a day you don't feel like it.
- A lifestyle change is needed once you start the program because it requires a significant time commitment. The program is eight weeks long and participants need to practice about six days a week for 45 minutes daily and also attend weekly meetings that could last over two hours. You may also have to take a day-long retreat and have a seven-hour mindfulness session.

To practice MBSR, Kabat-Zinn gives the following foundational attitudes that are essential to the practice:

- A non-judgmental attitude
- Patience
- Trust

- A beginner's mind
- Acceptance
- Learning to let go and not striving to be perfect

MBSR can be used alone or combined with other methods to relieve stress and other conditions that might induce stress effectively. However, there are some things you should keep in mind before starting your mindfulness practice:

1. When you begin, you will find that it is different than what you were expecting. So it is important to maintain realistic expectations. You might end up pleasantly surprised, but keep an open mind and understand that while mindfulness is a wonderful technique, it is not a cure-all.
2. Mindfulness is not about fixing you, but rather it is about noticing your thoughts, actions, habits, and feelings.
3. It is also not about stopping your thoughts, but rather about helping you become aware of them and changing them to better, healthier thoughts, emotions, actions, and habits.
4. Some people are wary of trying mindfulness out because they think practicing it means that they have converted to another religion. This is not true. Even though MBSR is based on Buddhist principles, it is not part of any religion.
5. It is not a way to escape your reality, but rather to change it.
6. It does more than just reduce your stress -- it can help your body thrive and boost your creativity.
7. Mindfulness can also boost your neural connections, help you build new neural circuits, boost your concentration, awareness, and flexibility.

Mindfulness techniques and exercises

As expected, mindfulness makes up a big part of most MBSR techniques and it is easy to think of it as a state of mind. These exercises are aimed at helping you become more mindful by emphasizing different areas. If you are interested in doing mindfulness meditation but don't know where to start, why not try some of these mindfulness exercises. Some of them can even be done in less than five minutes.

Techniques

- Focused mindfulness – An important aspect of mindfulness is the ability to calm and focus your mind. Focused mindfulness, therefore, emphasizes on focusing on what's happening internally and observing your mind. It can be likened to keeping your eyes on the road by focusing on a particular occurrence. You can choose to focus on your breath, bodily sensations, or an object to keep you grounded in the present moment.
- Cognizance or awareness mindfulness – Unlike focused mindfulness, this technique emphasizes looking outwards rather than inwards. It entails looking at your mind from an outside perspective. When trying the awareness approach, you view your mental activity as if it belonged to someone else. Put differently, it can be described as observing your thoughts and emotions from outside your usual self-centered point of view. You view your mind as a consciousness stream without attaching any judgment to it.

You can also switch between these two techniques. To do this, take notice of your consciousness, rationally, and select something to focus on or become aware of.

Exercises

This section outlines some of the exercises you can use to develop your mindfulness.

1. Breathing exercises – These exercises facilitate mindfulness by helping you focus on your breath. In the previous chapter, we explored deep breathing in-depth and stated a few breathing techniques you can use to help develop your mindfulness.

2. Body-scan meditation – This exercise involves becoming aware of the sensations in your body. Body-scan meditation allows you to transfer your awareness throughout your body by focusing on a single body part at a time. When you find an especially tense or sore area, use your breath and focus on this area until you relax. You can even combine it with a healing visualization, such as a ball of warm light melting the soreness away. We also looked at how to practice body-scan meditation in chapter eight, so you can refer to this technique here, as well.

3. Object meditation – This involves focusing your attention on an object. You can use something special to you if it helps you focus more. Hold it in your hand and let it be the center of your attention. Direct all your senses to it and take note of the sensations you observe. These can include its color, taste, smell, shape, texture, size, or even the sound it makes when you manipulate it, either by squeezing, hitting, dropping it, and so on.

4. Walking meditation – This involves developing mindfulness as you take a leisurely meditative walk. As you take your leisurely walk, keep a calm pace and take note of how you are walking. Is your back straight? Do you swing your hands? Or do you swing your hips a bit? Also, focus on the sensations you feel as you walk. Are your shoulders feeling tight or loose? How are your feet touching the ground? At the end of the path, turn and continue walking while maintaining your awareness of these sensations.

5. Mindful eating – This exercise calls for you to pay attention to what you are eating. Take note of what you are holding, how it feels in your hand, how heavy it feels, the color, smell, etc. Then move on to eating it, but do this slowly as you savor how it tastes, the way its texture feels on your tongue, and its smell. This exercise can help you discover new sensations using familiar foods.

A great example of mindful eating is the raisin exercise. It is a great introductory exercise for those looking to try mindfulness. You can use any food you want, as long as it has an unusual smell, taste, or feel to it. Take a raisin and imagine that you have never seen one before. Pay attention to how it looks, feels, smells, how the skin moves when you touch it. Then, eat it. While it's in your mouth, savor how it tastes, the way the skin feels on your tongue and how the taste changes when you chew on it. Let it linger and then swallow it.

By focusing on the raisin or whatever food you are mindfully eating, you are less likely to spend time or waste energy and attention on worrying about what was stressing you. This exercise helps you take notice of what is in front of you and focuses your attention on it. Even if your mind wanders, you can guide it back to the exercise.

6. Take 10 seconds every hour to yawn and stretch. Yawn, even if it's fake -- it will trigger a real one. Breathe in deeply and exhale, saying, "ahh". Notice how your yawn disrupts your thoughts and centers your focus on the present. Next, stretch slowly for another 1- seconds. Take non-judgmental notice of the tense areas and say to them "ease". Do this for about 20 to 30 seconds then resume what you were doing.

7. Stretching mindfully – You can practice applying mindfulness to any stretching exercises you want, but if you are looking for a guided version, then try yoga. Many videos can be used for guided yoga practice and, once you get used to them and know the poses, you can move to audio recordings or practice without any guidance.

8. STOP – This acronym means Stop, Take a Breath, Observe, and Proceed. Jon Kabat Zinn, the pioneer of this meditation technique suggests you:

   First, stand up and breathe. This allows you to feel your connection to the ground.

Secondly, tune into your body. Look at yourself and scan your body, taking notice of all your sensations, thoughts, and emotions. Use your breath to release negative thoughts, emotions, and sensations, such as tension, and occupy your mind with pleasant ones as you breathe in.

Thirdly, observe. Use your eyes to look at your surroundings and take it in. Take notice of something beautiful and be grateful for it.

Lastly, think of the possibility. Explore your possibilities by asking what's new, what steps can be taken as you move forward, or what is possible.

If you find yourself reacting to any of these steps, pause and take a few deep breaths. You can also repeat the following phrases, "calm down", or "clear head" and take in more deep breaths as you exhale saying "melt", "relax", and other calming words.

9. Try loving-kindness meditation – This exercise involves repeating phrases that highlight your good qualities in yourself and others. In other words, it means being kind to yourself and others. You can start by delighting in your goodness. Think of the deeds you have done out of the goodness of your heart, rejoicing in their memory, and celebrating your potential for good. Now silently repeat phrases that idealize what you'd wish for most earnestly.

   For instance, repeat the following phrases: "May I be physically, mentally, and emotionally whole", "May I forgive", "May I live with ease", and so on. Repeat these words in a pattern that pleases you, paying attention to one phrase at a time. If your thoughts wander, that is fine, just refocus. Now visualize yourself in the midst of those who have been kind to you or whose kindness has inspired you. See yourself as the recipient of their love and kindness as you keep repeating the phrases. As the session ends, let go of the visualization but keep repeating the words for a bit longer. In doing so, you are transforming the hurtful relationship you had with yourself and now you can move towards a kinder future.

There are very few things that can stop you from practicing MBSR because, if you have a mind, you can practice mindfulness and if your body is capable of moving, you can do yoga. Through mindfulness meditation, we can address current stressors and also help us develop our resilience to future stressors. It can help us get healthier while gaining a deeper, lasting sense of peace.

CHAPTER TEN:

Managing Stress At Work

If you have ever held a job, at some point, you probably have experienced work-related stress. Even if it is something you love, every job has its stressful elements. The American Psychological Association's annual stress surveys have consistently shown that work is a significant stressor for many people. Examples of short-term workplace stress include pressure to meet a deadline or to find a way to complete a challenging task. But when this stress becomes chronic, due to having a difficult boss or coworker, on top of a continually growing workload, it can easily overwhelm you and adversely affect you, both physically and mentally, and can even affect your performance.

You can't always avoid work stress, but you can take steps to manage it and reduce its damaging effects.

Coping with stress at work

On average, people have anywhere from 30 to 100 projects or tasks to work on at a job. In a day, the modern worker gets interrupted about 10 times an hour and can get distracted for up to two hours a day. If you remove family time and time spent either sleeping, in traffic, or doing other activities, it doesn't leave you with enough time to adequately take on these projects. In large companies, four out of

10 workers are experiencing corporate restructuring and facing a lot of uncertainty about their futures at these companies. You might be in the middle of a project when your boss drops another urgent one on your lap, or your coworker messes up a group project. All of these scenarios can occur in the workplace and induce stress.

According to the American Institute of Stress, 40 percent of people with jobs, whether employers or employees, said that their job was their main stressor. 80 percent of workers feel that they need help in learning how to manage their stress while noting that about 42 percent of their coworkers also need such help. Also, most adults lay awake at night, plagued by the stressful events that took place that day. And even though many lists are showing the most and least stressful jobs, what we must understand is that it is not the job that matters but the person-to-environment fit. For instance, some people work well under pressure, while others don't. Others like doing things that would be too much for most of us, as long as they perceive that they are in control. Others prefer shunning responsibility and doing the bare minimum when performing tasks. This is an important aspect of workplace stress that we need to understand, as it greatly impacts how you will deal with work-related stress.

Even in identical situations, two people can experience different levels of stress. When trying to find how to best cope with work-induced stress, you must remember that it is a highly personalized experience that varies, even in identical situations, for various reasons.

Here are some of the factors that can cause work-related stress:

- Low salary
- More unpaid overtime and excessive workload caused by staff cutbacks
- Fear of losing your job
- Few opportunities for growth or advancement in one's career
- The pressure to work optimally all the time
- The work isn't engaging or challenging mentally
- The pressure to perform better to meet rising expectations, but no increase in job satisfaction

- Lack of social support
- Not enough control over job-related decisions; no control over how you do your work
- Conflicting demands or unclear performance expectations; unclear on how to handle certain tasks; let down by a colleague because they did not perform how you wanted

Some of the warning signs of work-related stress include:

- Increased anxiety, irritability, or even depression
- Indifference and losing interest in your work
- Inability to sleep; you keep tossing and turning
- Fatigue, even after getting up in the morning
- Trouble concentrating on anything
- Muscle tension or headaches
- Problems with your stomach
- Withdrawing socially
- Loss of sex drive
- Abuse of alcohol and drugs to help you quiet the thoughts and cope

Dean was working in what he thought was his ideal job. He had worked hard to get there, staying long hours at the office, working while at home and even during the weekends, and spent a lot of time away from his family and friends. All his hard work didn't go unnoticed and soon he got an offer from another company. They offered him a senior post, managing a small group. Dean was thrilled. Shortly after starting his new job, he noticed that the pressure to perform was always there. He had demands from upper management and also pressures from managing a team and their various needs. His home life was also chaotic since he and his wife had just had a baby girl and she was not sleeping well, which meant that they weren't sleeping well either. This was causing a lot of tension at home.

His team was put in charge of a very important ad campaign and a lot was riding on it and making a good presentation to their clients. Dean was already on edge since he wasn't sleeping that well, he couldn't eat, and his mind was racing. He felt like he didn't have time to do anything anymore and his concentration was dwindling. He couldn't think through problems that were brought to his attention and he started getting sick a lot, too. Now he had to oversee this big project and that only added to the pressure he felt.

On the day of the presentation, Jamie, one of Dean's interns, spilled coffee on his desk, soaking a few of his presentation notes, just as he was leaving for the meeting. Dean snapped. He started shouting at Jamie, causing a scene as everyone wondered why sweet Dean was tearing off poor Jamie's head. But then something happened. During his outburst, he suddenly clutched his chest and collapsed. He was rushed to the emergency room, where doctors determined that he had suffered a heart attack.

When he regained consciousness, the doctor told him what happened and he told Dean that what was really affecting him was the stress and pressure he was under. It's what caused the heart attack. This served as a wakeup call to Dean that he needed to change. So, when he got discharged, he started seeing a counselor who helped him identify his stressors and taught him different ways he could deal with stress, whether at home or work. He learned how to prioritize better and only take on what he could handle. He went back to exercising, something he loved, and watched what he ate. These few changes made a big difference over time and helped him lead a better life and attain a new level of job satisfaction.

When you feel that your job is demanding too much from you and you have no control over it, you are at risk of getting diseases, such as heart disease or high blood pressure. The severity of your job stress depends on its demands, your sense of control, and the decision-making state of mind you are in when handling the demands. Can you identify some of Dean's stressors? Let's look at the different ways you can manage your stress and see if you could identify a few that could have helped Dean out.

Ways you can manage stress at your workplace

Job-related stress doesn't just disappear once you get home. It can persist and take a toll on your health and well-being. Uncontrolled stress can cause you to have headaches, an upset stomach, sleeplessness, a shorter temper, and difficulty concentrating. If it persists, you can get anxiety, depression, insomnia, stomach problems, cardiovascular issues, and because you have lowered immunity, opportunistic infections. How you choose to deal with your stress can compound your condition, such as overeating, eating a lot of junk food, or abusing alcohol and drugs.

While stress at work is expected, excessive stress can affect your productivity and performance. Whatever your work demands of you, according to the American Psychological Association, there are techniques, skills, and steps you can take to protect yourself from its harmful effects, boost your well-being, and give you more job satisfaction in and out of where you work. Let's look at some of them.

1. Track your stressors

Take note of things that might be inducing stress at your workplace. By identifying your stressors, you can easily find ways to relieve or avoid them. You can keep a journal for about a week and identify any situations that created stress and also note how you responded to them. Record your thoughts, feelings, and any information about the situation, also noting the people and circumstances involved. Think about how you reacted -- did you raise your voice? Did you think of eating? Or did you go out for a walk? Taking note of these reactions, they can help identify underlying patterns among your stressors and how you habitually react to them.

2. Have healthy responses

Sit back and think about how you respond to stressors. If you find yourself in a stressful situation at work, do you have an angry outburst, stuff your feelings away, walk away, or try to eat or drink your feelings away? Or do you confront whomever it is that might be causing you problems? Rather than using these negative ways to fight stress, why not try responding more healthily? There are many things you can do to relieve stress, such as exercise, yoga, meditation, eating a healthy diet, or deep breathing.

You can also make time for your hobbies and other favorite activities, such as reading a book, going to a concert, playing games, and so forth. Setting aside this time to spend on something you like doing something or with people you love can greatly reduce your stress levels. By developing healthy ways to respond to stress, you reduce its adverse effects on your body and the strain it puts on you and others.

3. Create boundaries

In today's world, it is easy to feel pressure because we are connected 24/7. So, it is important to develop some work-life balance by establishing some boundaries for yourself. This could mean not taking your work home, checking your emails, or your phone during family time or answering work calls while at home. Everybody has different preferences when it comes to how much they value their work or home life. But creating very clear boundaries between these two worlds reduces the chances for conflict and the stress that ensues.

4. Prioritize and organize

You don't have to do everything by yourself. Learn to prioritize, organize, and delegate tasks to lighten your workload. Taken on high-priority tasks first and break them down to tackle them more easily. Delegate duties and be more accommodating. Create a balanced schedule and take enough time to spend with your family, on social activities, other responsibilities, and downtime to prevent burnout. Learn to leave earlier, plan regular breaks, and establish healthy boundaries. Also, do not over commit yourself to a task. It is okay to say you may not be able and not feel like you will be letting people down. Understand what you should be doing and what you must be doing and drop unnecessary tasks.

5. Break bad habits

If you think about it, it is our negative thoughts and behaviors that often make job stress worse for us. If you can change them, you can decrease your stress and improve your working conditions. Resist the urge for perfectionism in everything you do because you are only setting yourself up for frustration. Rather, have realistic goals and expectations, do your best, and be okay with quality work. You can't control everything, so don't try to. Learn how to be okay with that. If you lack the motivation or the energy needed to work, try changing how you think about your job. Be more positive, stay away from negative coworkers, and always appreciate the small achievements you make, even if no one else does.

6. Take time to recharge

Take time off and relax. This can help avoid burnout and also keep you motivated and energized. Your body needs time to recover, so set aside time when you don't engage in work-related activities or even think about work. Make use of your vacation days and go somewhere to relax. This disconnection is critical in helping you unwind.

7. Sleep well

You must get a good night's sleep. Skimping on sleep interferes with your productivity, creativity, and your ability to solve problems and focus. When you are rested, you are better equipped to handle your job responsibilities and cope with stress. Find ways to improve the quality of your sleep. It is not about the number of hours you sleep, but the quality of the sleep. Try to sleep and wake up at the same time every day, even during the weekend, avoid caffeine a few hours before you sleep, and change your bedroom to make it more conducive to sleep.

Try and get about eight hours of sleep. This is the amount recommended for most adults. Turn off your TV screen, tablet, phones, computers, and other electronic devices that can suppress your body's production of melatonin and affect your circadian (sleep/wake) rhythm. Engage in soothing, calming activities before bed, such as reading, listening to music, or meditating, rather than trying to catch up on work before you sleep.

8. Reach out to someone

Consider getting some support by accepting help from friends, family members, and even coworkers you trust to build resilience and your ability to manage work-related stress. However, if you continue feeling overwhelmed, consider talking to a mental health care professional, such as a psychologist, who can help you get to the root of the problem, alter your self-destructive behavior, and get your stress under control.

9. Be proactive about your job

Regaining some control over your job or your career can help you manage your stress. Consider talking to your supervisor about the stressors in your workplace. Since many companies are aware of the detrimental effects stress can have on their workforce, they are proactive in fighting it.

Ask for a clear description of what your job entails, your responsibilities, and duties. This way, you will not be assigned something that is out of the parameters of your job. You can also request a transfer to escape a toxic environment. If you feel that your current job does not offer you any way to advance in your career, why not ask for new duties? Look for job satisfaction and find meaning in your work. This could mean a different list of duties, working in a different department, and so on.

10. Learn how to relax

Learn more about the different techniques you can use to relieve and manage stress, such as meditation, breathing exercises, and mindfulness. Take a look at the previous chapters to see the many different techniques that you can use to deal with your stress and how to practice them.

If Dean had applied some of these techniques, such as keeping up with exercise, finding ways to solve his sleeping problem, talking to his supervisor about getting some help on the ad project, eating better, and taking better care of himself, maybe he would have been able to handle that coffee situation and his overall stress a lot better.

Simple tips that can help reduce your work-related stress:

- Start the day off right, preferably with some meditation to get you in the right mindset
- Have a clear list of requirements for your job and the tasks you are delegating to others
- Avoid conflict, but where you can't deal with it, don't let it fester
- Keep yourself organized, clear any mess on your desk, and plan out what you have to do
- Don't try and do too many things at once
- Take a nature walk during your lunch and mindfully engage in walking meditation
- Don't be a perfectionist or a procrastinator
- Listen to music to soothe you

FINAL WORDS

In our technologically advanced world, we are faced with threats and demands that can trigger our stress response and the cascade of unhealthy biological reactions that ensue, resulting in stress. As I stated before, this can lead to a slew of stress-related diseases, some of which include cardiovascular conditions, anxiety disorders, depression, obesity, and a host of other conditions triggered by low immunity and disrupted digestion processes. This book teaches you the different ways you can mitigate your stress, its effects, and learn how to control it.

You might be hard-pressed to find a collection of stress reduction and management techniques like those collected in this book. They are a combination of mind and body calming techniques aimed at teaching you how you can respond to stress differently. They are backed by science and are also practical, written in an engaging, easy to read format that allows you to pinpoint exactly what you are looking for. If you need quick ways to relieve stress, just jump to chapter two or try some of the relaxation techniques in chapter eight. This book also teaches psychological practices, such as meditation and mindfulness, that can help combat unhealthy reactions to stress while building your resilience.

I've covered a lot throughout this book, but let's recap some of the major points:

Chapter one was all about the basics of stress. What is stress? How do our bodies react to it? What is the stress response? What takes place during a stress response? And what are some of the causes of stress? We defined stress as to how we react to the demands of changes in our environment and it can be good or bad. We looked at the different types of stress, such as acute stress and chronic stress. Acute stress is also known as short-term stress and it is what we feel when we are in a stressful situation, but it quickly goes away. Chronic stress, on the other hand, doesn't. You may not even be aware that is suffering from chronic stress -- you might think that the situation you are in is normal. However, after studying this book, it should be clear that the constant pressure you feel is not good for you and something should be done about it.

Chapter two is an overview of some of the few stress management techniques you can use. It includes a breakdown of quick stress relievers and other long-term techniques to help build your resilience to stress. The third chapter showed you how to identify stressors. These are the factors contributing to your stress. By going through a simple list of the known stressors that I listed or by journaling, you can pinpoint what is inducing your stress. Chapter four looked at the four pillars of stress management. By understanding what each of these pillars entails, you are able to learn when it is best to avoid a stressor, alter it, adapt to it, or accept it.

In subsequent chapters, we looked at how to worry less and enjoy your life more, find out what might be worrying you, and how to deal with it. We also looked at what emotional resilience and mental toughness are and how you can build them to help you combat stress. By developing emotional resilience and mental toughness, you are better equipped to tackle anything that comes your way and you are not easily affected by it. We also took a look at different relaxation techniques and how you can also use them to boost your emotional resilience and mental toughness. We explored how to apply mindfulness in the techniques we use to relieve stress and, finally, we looked at work-related stress and how you can manage it.

All of the techniques mentioned in this book are guaranteed to help you better manage your stress. I showed you how you could use techniques such as mindfulness, meditation, and relaxation methods to help build your resilience and stay calm under pressure. This way, you can look at the situation objectively rather than subjectively and, in doing so, gain a different perspective on it. You can then come up with new ways on how to deal with your situation.

So rather than sitting at your desk, worried about how much work you have to get done, why not organize your tasks in order of importance and focus on those first. If you can delegate the work, that's even better. However, you have to remember that we all have different standards, so don't expect that everyone will meet yours. What is perfect to me may still need some work, according to you. But ask yourself, were the conditions of the task you assigned met? If the answer is yes and the work is good enough, accept it. Letting go of perfectionism will take away a lot of the unnecessary stress you put on yourself and others.

The most valuable take away from this book is that you don't have to suffer through your stress. By applying the techniques in this book, you can regain control over your work and home life and improve their quality. Take action against stress now and start living your life to the fullest.

RESOURCES

The American Institute of Stress. (n.d.). Retrieved from https://www.stress.org/what-is-stress

Mayo Clinic Staff. (2017, March 31). Stress management. Retrieved from https://www.mayoclinic.org/healthy-lifestyle/stress-management/basics/stress-basics/hlv-20049495

Alarm Stage of Stress: Definition & Explanation. (2015, June 16). Retrieved from https://study.com/academy/lesson/alarm-stage-of-stress-definition-lesson-quiz.html.

Higuera, V. (n.d.). What Is General Adaptation Syndrome? Retrieved May 1, 2017, from https://www.healthline.com/health/general-adaptation-syndrome#definition

Felman, A. (2017, November 28). Why stress happens and how to manage it. Retrieved from https://www.medicalnewstoday.com/articles/145855.php#what_is_stress

DeMorrow S. (2018, March 26). Role of the Hypothalamic-Pituitary-Adrenal Axis in Health and Disease. International journal of molecular sciences, 19(4), 986. doi:10.3390/ijms19040986

Mayo Clinic Staff. (2019, March 28). Stress management. Retrieved from https://www.mayoclinic.org/healthy-lifestyle/stress-management/in-depth/stress-management/art-20044151

Scott, E. (2019, September 11). 5 Ways to Calm Down Quickly When You're Feeling Overwhelmed. Retrieved from https://www.verywellmind.com/ways-to-calm-down-quickly-when-overwhelmed-3145197

Scott, E. (2019, October 8). An Overview of Stress Management. Retrieved from https://www.verywellmind.com/stress-management-4157211

Moore, C. (2019, June 28). What Is Mindfulness? Definition + Benefits (Incl. Psychology). Retrieved from https://positivepsychology.com/what-is-mindfulness/

Martin, B. (2019, June 19). In-Depth: Cognitive Behavioral Therapy. Retrieved from https://psychcentral.com/lib/in-depth-cognitive-behavioral-therapy/

Olpin, M., & Hesson, M. (2012). Stress Management for Life: A Research-Based Experiential Approach. Boston: Cengage Learning.

Alidina, S. (2015). The Mindful Way Through Stress: The Proven 8-Week Path to Health, Happiness, and Well-Being. New York City: Guilford Publications.

Alpert, J. (2014, June 8). 6 Powerful Steps to Stop Worrying and Start Living. Retrieved from https://www.huffpost.com/entry/6-powerful-steps-to-stop-_b_5265123

Robinson, L., Smith, M., & Segal, J. (2019, October). How to Stop Worrying. Retrieved from https://www.helpguide.org/articles/anxiety/how-to-stop-worrying.htm

American Psychological Association. (n.d.). The Road to Resilience. Retrieved from https://www.apa.org/helpcenter/road-resilience

Chowdhury, M. R. (2019, July 4). What is Emotional Resilience and How to Build It? Retrieved from https://positivepsychology.com/emotional-resilience/

Scott, E. (2019, October 6). Why Emotional Resilience Is a Trait You Can Develop. Retrieved from https://www.verywellmind.com/emotional-resilience-is-a-trait-you-can-develop-3145235

Daskal, L. (2015, July 13). 18 Powerful Ways to Build Your Mental Toughness. Retrieved from https://www.inc.com/lolly-daskal/18-powerful-ways-to-build-your-mental-strength.html

Stulberg, B. (2019, September 9). How to Develop Mental Toughness. Retrieved from https://www.outsideonline.com/2401678/mental-toughness-tips

Collis, R., & Archer, R. (n.d.). WHAT IS PSYCHOLOGICAL FLEXIBILITY? Retrieved from https://workingwithact.com/what-is-act/what-is-psychological-flexibility/

Ribeiro, M. (2019, December 5). How to Become Mentally Strong: 14 Strategies for Building Resilience. Retrieved from https://positivepsychology.com/mentally-strong/

Jeffrey, S. (n.d.). 7 Steps to Discover Your Personal Core Values. Retrieved from https://scottjeffrey.com/personal-core-values/

MacDonald, A. (2015, November 10). Using the relaxation response to reduce stress. Retrieved from https://www.health.harvard.edu/blog/using-the-relaxation-response-to-reduce-stress-20101110780

Scott, E. (2019b, October 11). Relaxation Response for Reversing Stress. Retrieved from https://www.verywellmind.com/what-is-the-relaxation-response-3145145

Robinson, L., Segal, R., Segal, J., & Smith, M. (2019, October). Relaxation Techniques for Stress Relief. Retrieved from https://www.helpguide.org/articles/stress/relaxation-techniques-for-stress-relief.htm

Scott, E. (2019a, August 15). How to Reduce Stress With Breathing Exercises. Retrieved from https://www.verywellmind.com/how-to-reduce-stress-with-breathing-exercises-3144508

American Psychological Association. (n.d.-a). Coping With Stress at Work. Retrieved from https://www.apa.org/helpcenter/work-stress

Visualization and Guided Imagery Techniques for Stress Reduction. (n.d.). Retrieved from https://www.mentalhelp.net/stress/visualization-and-guided-imagery-techniques-for-stress-reduction/

YOUR FREE GIFT

Thank you again for purchasing this book. As an additional thank you, you will receive an e-book, as a gift, and completely free.

This guide gives you 14 Days of Mindfulness and sets you on a two-week course to staying present and relaxed. Practice each of the daily prompts to learn more about mindfulness, and add it to your daily routine and meditations.

You can get the bonus booklet as follows:

To access the secret download page, open a browser window on your computer or smartphone and enter: **bonus.derickhowell.com**

You will be automatically directed to the download page.

Please note that this bonus booklet may be only available for download for a limited time.

CPSIA information can be obtained
at www.ICGtesting.com
Printed in the USA
BVHW041640190321
603028BV00003B/23

9 781647 801403